PORTF

THE UNUSUAL BILLIONAIRES

Saurabh Mukherjea is a bestselling author and the CEO of Institutional Equities at Ambit Capital, an Indian investment bank. In 2014 and 2015, he was rated as the leading equity strategist in India by the Asiamoney polls. A London School of Economics alumnus, Mukherjea is also a CFA charter holder.

PRAISE FOR THE BOOK

'Saurabh Mukherjea describes incisively how some great Indian companies have achieved corporate success and made a great deal of money for investors along the way'—John Kay, professor of economics, London School of Economics

'Saurabh's book highlights that the recipe for outstanding corporate results hinges on old-fashioned values'—Ashoka Wadhwa, group CEO, Ambit Holdings

THE
UNUSUAL
BILLIONAIRES

SAURABH MUKHERJEA

FOREWORD BY VINOD RAI

**PENGUIN
PORTFOLIO**

An imprint of Penguin Random House

PORTFOLIO

USA | Canada | UK | Ireland | Australia
New Zealand | India | South Africa | China

Portfolio is part of the Penguin Random House group of companies
whose addresses can be found at global.penguinrandomhouse.com

Published by Penguin Random House India Pvt. Ltd
7th Floor, Infinity Tower C, DLF Cyber City,
Gurgaon 122 002, Haryana, India

Penguin
Random House
India

First published in Portfolio by Penguin Random House India 2016

ISBN 9780143426738

Typeset in Adobe Caslon Pro by Manipal Digital Systems, Manipal
Printed at Replika Press Pvt. Ltd

www.penguin.co.in

To my paternal grandparents, Shephalika and Nirmal Mukherjea, for believing in me before anyone else did

Contents

Contents

Acknowledgements

It was in the summer of 2013 that my friend and guru, Sanjoy Bhattacharyya, drew my attention to William Thorndike's book, *The Outsiders: Eight Unconventional CEOs and Their Radically Rational Blueprint for Success*. The book changed the way I perceived and analysed companies which have been successful over long periods of time (we are talking decades here). Until I read Thorndike's masterwork, I had seen companies solely through the lens of the 'sustainable competitive advantage' framework created by my first guru, John Kay, and outlined in Appendix 1.

What Thorndike helped me grasp was that the truly great companies take the surplus cash flows created by their sustainable competitive advantages and then either return those to shareholders or reinvest those in their core franchise, or—and this is the litmus test of greatness—reinvest those successfully in new activities or markets. It is in those latter set of investments outside the core franchise that a great company assures its future regardless of how economic circumstances and customers' tastes pan out. Without that insight from *The Outsiders*, there would be no *The Unusual Billionaires*.

Whilst the easy part of this adventure was the conceptualization of the book, I soon realized that there was a gargantuan amount of work to do. Many decades of data for dozens of companies had to be crunched. In-depth interviews with executives and promoters had to be conducted across the length and breadth of India. Hypotheses had to be created, tested, scrapped, recreated, finalized and then finally turned into a coherent narrative. There is no way I could have done even a fraction of this work on my own whilst grappling with my day job. Fortunately for me, several of India's top analysts volunteered to help pull this book together. This book therefore is a team effort and I am merely representing a talented group of individuals.

I thank Gaurav Mehta, Prashant Mittal, and Karan Khanna, who formed the strategy team in Ambit's Institutional Equities team, in helping me crunch decades of data to build the 'first among equals' list. The same team, building on Robert Kirby's idea, then created the Indian Coffee Can Portfolio that eventually paved the way for the seven companies mentioned in this book. (Gaurav Mehta now works as a fund manager in Ambit's investment management business.)

I thank Ambit's sectoral analysts, Rakshit Ranjan, Ritesh Vaidya and Dhiraj Mistry, for analysing the four consumer franchises described in this book. I thank Pankaj Agarwal and Ravi Singh for their help in researching the two banks in this book—HDFC Bank and Axis Bank. Nitin Bhasin, Ambit's head of research, is an ardent follower of Warren Buffett and I thank him and his colleague, Achint Bhagat, for their work on Astral Poly and for Nitin's valuable suggestions in simplifying the Coffee Can construct.

My friend, Anupam Gupta, acted as a reality check on my obsessively analytical writing style. If *The Unusual Billionaires* is an accessible book, it is largely because of the hundreds of interventions Anupam made in different parts of the book to give it lucidity and clarity whilst reducing technical jargon. Anupam injected verve and vigour into the narrative that drives *The Unusual Billionaires*.

(L–R): Ritesh Vaidya, Achint Bhagat, Prashant Mittal, Ravi Singh, Rakshit Ranjan, Karan Khanna, Anupam Gupta, Nitin Bhasin, Pankaj Agarwal, Gaurav Mehta and Saurabh Mukherjea (sitting).

The deep dive into the seven companies analysed in this book meant that Ambit's analysts conducted close to a hundred interviews spread over the course of a year in many different cities. The Herculean job of organizing these meetings and persuading corporate captains to coordinate their diaries with Ambit's analysts fell on another colleague, Nitesh Bhadani, who delivered everything that I could have asked for and more.

During the interviews for this book, I had the honour of meeting some of India's most enlightened managers, owners and promoters. Listening to their experiences, aspirations and ambitions has been a tremendous learning experience for me and I thank the companies for generously sharing their time with us.

I thank Jalaj Dani, K.B.S. Anand and Jayesh Merchant at Asian Paints who welcomed us at their Mumbai offices in Kalina. I thank Kuldip Singh Dhingra, Abhijit Roy and Srijit Dasgupta for meeting me and my team at Berger Paints offices in Delhi and Kolkata. In the city of my birth, I also met Nazeeb Arif, Supratim Dutta, Neel Kingston Jasper and Nandini Basu from ITC and I am grateful to them for their time. In Bangaluru, I thank Sunder Genomal, Vedji Ticku and Pius Thomas at the offices of Page Industries, India's exclusive franchisee for Jockey. At Marico, I thank Harsh Mariwala, Saugata Gupta and Vivek Karve who helped us for the purposes of this book. Closer to my office, I thank Shikha Sharma, V. Srinivasan, Jairam Sridharan, Rajiv Anand, Sidharth Rath, Suresh Warrier and Abhijit Majumder at Axis Bank for giving us their time. Literally next door to us, I thank Sashi Jagdishan and Paresh Sukhtankar at HDFC Bank. Finally, I thank Sandeep Engineer, Hiranand Savlani and Yogesh Shah at Astral Poly, the youngest company in our book, for explaining their journey.

In addition to the management teams of these eight companies, I also thank Anoop Hoon, Nirmesh Prakash, Mangesh Pathak, Biji Kurien, Madhu Mansukhani, Milind

Sarwate, B.S. Nagesh, Latha Venkatesh, Hemant Kaul, Sujan Sinha, Dr V.K. Ramani, Dr P.J. Nayak, Shailendra Bhandari, Luis Miranda, Manisha Lath-Gupta, Tamal Bandyopadhyay, Samir Bhatia, H. Srikrishnan, Pankaj Kajaria, Haresh Ajmera, Shabbir Malwawala, Miten Mehta and Chandan Nath for sharing with me their time and insights.

I thank Rama Bijapurkar and Sanjoy Bhattacharyya for sharing their collective learnings over many years. Their insights into India's corporate history and their anecdotes made for enthralling discussions and I can now see how Rama produces a bestseller every other year.

I am grateful to Lohit Jagwani for reaching out to me with the idea that I could write for as august a publishing house as Penguin. Lohit is also solely responsible for calming me down and getting me back on track whenever I would throw my toys out of the pram during the painstaking process of negotiating the contract for this book with Penguin.

Finally, whilst I might never become a billionaire, I have someone in my life who enriches my life in manifold ways. Sarbani Mukherjea remains the most unusual woman I have ever met and I thank my lucky stars that the first sensible decision I made in my life was to marry her when we were both barely out of college. Now that we have Jeet and Malini Mukherjea in our lives as well, I live in the hope that the Mukherjea franchise will endure for many, many decades.

Foreword

Entrepreneurship is in the air. Over the past few years, Indian start-ups have attracted billions of dollars from venture capitalists all over the world. Old business models, in India and elsewhere, are seemingly being disrupted by a new wave of technological innovation. At the opposite end of the corporate spectrum, the sheer size of non-performing assets in the Indian banking system and the profligacy of some Indian promoters are making headlines almost every day. Clearly, the old order has not yet fully given way to the new and in India, we have become all too familiar with the nexus between big business and politics. Yet, even in the midst of these imperfections, I believe that there is a new wave of transparency and good governance that is, slowly but surely, disrupting the old way of doing business.

Corporate India knows this and is gradually adapting to this new environment. After all, change isn't exactly new for Indian promoters given that 2016 is the twenty-fifth anniversary of the 1991 reforms that ended the 'Licence Raj' and opened up most Indian businesses to foreign competition. In fact, the roster of companies in this book is a textbook case study of corporate India successfully grappling with change. Companies like Asian Paints, Berger Paints, and Marico survived and thrived after 1991, while HDFC

Bank, Axis Bank, Page Industries and Astral Poly were born and took flight post-1991. The journey wasn't easy for these companies and yet all seven of them have shown that they have what it takes to succeed regardless of what might be taking place in the external environment.

In fact, there are many lessons for all of us in the success of these companies. One lesson is that clean, well-managed companies cannot just survive but can actually thrive in India. A promoter who looks beyond his own and his family's selfish interests can achieve a lot for the company, for society (in terms of jobs created), and for shareholders. Secondly, hard work and integrity will never go out of fashion. Saurabh Mukherjea correctly notes that single-minded focus on the company's business and prudent capital allocation are core virtues that promoters who deliver long-term success possess. This comes as a welcome relief from the all-too-familiar tendency of Indian promoters to divert attention to flavour-of-the-month businesses and short-changing minority shareholders for personal gain.

I have followed Saurabh's work for a few years now and admire his intellectual rigour, clarity of thought, and diligence in analysing companies. All of these qualities are on display in this book. By speaking to both insiders and outsiders, Saurabh provides a unique perspective on how these companies have built and sustained their competitive advantages over long periods of time.

Saurabh's obsession with rigorous financial data analysis is well known. By defining 'greatness' in financial parameters, Saurabh has taken away biases in choosing winners. I am sure readers will appreciate the simplicity of the filters he has used to identify great Indian companies—10 per cent revenue growth and 15 per cent return on capital employed

(ROCE) for every consecutive year over the past decade. Based on his data crunch, Saurabh reaches a grim conclusion: over 99 per cent of the 5000 companies that are listed in India simply fail to fulfil his filters over the past decade.

This is indeed a disappointing result because if the purpose of business is to grow consistently and grow in a profitable manner, an overwhelming majority of Indian companies have failed. Is it any surprise then that our banking system is clogged with loans that will never be recovered? Can we now conclude that Indian promoters focus more on lining their pockets than achieving profitable growth? These are some of the more difficult questions that I was left asking after reading the book.

And what are the answers? What is the way ahead? We can learn from the elite set of firms profiled in-depth in this book. Most of them are well-known franchises that own some of India's most familiar brands. They have created their own roads to success and growth without compromising on profitability or integrity. As chapter after chapter of this book shows, the secret of success isn't complex. Manic focus on running a business efficiently, creating and sustaining competitive advantages, and prudent capital allocation lie at the heart of these winning companies. No wonder then that a portfolio consisting of these companies beats the Sensex hollow year after year (even if the portfolio itself is left untouched for a decade).

The Unusual Billionaires is a compelling read with simple themes. The in-depth stories of the journeys of these seven companies are almost like a highlights package of corporate India's achievements and inflection points over the past few decades. In the ups and downs of these companies, there are plenty of anecdotes that you will enjoy and lessons that you will find heart-warming. At its heart though, this book is about perseverance and integrity and about the fact that even as the wrong sort of corporates grab the headlines, the corporate outperformers quietly go about building outstanding businesses which enrich our lives in multiple ways. I hope that you enjoy reading the book as much as I did.

Vinod Rai
Chairman, Banks Board Bureau,
Former Comptroller and Auditor General of India

New Delhi,
April 2016

CHAPTER 1

Searching for Greatness

'Greatness is not a function of circumstance. Greatness, it turns out, is largely a matter of conscious choice.'

—Jim Collins, *Good to Great* (2001)

'It is a rough road that leads to the heights of greatness.'

—Seneca

Asian Paints on the Rajdhani Express

As I stood on the railway platform waiting for the Rajdhani Express to arrive, I was thinking about how lucky we had been to get first-class tickets on this premier express train. It had been a long, hot day in the city of Kota for me and my colleague. We had come to Kota, a city in the middle of Rajasthan, to visit a few companies and, with the day's work done, we were now looking forward to a hot meal on the train followed by some sleep, before our train pulled into Mumbai Central at 7.30 a.m. the following day. The

Rajdhani Express arrived bang on time and we clambered into its cool compartments.

As we entered our first-class compartment, I noticed an elderly gentleman sitting in the seat opposite ours. I greeted him and his response betrayed an unmistakable Bengali accent. As dinner was being served (chapattis, paneer, dal—all steaming hot—with chicken cutlets for carnivores like me), I struck up a conversation with the Bengali gentleman. It turned out that he ran his own company which, for the past forty years, has been providing consultancy services to the Indian oil-refining industry. The consultancy service was of a specialized kind—it was focused on helping oil refineries identify the correct coatings, paints and dyes for their oil tankers and oil-storage tanks. So, which company's coatings, paints and dyes did he recommend, I asked. 'Asian Paints,' was the unhesitating reply. 'There is no one else in the same league as Asian Paints. In the industrial paints and dyes segment, they are the unquestionable leaders and have been for most of my career.'

'Why is Asian Paints the number one in industrial paints and dyes? Are they the cheapest? Do they have the best-quality products?' The industrial paints expert took his time to think about my question. He then said, 'You know, I don't have an easy answer to your question. Asian's paints and dyes are the most expensive in the market. They're also the best in quality, but then other companies can also provide high-quality products. In fact, if you or I wanted, we too could manufacture industrial paints and dyes of the same quality. And yet we don't and nobody else does. So I can't really tell you why Asian Paints is number one, but it is the company that I recommend to all of my clients.'

Soon, the lights were dimmed in our compartment and we retired for the night. But as our train hammered through the Rajasthan countryside and then entered Gujarat in the early hours of the next day, I was intrigued by the veteran consultant's endorsement of Asian Paints as the 'number one company'. Indeed, in a country with so many paints brands, I asked myself: 'What made Asian Paints so special? Why has nobody else been able to catch up with them?' By the time we arrived in Mumbai Central, I decided that my colleagues and I would devote a substantial amount of our time and resources to answering these questions.

To help you understand why I was so fixated on Asian Paints and why there are so few outstanding companies like Asian Paints in India, it is worth defining greatness in the context of corporate life in India.

Defining Greatness

'The ancient Romans were used to being defeated. Like the rulers of most of history's great empires, they could lose battle after battle but still win the war. An empire that cannot sustain a blow and remain standing is not really an empire.'— Yuval Noah Harari, *Sapiens: A Brief History of Humankind* (2011)

Many historians take the view that the greatness of a kingdom or an empire should be measured by its longevity. How long did the empire sustain? How durable was the empire? By this measure, the first great empire was arguably the Persian Empire. Founded around 550 BC, it lasted for around 200 years until Alexander the Great brought it to an end in 330 BC by defeating King Darius III. However, if longevity is the measure of a great empire, the Roman Empire is by some distance the greatest empire the world has ever seen. Whilst the first Roman republic, headquartered in Rome, lasted from 100 BC to 400 AD, the imperial successor to the Republic lasted for a staggering 1400 years before falling to the Ottoman Turks in 1453.

In sports on the other hand, if you measure greatness using quantitative metrics such as averages, title counts and win:loss ratios, sportsmen like Sachin Tendulkar and Michael Schumacher are far ahead of their peers in their respective sports over the past few decades.

Exhibit 1: Greatness in the context of sports

Top Five Test Batsmen of All Time	Number of Runs Scored	100s Scored	Batting Average
Sachin Tendulkar	15,921	51	53.8
Ricky Ponting	13,378	41	51.9
Jacques Kallis	13,289	45	55.4
Rahul Dravid	13,288	36	52.3
Kumar Sangakkara	12,400	38	57.4

Top Five Formula One Drivers of All Time	Number of Grand Prix Wins
Michael Schumacher	91
Alain Prost	51
Lewis Hamilton	43
Sebastian Vettel	42
Ayrton Senna	41

Top Six Women Tennis Players of All Time	Grand Slam Titles
Margaret Court	24
Steffi Graf	22

(Contd)

Top Six Women Tennis Players of All Time	Grand Slam Titles
Serena Williams	21
Helen Wills Moody	19
Chris Evert	18
Martina Navratilova	18

Source: Espncricinfo.com; http://www.f1-fansite.com/f1-results/all-time-f1-driver-rankings/; http://www.sportsmuntra.com/top-10-greatest-female-tennis-players-time/.

In contrast, in cinema, if you measure greatness as being related to box-office success, actors like Aamir Khan, Tom Cruise, Angelina Jolie, and Harrison Ford have been star actors over multiple decades. In art, the works of Leonardo Da Vinci, Rembrandt and Picasso are recognized as great and have been commanding astronomical sums in auctions held in different countries over decades. Thus, the rarity of these individuals' achievements, measured in crude commercial terms, marks them out as great.

Paradoxically, the question, 'What is a great company?' is harder to answer. A great company attracts the best talent, commands respect in the business community and, more often than not, trades at a premium in the stock market. However, there is no standard definition of greatness. As the Bengali gentleman mentioned during dinner on the Rajdhani Express, there is no easy answer for what makes Asian Paints a great company. Moreover, as Phil Rosenzweig points out in his insightful book, *The Halo Effect*, most of us end up viewing contemporary successful companies as great companies because of the positive press around them. We also do this because of the veneer of success—the halo—that surrounds them. It is the business community's analogue to what is called the herd instinct in the stock market—everyone else thinks the company is great; hence the company must be great.

What, then, is a credible measure of greatness that is not polluted by the halo that surrounds successful companies? The instinctive answer is market capitalization—or the number of outstanding shares of a company multiplied by the last traded market price. Used ubiquitously by global benchmarks like the S&P 500, the yardstick of market capitalization appears to be the most common measure of greatness. After all, if the stock market is rational, the share price is the best possible measure of the value of the company. And higher the value, greater the company.

Take Apple Inc. for instance. Apple is seen as the universally loved company that gave us fantastic products like the iPhone, iPod and iPad. Brought back from near collapse by its iconic founder, Steve Jobs, Apple's products generate billions of dollars of revenue and is the world's largest company by market capitalization.

Similarly, in India, Tata Consultancy Services (TCS) is India's largest company by market cap. TCS's market capitalization went up to Rs 4.8 lakh crore in 2015 from Rs 0.6 lakh crore in 2004, implying a growth rate of 20 per cent per annum. This was much higher than the Sensex's growth rate of 13.3 per cent per annum over the same period, making TCS an enormous wealth creator for its investors. Surely, this achievement suggests that TCS is a great company.

Whilst there is no disputing TCS's or Apple's stature, measures of a company's greatness based on stock price tend to be short-sighted. Stock prices change every day, whereas greatness is meant to be an enduring quality. More importantly, stock prices are an effect and not a cause of a company's greatness—investors reward winning business strategies that help companies perform better than their rivals, not the other way around. It takes a long time for a company to build its brand, its management team, its systems and protocols and, in the process, deliver profits. Not many companies are able to sustain this over long periods of time. To use our example, Asian Paints's superior product quality is well known, but its massive network of dealers and distributors, built assiduously over the years, poses a huge barrier of entry. Tomorrow, if you or I, with backing from a deep-pocketed investor, decide to make the same quality of paints, we will find it next to impossible to compete with Asian Paints.

So, how do we quantify the greatness of firms like Asian Paints and how do we compare such firms with each other using quantitative metrics which capture greatness? My research provides two pointers which help answer this question. First, over long periods of time, financial performance is the best reflection of a company's business strategy. Secondly, greatness is not temporary and is surely not a short-term phenomenon. Greatness does not change from one quarterly result to another. Think of an enduring brand—Apple, General Electric, Hindustan Unilever, Colgate—chances are they have been around for decades and they have endured. Using these two pointers, I define greatness as the ability of a company to sustain superior financial performance for a long period of time. Such companies are rare. They can endure difficult economic conditions. Their growth is not beholden to domestic or global growth; they thrive in economic down cycles as well. Their management teams have strategies that deliver results better than their competitors. Over time, these companies learn from their mistakes and increase the distance between themselves and their competitors. Often, such companies appear conservative. However, they do not confuse conservatism with complacency—these companies simply bide their time for making the right moves. These traits are common among great companies and rarely found outside great companies. Having defined greatness in these intuitive terms, we can now begin the search for great Indian companies.

Quantifying Greatness

I now set the parameters or the guard rails within which I will define great companies in financial terms. This is a three-step process:

Step 1: Define Companies: Given that it is hard to collect data on unlisted companies, my search for great companies will have to stay restricted to listed companies (of which there are approximately 5000 in India). Even within the listed universe, I will limit my search to companies with a minimum market capitalization of Rs 100 crore as the reliability of data on companies smaller than this is somewhat suspect. There are around 1500 listed companies in India with a market cap above Rs 100 crore.

Step 2: Define Long Periods: I believe a decade is long enough to measure a company's financial performance. A decade in India usually accommodates both the up and down cycles in the economy. For example, the decade from FY06 (i.e. the financial year ending 31 March 2006) to FY15 (i.e. the financial year ending 31 March 2015) coincides with six years of strong economic growth (FY06 to FY11, where average nominal GDP (gross domestic product) growth[1] was 15.7 per cent) and four years of weak economic growth (FY12 to FY15, where average nominal GDP growth was 12.8 per cent). Hence, measuring greatness over a decadal period should not unfairly penalize cyclical companies, nor unfairly advantage companies in more stable, steady sectors.

Step 3: Define Superior Financial Performance: At the very basic level, a company doing well would mean that it is profitable and it is growing (by successfully reinvesting its profits). Over very long periods of time, the twin filters of growth and profitability, in my view, are sufficient to assess the success of a franchise. Thus, my stock-selection filters are companies that deliver revenue growth of 10 per cent and ROCE of 15 per cent every year for the past ten years. Let's look at these filters in more detail:

(a) Why revenue growth of 10 per cent every year? India's nominal GDP growth rate has averaged 14.5 per cent over the past ten years. A firm operating in India should, therefore, be able to deliver sales growth of at least 14.5 per cent per annum. However, very few listed companies—only nine out of the approximate 1500 firms on my screen—have managed to achieve this! Therefore, I reduce this filter rate modestly to 10 per cent, i.e. I look for companies that have delivered

---

[1] Nominal GDP growth rate ignores the impact of inflation, unlike real GDP growth which is an inflation-adjusted measure. For the purposes of this book, we use nominal GDP growth rate because inflation provides a natural tailwind for all companies in general. Consumer price inflation in India has averaged 8.4 per cent in the past decade and this would inflate revenue growth for most companies.

revenue growth of 10 per cent per annum every year for ten consecutive years.

Whilst management teams have a natural desire for growth and scale, growth creates shareholder value only when the returns on capital exceed the cost of capital. To put this simply, owners create value for shareholders only when the capital they use in their business generates a higher rate of return than the cost they are paying for using that capital.

(b) Why ROCE? Return on Capital Employed (ROCE) is defined as 'earnings before interest and tax/capital employed' where capital employed is defined as the fixed assets used by the business, e.g. plant and machinery plus the working capital being used to finance the business. If this sounds too technical, there is another more intuitive way to understand ROCE. Over the long run if a business produces 18 per cent ROCE i.e. a 18 per cent return on the capital that it is investing, then that is the annual return you are likely to get from holding that stock. A company uses capital to invest in assets, which in turn generate cash flows and earnings. This capital invested consists of equity and debt, and the sum of the cost of equity[2] and the cost of debt[3] (weighted in proportion to their share in total capital) is known more popularly as the weighted average cost of capital (WACC). In other words, WACC is the bare minimum cost that an owner pays for the capital required for running his business. Therefore, for the owner to create value for himself, the return on his capital (or the ROCE) must be more than

---

[2] The rate of return that a company's equity shareholder demands as compensation for the risk of investing his money in owning the company's stock.

[3] The rate of interest paid on loans taken by the company.

the money he is paying to use the capital (or WACC). Hence, when a promoter makes a high ROCE that covers his business's WACC and leaves an 'extra' for his shareholders, it is a good indication of that promoter investing his capital judiciously. In comparison, a bad businessman wouldn't even earn enough to pay his shareholders and lenders. Companies with low ROCEs keep requiring external infusions of capital to fund their growth. Therefore, this excess of ROCE over WACC is a measure of the excess returns to an investor in the company. It follows, therefore, that if a company grows without excess returns, it creates no value for equity investors.

In the Indian stock market, ROCE is the single biggest factor affecting a company's stock price. If I split India's listed companies into four equal groups, ranked by their ROCE and revenue growth,[4] companies with the highest ROCE (i.e. in the topmost 25 per cent or top quartile) have beaten the BSE200[5] by 7.7 per cent per annum. Contrast this with the same top quartile for companies with high revenue growth—they have beaten the BSE200 by only 4 per cent per annum. As you would expect, companies which delivered on both fronts (i.e. a combination of top quartile on ROCE and top quartile on revenue growth) have performed even better on the stock price front—they have outperformed the BSE200 by an impressive 11.5 per cent per annum.

---

[4] Measured over FY05–15; i.e. we take median ROCE over FY05–15 and revenue growth over FY05–15.

[5] The Bombay Stock Exchange (BSE) launched the S&P (Standard and Poor's) BSE200 Index on 27 May 1994. As per the BSE website, the selection of companies was primarily done on the basis of current market capitalization of the listed scrips. As per the BSE200 factsheet, it is a broad-based index comprising 200 large, well-established and financially sound companies across sectors.

(c) Why minimum ROCE of 15 per cent? The minimum return that one would rationally expect from equities is the risk-free return, i.e. what you would earn if you invested in the safest investment in India, namely, the Government of India's bonds. In early 2016, the Government of India's ten-year bonds gave a return of around 8 per cent and that is the risk-free return in India. However, given that equities carry an element of risk that government bonds don't, an equity investor would want a premium return for this extra risk. This is the equity risk premium—the extra return an investor expects over and above the risk-free rate for investing in equities. The equity risk premium, in turn, is calculated as 4 per cent (the long-term US equity risk premium) plus 2.5 per cent to account for India's rating (BBB—as per S&P). Hence, adding the risk-free rate of 8 per cent and an equity risk premium of 6.5 to 7 per cent gives a cost of capital of around 15 per cent. Note further that over the past twenty and thirty years, the Sensex has delivered returns of around 15 per cent per annum, thus validating my point of view that 15 per cent is a sensible measure of the cost of capital for an Indian company. Therefore, if a company is to be deemed great, it has to deliver an ROCE in excess of 15 per cent per annum over long periods of time.

It is worth noting that I am not looking for companies with the highest revenue growth or the highest ROCE. There is no point in doing that because companies which generate outstanding levels of growth or ROCE at a specific point in time generally mean revert, i.e. over long periods of time, their performance reverts to that of the average corporate. Hence, I base my selection on a system of guard rails—the first rail being revenue growth of at least 10 per cent and the second one being minimum ROCE of 15 per cent—which help us assess which firms have what it takes to protect themselves and march ahead through good as well as bad times. As Exhibit 2 below demonstrates, Asian Paints is one of the few Indian companies able to stay within my guard rails.

Exhibit 2: Asian Paints's revenue growth and ROCE over FY06–15

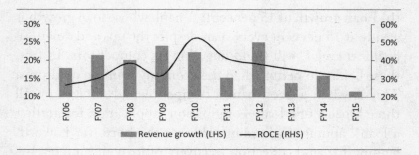

Source: Capitaline, Ambit Capital research.

In fact, whilst thirty-six Indian companies have generated revenue growth of at least 10 per cent per annum over FY06–15, and 102 companies have clocked ROCEs of at least 15 per cent per annum over that period, a mere eighteen companies have satisfied both criteria over this decadal period.

Quantifying Greatness, Specifically for Financial Services Firms

While the above filters apply to companies in the manufacturing sector, an important distinction needs to be made for companies in the banking and financial services industry (BFSI). Obviously, BFSI companies have neither revenues nor ROCE, since they borrow and lend money, and earn interest and investment income on these operations. Hence, for BFSI companies, I use the following filters:

(a) ROE of 15 per cent: I prefer Return on Equity (ROE) over Return on Assets (ROA). For the uninitiated, equity is the value of an asset minus the total liability. I feel this is a fairer measure of the bank's ability to generate higher income efficiently on a given equity capital base (i.e. shareholder equity plus reserves and surplus) over time.

(b) Loan growth of 15 per cent: A bank whose loan growth is steady at 15 per cent every year, despite the ups and downs of business cycles, will stand out from its competitors. In fact, these banks do better when the economy is in the doldrums. This is when a good bank's competitive advantages on all three aspects of a loan—origination (application for getting a loan), appraisal (deciding whether the borrower is worth lending to), and collection (recovery of loan and interest)—gets tested most comprehensively. Thus, during a down cycle, banks with weaker processes will suffer and cede market share to stronger banks. During a down cycle, stronger banks—with better balance sheet and risk-assessment capabilities—can up the ante by lending to sectors that are resilient.

Whilst seven Indian lenders have generated loan book growth of at least 15 per cent per annum over FY06–15, and thirteen lenders have clocked ROEs of at least 15 per cent per annum over that period, only six lenders have satisfied both criteria over the period of this decade.

Enter the Coffee Can Portfolio

'In investing, as in auto racing, you don't have to win every lap to win the race, but you absolutely do have to finish the race. While a driver must be prepared to take some risks, if he takes too many risks, he'll wind up against the fence.

There are sensible risks—and there are risks that make no sense at all.'—Capital Group fund manager Robert Kirby quoted in Charles D. Ellis's *Capital: The Story of Long-Term Investment Excellence.*

Robert Kirby was not only a senior fund manager for the Capital Group companies, one of the world's largest asset management firms with assets under management in excess of US$1.4 trillion, he was also a leading amateur race car driver. As exemplified by the quote above, his experience of investing and racing intertwined to give him a very practical sense of risk management. Many investment professionals— lost in the world of probability distributions and value at risk models—lack it.

In the late 1960s, the Capital Group, then as now headquartered in Los Angeles, set up an entity called Capital Guardian Trust Company whose aim was to provide traditional investment counselling services to wealthy individuals. Kirby joined Capital in 1965 as the main investment manager in Capital Guardian Trust. Nearly twenty years later, he wrote a remarkable note which introduced to the world the concept of the Coffee Can Portfolio (CCP).

Kirby, in a note[6] written in 1984, narrated an incident involving his client's husband. The gentleman had purchased stocks recommended by Kirby in denominations of US$5000 each but, unlike Kirby, did not sell anything from the portfolio. This process (of buying when Kirby bought but not selling thereafter) led to enormous wealth creation for the client over a period of about ten years. The wealth creation was mainly on account of one position transforming

---

[6] https://thetaoofwealth.files.wordpress.com/2013/03/the-coffee-can-portfolio.pdf.

to a jumbo holding worth over US$800,000, which came from a zillion shares of Xerox. Impressed by this approach of buy and forget followed by this gentleman, Kirby coined the term Coffee Can Portfolio, in which the 'coffee can' harkens back to the Wild West, when Americans, before the widespread advent of banks, saved their valuables in a coffee can and kept it under a mattress.

Although Kirby made the discovery of the CCP sound serendipitous, the central insight behind this construct— that in order to truly get rich an investor has to let a sensibly constructed portfolio stay untouched for a long period of time—is as powerful as it is profound. After all, the instinctive thing for a hard-working, intelligent investor is to try to optimize his portfolio every so often, usually once a year. It is very hard for investors to leave a portfolio untouched for ten years. A retail investor will be tempted to intervene whenever he sees stocks in the portfolio sag in price. A professional investor will feel that he has a fiduciary responsibility to intervene if parts of the portfolio are underperforming. But Kirby's counter-intuitive insight is that an investor will make much more money if he leaves the portfolio untouched.

Thirty years after Kirby formalized the concept of CCP, the Silicon Valley–based venture capitalist and founder of PayPal, Peter Thiel, provided a lucid explanation in his 2014 book, *Zero to One*, why leaving a portfolio untouched for long makes investors very rich. Thiel begins by talking about the Pareto Principle, conceptualized by Italian economist Vilfredo Pareto, which says that 80 per cent of the effects come from 20 per cent of the causes. In the investment management paradigm, what it essentially implies is that a few companies in the portfolio attain exponentially greater value than all the others when held for a long duration.

Thiel, in his book, highlights this principle using an example of the venture capital industry wherein a fund typically invests in a portfolio of high-potential, early-stage companies, expecting a few of them to hit exponential growth and increase the value of the fund multifold. The increase in value takes place over a period of time with the top one or two firms in the fund becoming more valuable than all others combined at the maturity of the fund (most venture capital funds typically have a ten-year lifespan). When I applied the CCP construct in the context of the Indian stock market, this is exactly what I found. To be more specific, I have found that holding a portfolio with a healthy mix of large-, medium- and small-cap stocks with sound fundamentals for ten years exhibits a similar phenomenon in which a handful of stocks are responsible for the majority of the increase in the value of the portfolio. Those who are keen to delve further into why leaving a portfolio untouched is a seriously lucrative proposition should refer to Appendix 2.

Exhibit 3: No divergence in returns at beginning of the portfolio*

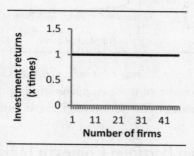

Source: Peter Thiel's *Zero to One*, Ambit Capital research.
*Distribution of actual returns of companies in our completed Coffee Can Portfolios at the beginning of the investment period.

Exhibit 4: Some companies start outperforming others at mid-stage (after five years)*

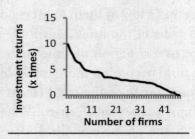

Source: Peter Thiel's *Zero to One*, Ambit Capital research.
*Distribution of actual returns of companies in our completed Coffee Can Portfolios after five-year period (mid-stage).

Exhibit 5: One or two firms generate exponential returns at the end of the portfolio term (ten years)*

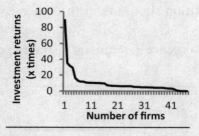

Source: Peter Thiel's *Zero to One*, Ambit Capital research.
*Distribution of actual returns of companies in our completed Coffee Can Portfolios after ten-year period (end of the term).

The Coffee Can Portfolio Comes to India

Having defined the parameters and criteria for measuring great companies, I can now screen listed companies.

Specifically, I can now build CCPs by screening on the basis of data for the past ten years and then I can let that portfolio run for the next ten years. For example, my first screening is for FY 1991 to FY 2000. I take the universe of listed stocks with a market capitalization of more than Rs 100 crore and look for companies that meet the parameters of:

(a) Revenue growth of 10 per cent and ROCE of 15 per cent every year for non-financial services companies; or

(b) loan book growth of 15 per cent and ROE of 15 per cent every year for financial services companies.

Using FY1991 to FY2000 screen, there are five companies that meet these requirements. These are NIIT, Cipla, Hero Moto, Swaraj Engines, and Housing Development Finance Corporation (HDFC) Limited. This gives us the Coffee Can Portfolio 2000. I now track the price performance of the Coffee Can Portfolio 2000 for the ten-year period, 30 June 2000 to 30 June 2010. For this, I allot an equal amount of money in each of these five stocks, say Rs 100. Thus the value of my portfolio at the start of my analysis is Rs 500. I find that at the end of ten years, the value of this portfolio has risen to Rs 2923. This implies an annual return of 19.3 per cent versus the 14 per cent per annum returned by the Sensex over the same period. Thus, the Coffee Can Portfolio 2000 outperformed the Sensex by 5.3 percentage points.

I repeat the above exercise for each year until the latest available financial year-end, FY2014–15. Given that each time bucket is ten years, I have six fully completed Coffee Can Portfolios: FY1991–2000, FY1992–01, FY1993–02, FY1994–03, FY1995–04 and FY1996–05.

The CCP of companies beginning from FY06 (i.e. Coffee Can Portfolio 2006) will complete its ten years of price performance only on 30 June 2016. Similarly, Coffee Can Portfolio 2007 will end on 30 June 2017 and so on. Thus, I have ten Coffee Can Portfolios which are incomplete in the sense that they have not yet run for ten years. For these uncompleted Coffee Can Portfolios, I use a cut-off date of 5 April 2016 for measuring price performance.

The results are revealing and can be summarized in one sentence: Each of the sixteen Coffee Can Portfolios (six complete and ten incomplete in that they have not completed ten years) has outperformed the benchmark large-cap index in India, the Sensex.[7] In fact, as can be seen in Exhibits 6 and 7, the outperformance of the Coffee Can Portfolios to the Sensex is almost always in excess of four percentage points per annum.

For more details on the portfolio constituents and the comprehensive manner in which almost every iteration of the Coffee Can Portfolio outperforms the Sensex, please refer to Appendix 2.

The Hunt for Rahul Dravid

'Primus inter pares' in Latin means 'first among equals'. It is typically used as an honorary title for those who are formally equal to other members of their group but are accorded unofficial respect, traditionally owing to their

---

[7] In fact, a subset of large companies in the CCP has also successfully beaten the Sensex on all sixteen occasions. These large companies were in the top-100 stocks by market cap (at the start of the period under consideration). We call this subset the large-cap portfolio.

Exhibit 6: Back-testing results of completed six iterations of the Coffee Can Portfolio (i.e. these iterations have run their complete course of ten years)

Kick-off year*	All-cap CCP (start)	All-cap CCP (end)	CAGR return	Outperformance relative to Sensex	Large-cap CCP (start)	Large-cap CCP (end)	CAGR return	Outperformance relative to Sensex
2000	500	2923	19.3%	5.3%	400	2602	20.6%	6.5%
2001	600	7362	28.5%	10.0%	300	2685	24.5%	6.0%
2002	800	6057	22.4%	4.1%	500	3348	20.9%	2.6%
2003	900	8668	25.4%	7.1%	600	6754	27.4%	9.1%
2004	1000	14618	30.8%	12.6%	500	3097	20.0%	1.9%
2005	900	5795	20.5%	6.0%	500	2517	17.5%	3.1%

Source: Bloomberg, Capitaline, Ambit Capital research.

Note: Portfolio at start denotes an equal allocation of Rs 100 for the stocks qualifying to be in the CCP for that year.

Exhibit 7: Back-testing results of incomplete ten iterations of the Coffee Can Portfolio (i.e. these iterations have not run their complete course of ten years)

Kick-off year*	All-cap CCP (start)	All-cap CCP (end)	CAGR return	Outperformance relative to Sensex	Large-cap CCP (start)	Large-cap CCP (end)	CAGR return	Outperformance relative to Sensex
2006	1000	4708	17.2%	8.1%	600	2,333	14.9%	5.8%
2007	1500	5322	15.5%	9.3%	1000	3,282	14.5%	8.3%
2008	1100	4346	19.3%	11.1%	800	2,689	16.9%	8.7%
2009	1100	3806	20.1%	11.8%	900	2,430	15.8%	7.5%
2010	700	1438	13.4%	7.3%	300	693	15.6%	9.5%
2011	1400	1864	6.3%	0.3%	400	682	11.8%	5.8%
2012	2200	4143	18.3%	8.4%	500	802	13.3%	3.4%
2013	1800	3784	30.7%	21.3%	600	1,068	23.1%	13.7%
2014	1600	2114	17.1%	18.3%	700	966	20.0%	21.1%
2015	2000	1957	-2.7%	10.6%	1,200	1,139	-6.6%	6.8%

Source: Bloomberg, Capitaline, Ambit Capital research.

Note: Portfolio at start denotes an equal allocation of Rs 100 for the stocks qualifying to be in the CCP for that year. *The portfolio kicks off on 30 June of the kick-off year. #CAGR returns for portfolios since 2006 have been calculated until 5 April 2016.

stature and the respect they command in their peer group. Amongst test cricketers, Rahul Dravid was the first among equals. As Edward Smith, the former England and Kent batsman who batted alongside Dravid in county cricket matches says,

> When Rahul Dravid walked into the dressing room of the St Lawrence ground in Canterbury on a cold spring morning, you could tell he was different from all the others. He did not swagger with cockiness or bristle with macho competitiveness. He went quietly round the room, shaking the hand of every Kent player—greeting everyone the same, from the captain to the most junior. It was not the mannered behaviour of a seasoned overseas professional; it was the natural courtesy of a real gentleman. We met a special human being first, an international cricketer second. The cricketer was pretty good, too. Dravid joined Kent for the 2000 season, and I spent much of it at number four, coming in one after Dravid (not that he was the departing batsman very often). That meant I had some wonderful opportunities to bat alongside the player who became the highest scoring number three of all time.[8]

I now look for the first among equals among CCP stocks.

The sixteen CCPs from 2000 to 2015 tell us two things. Firstly, in any given year, there are around twelve companies in the CCP. The smallest CCP was for 2000 with just five companies, while the largest CCP (with twenty-two stocks) was the portfolio which kicked off in 2012.

Secondly, the CCP has, on average, a churn of 26 per cent. This means that, in every cycle, for every ten

---

[8] http://phone.espncricinfo.com/magazine/content/story/557122.html.

companies in the CCP, three companies are replaced in the next cycle. Thus, very few companies actually manage to sustain their ten-year track record over the next ten years.

Therefore, we define those companies as first among equals which appear the most number of times in our CCPs. Repeating ten years of revenue growth of more than 10 per cent and ROCE of more than 15 per cent in multiple ten-year periods is not easy. So, if a company features repeatedly in the portfolios, by implication the company is delivering the test-cricket equivalent of hitting double centuries repeatedly.

To find the corporate equivalent of Rahul Dravid among our Coffee Can Portfolios, I search for those companies that have featured four or more times in the past ten iterations (2000–15). Only fourteen companies (including five from the financial services domain) have featured in the CCPs four or more times. This list has nine manufacturing and general services companies—Asian Paints, Astral Poly, Berger Paints, Cipla, Infosys, Ipca Labs, ITC, Marico, and Page Industries—and five financial services companies—HDFC, HDFC Bank, Axis Bank, Punjab National Bank (PNB), and Dewan Housing.

Of the five financial services companies mentioned above, three have shown a marked slide in the metrics over the past three years as the economic slowdown has bit deep into the Indian economy:

- Punjab National Bank's ROE has plummeted from 27 per cent in FY10 to 10 per cent in FY14 and 9 per cent in FY15. Alongside this, this public sector bank, whose loan book was growing at a brisk 20 to 30 per cent until

FY12, has seen a sharp drop in its loan book growth. In FY13, FY14 and FY15, this metric was well below 15 per cent for PNB.

- HDFC's loan book growth has dropped from 23 per cent in FY13 to barely 15 per cent in FY15.
- Dewan Housing's ROE has dropped from 22 per cent in FY11 to barely 15 per cent in FY15.

Hence, I exclude these three lenders from the first among equals list.

Of the nine other companies mentioned above, three have shown a pronounced slide in their performance:

- Cipla's ROCE has dropped rapidly from 24 per cent in FY13 to marginally above 15 per cent in FY15. This drop is in part driven by a halving in revenue growth from 23 per cent in FY14 to 12 per cent in FY15.
- Infosys's sales growth went from 5 per cent in FY10 to 24 per cent in FY14 and then dropped to 6 per cent in FY15.
- Ipca's ROCE halved from 28 per cent in FY14 to 14 per cent in FY15. This was in part driven by revenues shrinking by 4 per cent in FY15 after healthy growth in the preceding years.

Hence, I exclude these corporates too from our list.

After excluding these six companies from my original list of fourteen companies, I am left with the eight shown in Exhibit 8. These companies—the first among equals in India Inc.—stand out for their consistent, sustained, long-term financial performance.

Exhibit 8: The eight companies which are first among equals

Number	Company name	Number of times ROCE> 15% (last 10 years**)	Number of times revenue growth > 10% (last 10 years**)
1	Asian Paints	10	10
2	Astral Poly	10	10
3	Berger Paints	10	10
4	ITC	10	10
5	Marico*	10	10
6	Page Industries	10	10
7	HDFC Bank Ltd***	10	10
8	Axis Bank Ltd***	10	10

Source: Capitaline, Ambit Capital research. N

Note: *Marico demerged its Kaya business in 2014. After adjusting for the demerged business, the revenue growth was greater than 10 per cent in FY14.

**Last ten years refer to FY2006–15.

***For the two banks we are using ROE and loan book growth >15 per cent as the filter.

These eight companies have shown that it is possible to deliver sustained growth without compromising on long-term profitability—a test that 99.8 per cent of the 1500 largest listed companies in India fail to meet. The stories of these unusual companies are rich with learnings for the rest of us. Not only are these companies unusual in their demonstration of superior financial performance, they also stand out in the way they are managed, and the extent to which they have been able to constantly deepen their competitive moats and peel away from competition.

The next seven chapters delve deep into the multi-decadal evolution of these great companies and how they have created sustainable competitive advantages.[9] Those who want to understand more deeply the concept of sustainable competitive advantage should turn to Appendix 1. Chapter 9 synthesizes the learnings from my research on the eight great companies into easily digestible takeaways. Finally, Chapter 10 builds upon the takeaways from the great companies and turns it into a checklist for investors.

For those who want to get their teeth into slightly more technical material, Appendix 2 gives detailed performance data on all CCPs since 2000 and also gives the latest CCP. Appendix 3, 'The Case against Churning', highlights why it makes sense to buy and hold the same portfolio for a decade.

---

[9] I have not included a chapter on ITC in this book in spite of the fact that the firm features in the first among equals list.

2

Asian Paints: Seven Decades of Excellence

'Persistence is what makes the impossible possible, the possible likely, and the likely definite.'

–Robert Half

The year 1942 was a tumultuous one. World War II was on and British forces were battling Germany in Europe and Japan in Sri Lanka. In the last few years of British rule, Gandhiji launched the Quit India movement at Gowalia Tank, Mumbai. Four years earlier, in 1938, J.R.D. Tata was appointed the chairman of the Tata Group. At thirty-four years, he was then the youngest member of the Tata Sons board. The Birlas were setting up their manufacturing empire. In those volatile days, the paints industry in India comprised a few foreign companies and Indian players like Shalimar Paints. A temporary ban on paint imports during World War II resulted in an opportunity for domestic production. Spotting this opportunity, a twenty-six-year-old entrepreneur, Champaklal H. Choksey and three of his friends—Chimanlal N. Choksi (not related to Choksey), Suryakant C. Dani, and Arvind R. Vakil—set up Asian Paints in Mumbai. By 1967, Asian Paints had become the largest paint company in India—a position it holds until this day. Champakbhai—as he was affectionately known—passed away on 31 July 1997, also the last day of his family holding a stake in Asian Paints. The families of the other three founders continue to own 52.8 per cent of the firm's shares outstanding.

As Asian Paints nears its seventy-fifth anniversary (in 2017), it stands out as an exemplary case study of a home-grown brand taking on competition (domestic and foreign) and winning in India. It is also a rare example of a large Indian company, held by multiple promoters and yet run by a high-calibre, professional, management team. The remarkable consistency in revenue growth, earnings growth, and disciplined capital deployment (see Exhibit 9) stands testimony to their calibre.

Exhibit 9: Decadal growth of revenue, profitability and capital employed for Asian Paints from 1952 onwards (growth measured through CAGR)

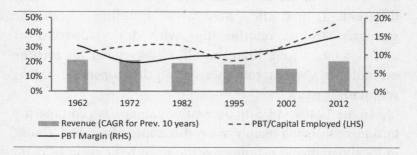

Source: Company, Ambit Capital research.

I now delve into the seven-decade history of Asian Paints across three phases: Phase 1 (1942 to 1967), Phase 2 (1967 to 1997), and Phase 3 (1997 to 2015).

Founders Take It to the Number One Spot

Phase 1: 1942–67

'Champaklal Choksey was a visionary, a father figure and a statesman to the paints industry. He laid the foundation of Asian Paints by being a superb gap analyst and looking at what the competition was not doing,' said Anoop Hoon, former national sales manager (decorative) of Asian Paints from 1991 to 1994, in our discussions with him in October 2015.

Choksey's strengths lay in identifying consumption trends and patterns early and devising strategies around them. Once this was done, he would test these strategies, choose the winning approach and focus consistently on improving processes. Back in the 1940s, Choksey chose the decorative retail segment instead of industrial paints. He saw that the industrial paints business was price-driven and the company with the lowest price won the business for that year. However, decorative retail was inherently different. It had the potential of building sustainable strengths around relationships with dealers/distributors and also had strong brand recall. Choksey bet his fortune on building a strong presence within this consumer-facing segment of paints.

In the 1940s and '50s, decorative paints was a commodity business consisting mainly of dry distemper, also called 'chuna' in local parlance. Distemper is the most basic form of paint and consists mainly of colouring agents, chalk and lime.

Choksey's challenge was to establish the Asian Paints brand in a business where a handful of distributors controlled the supply of paint across India. After being ignored by these distributors in big cities like Mumbai and Pune, Choksey and his partners took to the villages to sell directly to the shopkeepers. This is where Choksey hit pay dirt. Asian Paints opened its first dealership in a small town called Sangli, near Satara, in south Maharashtra. K.B.S. Anand, MD and CEO of Asian Paints, recalls: 'Shopkeepers in smaller towns felt pampered while dealing directly with the company, rather than dealing with distributors. They were also getting the product at a better price.'

The company's abilities to understand consumption patterns are legendary as can be seen in this example: During the Pongal festival in Tamil Nadu (January) and the Pola festival in Maharashtra (August), villagers worship their bulls. Choksey noticed that these festivities brought with it a unique demand for painting the horns of bulls, where paint was required in bright colours and in small quantities (50–100 millilitre packs). He saw the opportunity and succeeded in breaking into this market. Similarly, the bottom panel of the front doors of homes in Tamil Nadu have small stripes painted in red and yellow which is considered auspicious. This was yet another market for Asian Paints. As a former employee of the company recalls: 'Champakbhai used to say that "*Gareeb apni dahleej zaroor rang karega, poora ghar chahe na kare*" (a poor household will always colour its entrance door even if they do not paint the rest of the house). Also, the cattle stick their horns into mud and marsh. So, the product packs have to be small, and product quality has to be long-lasting. If that means our margins will be under pressure, so be it.'

As demand for their products rose, dealers in small towns and cities started stocking them. As a result of this, the larger distributors in bigger cities who previously did not want to sell their products started partnering with the company. This approach of building the business from rural to urban India, and delivering on untapped consumer demand helped the company reach an annual turnover of Rs 0.23 crore with only 2 per cent PBT margins[10] in 1952, a decade after it was founded.

Choksey kept noticing gaps in consumer demand. In the cities, for example, he saw the difference between basic distemper and the more expensive plastic emulsion paint (which was launched by Jenson and Nicholson under the brand name Robbialac). While dry distemper was cheap, it had a tendency to peel off walls, stick to clothes, and stink badly. On the other hand, plastic emulsion was free from these problems but was five times costlier than dry distemper, and hence unaffordable. Thus, during the 1950s, Asian Paints launched a new innovative product— the washable distemper, placed between dry distemper and plastic emulsions. This was supported by a highly successful advertising campaign which said, 'Don't lose your temper, use Tractor Distemper.'

Effective advertising remains a cornerstone of the company's marketing strategy. In 1954, the company introduced its mascot—Gattu, the mischievous kid (see Exhibit 10).

---

[10] Profit before tax margin (or PBT margin) is a measure of profitability of a company. It is derived by dividing pre-tax profits with sales, and expressed as a percentage. Hence, a high PBT margin implies a highly profitable company.

Exhibit 10: Asian Paints mascot—Gattu, the mischievous kid—introduced in 1954

Source: Company, Ambit Capital research.

The mascot appealed to India's middle-class households. Once again, it was a daring experiment by Choksey and it paid off. During the 1950s and '60s, most of its competitors had foreign ownerships and focused mainly on industrial paints, marine paints, and large distributors or institutional orders for decorative paints.

In 1967, twenty-five years after commencing operations, Asian Paints became India's largest paints company by revenue. During this phase, the company's promoters focused on establishing the right product portfolio, the right distribution channel and strong brand recall. Thus, although the firm was not very profitable during the 1950s (2 per cent PBT margin and 5 per cent PBT/capital employed ratio[11] in 1952), during 1952–62, its revenues grew at a CAGR of 21 per cent with margins rising to 13 per cent by 1962 and PBT/capital employed rising to 26 per cent.

Professional Management Helps Scale Up Operations

Phase 2: 1967–97

'The promoters realized that the world is evolving around us and home-grown talent is probably not best equipped to scale up the organization in this environment. Hence, we needed to hire professionals. A lot of the strengths of the company that we see today evolved from that one basic decision,' said K.B.S. Anand, in my discussions with him in November 2015

After Asian Paints became the country's largest paint company in 1967, Choksey realized that scaling up the firm's operations subsequently required developing abilities to handle the complexities of an expanding direct-to-dealer distribution network and streamlining of systems and processes across various functions. To overcome this hurdle, Choksey started hiring fresh graduates from Indian Institute of Management, Ahmedabad (IIM-A), and Indian Institute of Management, Calcutta (IIM-C), and offered them complete authority and responsibility in their roles.

---

[11] PBT/capital employed ratio compares a company's profits with the capital employed to generate that profit. It is similar to ROCE and hence, the higher a company's PBT/capital employed ratio, the more profitable the company is.

The strategy worked and people like Biji Kurien and P.M. Murty joined Asian Paints in the late 1960s and early 1970s. Anand, an Indian Institute of Technology, Bombay (IIT-B) and IIM-C alumnus, was hired from the campus in 1970. While Kurien left to lead Berger Paints in the 1970s, Murty, an IIM-C graduate, went on to become Asian Paints's head of decorative business, and was elevated to MD and CEO in 2009. Anand took over as MD and CEO in 2011. Both Anand and Murty have been with Asian Paints since the 1970s, a testimony to the loyalty that the promoters have enjoyed with their best hires.

In the early 1970s, Asian Paints bought its first mainframe computer. I reckon, based on the best of my knowledge, that they were the first Indian company to buy a mainframe computer back then. Anand recalls, 'I graduated from IIT-B around the same time and I know that Asian Paints's mainframe was better than IIT-B's!' Interestingly enough, this mainframe was not used for payroll or administration processes. Instead, it was used for demand forecasting and improving service levels across the country. Since then, Asian Paints has nurtured the use of data analytics to forecast demand and consistently improve its supply chain efficiency—the single largest driver of competitive advantage for Asian Paints to date.

Through the 1970s, the company focused on upgrading its facilities. In 1974, a major modernization programme was undertaken to streamline the paint production facilities by improving the layout of machines and replacing old machinery. Hoon recalls, 'During the period 1967–87, the internals of the organization were made superstrong. This included computerization of various functions, improvement of supply chain efficiencies and manufacturing plants' productivity, and expansion of capacities. All the other companies couldn't react adequately to what was happening inside Asian Paints, thus taking the company beyond the reach of competition.'

In 1984, Choksey was succeeded by his son, Atul Choksey, as the managing director of Asian Paints. Choksey continued investments in IT automation to strengthen efficiencies. He also focused on expanding the company's manufacturing facilities beyond the west (Maharashtra and Gujarat), into the south (Andhra Pradesh in 1985, backward integration in Tamil Nadu in 1987) and north (Uttar Pradesh in 1990). These plants would go on to have their capacities expanded in the late 1990s. In 1982, two years before Atul became the managing director, Asian Paints had done its initial public offering (IPO) on stock exchanges to raise capital which partly funded this expansion of manufacturing units. On the brands front, Choksey—known to be aggressive with advertising—launched Utsav and Royale in interior paints, and a new segment of exterior paint emulsions under Apex. Finally, he also ventured beyond India and beyond decorative paints. Under him, Asian Paints entered into a technical collaboration arrangement with Nippon Paints for automotive finishes in 1995 and powder coatings in 1992, joint ventures for paints in Fiji, Tonga, Nepal and Vanuatu in 1990 and Queensland (Australia) in 1995, and a joint venture in 1997 with PPG Industries Inc., USA, to manufacture automotive paints and certain industrial products.

During these thirty years, its competitors, barring Berger, were either making mistakes around capital misallocation (e.g. Garware Paints, Jenson and Nicholson) or were focusing on only the premium segment of the industry (e.g.

ICI). This allowed Asian Paints to widen its gap versus peers during this phase.

Exhibit 11: Asian Paints's share price chart during 1991–97

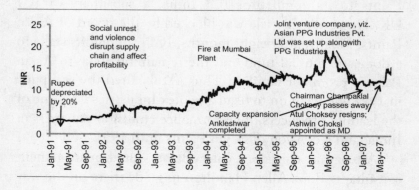

Source: Bloomberg, Ambit Capital research.

Business Process Re-engineering and Acceleration of Market Share Gains

Phase 3: 1997–2015

On 31 July 1997, Choksey passed away at the age of eighty-one. At that time, media reports indicated dissent between Choksey's son Atul and the remaining three promoter families. The magazine, *India Today*, reported[12] as follows in its September 1997 issue, 'While Choksey's co-promoters—Abhay Vakil, Ashwin Choksi and Ashwin Dani—dismiss charges of infighting, there's no denying that many of Choksey's plans for the company had not met with their

---

[12] 'A high stakes battle', *India Today*; http://indiatoday.intoday.in/story/british-major-icis-acquisition-of-9.1percent-stake-in-asian-paints-raises-spectre-of-takeover/1/274760.html.

approval. Choksey wanted to expand aggressively. This meant raising equity and diluting control, which the other three vehemently opposed.'

Eventually, Atul sold his 9 per cent stake in Asian Paints to its competitor ICI India, a subsidiary of ICI UK. However, this sale was blocked by the board of Asian Paints. Finally, after eight months, ICI sold half its stake to a domestic mutual fund and the remaining stake to Asian Paints's promoter families. Thus, Atul exited the company in 1997 and went on to head Apcotex Industries Ltd, one of the leading producers of performance emulsion polymers in India, and a division of Asian Paints until 1991.

After this episode, Asian Paints hired management consultants Booz Allen Hamilton to guide them on the way forward. The key benefits of this exercise were:

a) the best practices of all the manufacturing plants were brought together to improve operating efficiencies;
b) working capital cycles were brought down by rationalization of both raw material and finished goods' inventory management processes;
c) freeing up of bandwidth of managers which allowed them to focus more on the core business rather than spend time managing inefficient manual processes; and
d) improved organizational structure across three business units—domestic decorative, international and industrial paints.

A former employee of Asian Paints recalls, 'All credit to the directors that they understood that if we have to keep the flag flying, we had to have a relook at several aspects of the business, like technology, formulations, etc.'

Separately, the professional management team shifted the firm's focus of relying on in-house development of Information Technology (IT) infrastructure to procuring IT from third-party vendors. In 1999, the first phase of this included procuring software for supply chain management from i2 Technologies (a US-based company), which centralized and automated a large part of the process of demand forecasting, production planning and raw material procurement. The second phase included setting up of ERP (Enterprise Resource Planning) software in July 2000 across India.

During our discussions with him, Anand said, 'The demand forecasting offered by i2's software helped us a lot. Earlier, there was manual demand forecasting with manual interpretation of data, whereas here, there was a demand planner with analysts, who were trained to look at demand patterns in a more systematic manner'. Through these initiatives, the firm saw a significant reduction in working capital cycle days and improvement in ROCEs as highlighted in Exhibits 12 and 13.

Exhibit 12: Working capital days and ROCE from FY95 to FY15

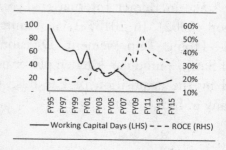

Source: Ambit Capital research.

Note: Working capital days = Debtors days + Inventory days – Creditors days.

Exhibit 13: Debtors days, creditors days and inventory days
from FY95 to FY15

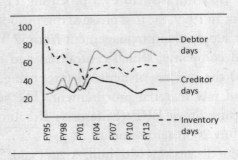

Source: Ambit Capital research.

In its decorative paints business in India, Asian Paints
gained substantial market share, especially from peers like
Akzo Nobel (ICI) and Kansai Nerolac during this phase (see
Exhibits 14–16). The firm also accelerated the expansion
of its international footprint with the acquisition of a paint
company in Sri Lanka (1999), setting up of greenfield
operations in Oman (2000), acquisition of a paint company
called SCIB Chemicals in Egypt (2002), and acquisition of
a controlling stake in Berger International, Singapore, for
Rs 580 million (2002). In 2013, Asian Paints launched a
new vertical—Home Improvement Division—with the
acquisition of Sleek, a modular-kitchen player in India. This
was followed by the acquisition of Ess Ess, a bathroom-
fitting company in India.

Exhibit 14: Asian Paints gained market share from Kansai Nerolac and Akzo Nobel during 1997–2015

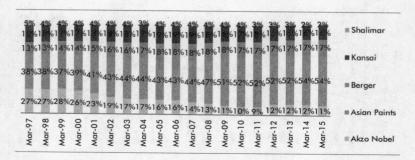

Source: Industry, Ambit Capital research.

Exhibit 15: Asian Paints's share price chart during 1997–2009

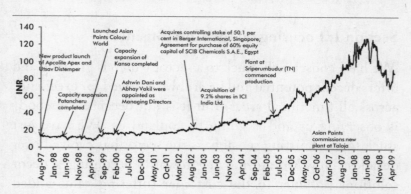

Source: Bloomberg, Ambit Capital research.

Exhibit 16: Asian Paints's share price chart during 2009–15

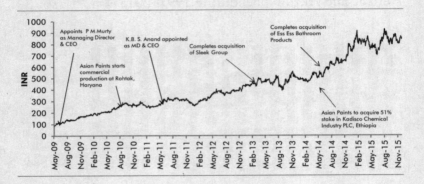

Source: Bloomberg, Ambit Capital research.

What Is Asian Paints's Secret Sauce?

Section 1: Focusing on the Core Business

'We have consciously stuck to a sector which is growing and offers decent potential and have always strived for excellence across all functional areas. But it is not because somebody is observing us and is going to applaud us. We have just stuck to our knitting sensibly as the sector has evolved over decades. Now we are moving towards becoming a decor solutions provider to the customer (offering value-added services like colour consultancies),' recalled Jalaj Dani, member from the promoter family, Asian Paints, in my meeting with him.

For the Choksis, Danis and Vakils, Asian Paints is the single biggest source of their wealth and to give them credit, the promoters have refrained from pushing the company towards major unrelated diversifications. On the contrary, erstwhile paint industry leaders like Jenson and Nicholson saw a steep decline in their market shares during the 1990s due to unrelated diversification into sectors like financial services, weigh bridges, weighing machines and hotels.

Asian Paints identified and understood the twin drivers for growth—supply chain efficiencies and brand power—early on and have relentlessly focused on entrenching themselves further in the paints sector using these drivers.

Following the departure of Atul Choksey in 1997, the remaining promoters have taken it upon themselves to focus on different divisions within Asian Paints, while the role of the managing director and CEO is held by an independent professional, K.B.S. Anand. Anand, in my meeting with him in December 2015, said, 'We have been lucky to have new jewels in the form of professional managers who attempted to do things that haven't been done before, and lucky to have a management that allowed them to do such things.'

Asian Paints is the only paints company in the sector which has not seen a change in its controlling shareholders (promoters) over the past seventy years. As shown in Exhibit 17, all its competitors have seen: a) a change in the controlling shareholder; and b) significant presence of a foreign entity on the board of directors. Industry experts say that this consistency at the board level has helped Asian Paints maintain focus on execution of a stable, long-term strategy over these decades.

Exhibit 17: Changes in promoters of paint companies since inception

Year	Change in ownership	Event details
Asian Paints		
1942	No	Formed by Choksey, Choksi, Vakil and Dani. Choksey moved out in 1997.
Berger Paints		
1923	No	Hadfields (India) was incorporated.
1947	Yes	Acquired by British Paints.
1965	Yes	British Paints was acquired by Celanese Corp.
1969	Yes	Berger, Jenson and Nicholson Ltd bought British Paints (India) from Celanese Corp.
1976	Yes	Foreign holding in the company was diluted to below 40% by sale of shares to the UB Group.
1988	Yes	Berger, Jenson and Nicholson sold controlling stake in Berger Paints India to UB Group.
1991	Yes	The business was sold to the Dhingra brothers.
Kansai Nerolac		
1920	No	Formed as Gahgan Paints. Entered into collaboration with Goodlass Group UK.
1933	Yes	Acquired by Lead Industries Group (creation of Goodlass Wall).
1957	No	Goodlass Wall became Goodlass Nerolac Paints and went public.
1976	Yes	Became part of the Tata Forbes group on acquisition of a part of the shareholding by Forbes Gokak.

(*Contd*)

Year	Change in ownership	Event details
1999	Yes	After selling 36% to Kansai Paint Co. in 1986, Kansai bought the remaining holding of Tata Forbes in 1999 and renamed it Kansai Nerolac in 2006.

Akzo Nobel

Year	Change in ownership	Event details
1911	No	Set up in India as Brunner Mond & Co.
1929	Yes	Name changed to Imperial Chemical Industries after a merger at the parent level.
1984	No	After entering several businesses, ICI merged all its group companies.
1987–2007	No	Entered and exited various businesses (pharmaceuticals, catalysts, rubber chemicals, adhesives, etc.).
2008	Yes	Akzo Nobel bought the entire share capital of Imperial Chemical Industries globally. The name of the company was changed to Akzo Nobel India.

Shalimar Paints

Year	Change in ownership	Event details
1902	No	Incorporated as Shalimar Paint Colour & Varnish.
1928	Yes	Pinchin Johnson bought the controlling stake and it became a part of the Red Hand Composition Group.
1963	No	After going public in 1961, changed its name to Shalimar Paints.
1964	Yes	Red Hand Composition bought over by International Paints, which became part of the Courtaulds Group.
1989	Yes	Sold to S.S. Jhunjhunwala and O.P. Jindal Group.

Source: Ambit Capital research.

Section 2: Deepening its Competitive Moats

Asian Paints has steadily built its competitive advantages across the four criteria of John Kay's IBAS framework—namely, innovation, brands and reputation, architecture, and strategic assets (for more details of this framework, please refer to Appendix 1).

I discuss each aspect below:

Innovation

Over seventy years, Asian Paints has repeatedly excelled as the first mover, thinking differently and being several steps ahead of the competition. This is evident across the firm's understanding of customer demand, use of technology and nurturing of professional talent. Competition has usually imitated Asian Paints, and even then, has always remained a few steps behind. There are three clear areas where Asian Paints has been ahead of competition.

First, product innovation: Asian Paints understands its customers better than its competition. This strength was possibly ingrained from its early days (the 1940s and '50s) when the promoters of Asian Paints deeply inculcated a culture of staying close to its customers. This proximity helped the company understand what product types (for instance, the launch of washable distemper in the 1950s), colour shades (deep shades rather than pastel shades), and pack sizes (smaller packs to help paint the horns of cattle and spokes of bullock carts) are in demand in various parts of the country. As a result, at a time when most paint companies in India were focusing on institutional customers and large distributors in urban areas, Asian Paints was able to build the business starting with smaller cities, rural markets and selling directly to dealers.

Second, supply chain management: In the 1950s and '60s, large multinational corporations (MNCs) used to offer at least 180 days of credit period to their distribution channel (i.e. shopkeepers, dealers and distributors who supplied paints to retail customers) and allowed the channel to extend the credit period to as long as one year in some cases. This hampered entry into the market for the smaller players, given the high and rising working capital requirements for them to deal with the channel partners at a time when the cost of capital was as high as 18 per cent. In that era, Asian Paints started the practice of offering regular payment performance discount, for example, a shopkeeper would get a 3.5 per cent extra discount if, without fail, he made payments on time throughout the year. This discount encouraged dealers to pay before time and the success of this practice led to the launch of cash discounts, where if a dealer made the payment in cash, he would get a 5 per cent discount on his procurement price. These initiatives were a win-win—Asian Paints delivered its products to its dealers faster than its competition and the dealers were able to manage their working capital cycles better.

Supply chain management is a critical aspect for success in the paints industry given the voluminous nature of products, low margins for dealers, seasonality of demand and the large number of stock-keeping units (SKUs). Asian Paints has a track record of remaining a leader on this front. Some initiatives it has taken to strengthen this moat include being the first company to

(a) use mainframes in the early 1970s to forecast demand for better inventory management;
(b) start branch billing on computers in the late 1970s;
(c) import a colour computer in 1979 which helped reduce tinting time from five or six days down to four hours; and

(d) use GPS (Global Positioning System) for tracking movement of trucks carrying finished goods in the channel (implemented between 2010 and 2015).

Asian Paints also established a network of regional distribution centres (RDCs) in the 1980s and 1990s. Over the previous five years, this has been replaced by larger distribution centres close to manufacturing plants.

Third and finally, empowerment of professionals: Asian Paints was unique amongst Indian promoter-led firms—it allowed professionals to take control of middle and senior management roles as early as 1969. Although many second-generation members of the four promoter families were engaged in the business in the 1970s and thereafter, they had been given strict instructions not to interfere with professionals, especially when the latter had been made responsible for a specific function.

Brand

Asian Paints's investments in its brands are legendary. I am reminded of a meeting, back in 2013, with a former employee of Kansai Nerolac (a competitor of Asian Paints), who told me, 'Asian Paints is the only paint company which has strong brand recall even for its sub-brands, both in economy, like Gattu and Utsav, as well as for premium products, like Royale and Apex. All the other paint companies have been able to create brand recall for only the mother brand—like Nerolac, Dulux and Berger.'

Asian Paints has consistently maintained its focus on advertising from as early as the 1950s. More importantly, its advertising campaigns have always kept pace with the changing profile of its customers. For instance, one of the recent advertisement campaigns of Royale Play, a premium emulsion, captures the emergence of nuclear families living in metropolitan cities with long office working hours. The advertisement campaign called 'Surprise Your Spouse' has the tag lines: 'He's working late? Watch your home's makeover transform his mood' and 'She is visiting her parents for the weekend? Let a transformed home welcome her back.'

As India's economy grew since the 1950s, so did customer demands. To its credit, Asian Paints capitalized on the emotional appeal of a house or *ghar* and linked it to paint. Indeed, a freshly acquired and newly painted house is a matter of pride for any family. Asian Paints and its advertising agencies have changed their messaging to maintain this emotional connection with their target audience.

Three examples can indicate this. First, Gattu—the mischievous kid—was launched as Asian Paint's mascot in 1954, mostly in print ads, with the tag line: 'Any surface that needs painting, needs Asian Paints.' Unlike its peers who were focusing on upwardly mobile, urban audiences in their adverts during the 1970s, Gattu—designed by R.K. Laxman, whose Common Man cartoons were famous throughout India—appealed to the masses and helped Asian Paints become a leader in the smaller cities. Gattu remained the mascot for Asian Paints until 2002; beyond this year, the firm started changing its positioning in favour of premium households. Second, in my discussions with him in December 2015, Anand highlighted: 'In 2002, we did the entire rebranding exercise having understood that paint is the most important thing driving the feel-good factor at home, which, after the family, is the most important thing for an individual. That is why we came up with the theme, *Har ghar kuch kehta hai, kyun ki iske andar koi rehta hai* (every house says something about it since someone lives in it). We tried to personify paint as a mechanism to transform and personalize every individual home.' And finally, in 2012, Asian Paints underwent another meaningful rebranding exercise. As Amit Syngle, vice-president (sales and marketing), stated in a media release in 2012, 'The change in our brand identity signifies our intent to establish a deeper connect with our customers as well as ensure that the Asian Paints brand is able to stir the consumer's imagination, ignite their creativity as well as expand their vision to a new vista of possibility. Our new logo conveys those elements with the flowing ribbon formation that creates the "AP" design highlighting the easy flow, smoothness, dynamism and possibility that our solution and offerings will provide.'

Architecture

I met Rama Bijapurkar, a leading market strategy consultant and an independent director on the boards of several notable companies in October 2015 whilst I was finalizing the 2015 Coffee Can Portfolio for Ambit's clients. Amongst other things, we discussed Asian Paints and how its internal processes stack up relative to the competition. Rama told me, 'I have known Asian Paints for thirty years and all through this period, they have been obsessed about hiring the best people, about having the best IT and the smartest technology-driven process. They started obsessing about talent and technology way before anybody else in India.'

There are three critical aspects to Asian Paints's architecture: a) creating a unique working culture that nurtures talent; b) using IT to improve competitive advantages; and c) creating a truly independent board of directors to help shape evolution of the firm.

Asian Paints does not offer the highest pay packages to business school graduates. Then how does the firm manage to achieve one of the lowest attrition rates in its junior and middle management team across the consumer sector in India?

Choksey began the tradition of hiring top management talent from the IIMs in 1969 and this practice has continued until date. One of India's most seasoned fund managers who invested in Asian Paints when it went public in 1982, explained this in our discussion with him: 'Asian Paints is not about a few individuals. The average quality of employees in any role is markedly superior to any other company, and that comes by hiring better people at all levels consistently.' Nirmesh Prakash, former manager (marketing) at Asian Paints during the period 2000–05, highlighted: 'Out of 100 people on the work floor, if one is not a cultural fit, he would be easily visible as a misfit. But the remaining ninety-nine would be very similar to each other in their intellect, motivation levels and work ethics.'

In my discussions with the recruitment coordinators at India's best business schools, I discovered that Asian Paints is a preferred employer. What is more interesting, however, is the manner in which Asian Paints maintains a professional working environment that enhances its attractiveness as a preferred company to work for. I spoke to several employees—past and present—to understand this unique feature.

My discussions lead me to believe that the following practices are instrumental in helping Asian Paints nurture talent: First, rapid career progression for those who perform. After management trainees join Asian Paints, they are given significant authority and responsibility in their roles, and if they perform, they get promoted very quickly to middle management roles. Mangesh Pathak, a former employee of Asian Paints, told me in October 2015, 'Within six months of joining Asian Paints in 1996 as a management trainee, I was given independent responsibility to manage one of the six regional distribution centres. In less than five years, I was handling a large portfolio of raw and packing materials as a purchase manager. Job rotation at regular intervals always ensured a steep learning curve and acted as a motivation for me.'

Second, empowerment allows creativity. Once an employee gains independent responsibility to manage a depot/branch/manufacturing plant, there is a high degree of accountability. Also, there is ample room for an employee to be creative and take independent decisions. Asian Paints has one of the best processes of internal reporting and budgeting and, therefore, performance of each individual or branch or business unit is clearly measurable. This is followed up with fairness in performance appraisal and a disciplined process of carrying out review meetings, which are attended by representatives of the three families, and all members of the senior management team. The fund manager cited previously told me, 'In these review meetings, there is no blame game. Instead, a genuine attempt is made to learn from what has happened so that things can improve in future.' Jalaj Dani, member from one of the promoter families of Asian Paints, also told us, 'You learn a lot from interacting with people in this organization if you have the humility to listen to them. This firm has had a culture that has allowed the professionals to do what they like to do, which results in people delivering great ideas and doing great things.'

And finally, senior employees are looked after well. Once an employee spends ten to fifteen years with Asian Paints, his relationships with the promoter families and senior management professionals become extremely strong. Thereafter, the organization will intervene to help the employee's family for any need in his personal life. Some examples of such interventions I came across in our interactions with some current and former senior employees of Asian Paints include ensuring the best quality of healthcare support when an employee or his family member encounters debilitating illness, and taking care of the well-being of employees' family members during any emergency situation.

As Jalaj Dani told me, 'It's about the feeling of being a family. From funerals to weddings to attending other personal events—it's the sensibility of being sensitive about it.' Hoon adds, 'I once asked Choksey why Asian Paints does not pay the managers well. He answered that whilst we are the best paymasters to salesmen, clerks and labourers, we don't need to pay the managers very highly. When I bring these boys from business schools, there is a price that they have to pay to get experience here. I know some of them will leave after getting trained because they will be offered a better salary within the first three to five years of joining. But those who will remain with me over the longer term will be looked after well by the organization on all fronts.'

Asian Paints's use of technology is well known. It invests capital to buy and use best-in-class technology to improve its supply chain efficiencies and working capital management—which are the two biggest drivers of competitive advantage in the paints industry. For instance, mainframes were used for demand forecasting as early as the 1970s. Hoon, who was the factory manager of the company's Ankleshwar plant (Gujarat) in the 1980s recalls: 'In 1980, the Bhandup plant (Mumbai) used to operate with 1600 workers. Ankleshwar started production with only around 250 workers for the same capacity. And the subsequent capacity expansion in Patancheru (near Hyderabad) was with less than 100 workers in 1985, all thanks to better technology to automate manufacturing processes and higher productivity.'

Many of its new plants across the country are controlled through IT servers placed in Mumbai. They are totally controlled over interfaces where operators sit and operate across all segments of manufacturing. IT encompasses other functions such as human resources as well. Key result areas (popularly known as KRAs in office parlance) are given to the middle management employees who are encouraged to increase the productivity of operations through their respective roles. Mangesh Pathak, former purchase manager, recalls, 'Around 2001, I was clearly told that if I take steps to improve the working capital pertaining to my portfolio of raw/purchase material, the firm would see a certain increase in percentage points in overall ROCE. A very clear link was established between company's overall goals and the key performance indicators (KPIs) of a functional manager.'

The benefits of using IT are also visible at dealer levels. As one of the largest dealers of Asian Paints located in South Mumbai told us, 'I order products from Asian Paints five to ten times in a day and receive supplies three to four times daily. Until 1995–96, we used to call the depot to place our orders. Then they started their call centres in 2002–03. Now they incentivize us to order online rather than through the call centres, by giving us between Rs 500 and Rs 10,000 extra per month depending on the size of our online orders. Even if others copy this in a few years, they will have frequent stock-outs, and hence won't meet our requirements.' Asian Paints's management told us, 'Over the period 2000–15, IT has become a go-to resource for everyone in the company rather than being just a low-priority support function. IT is like electricity. It is part of daily life. It works as a great integrator of all operating functions across the firm'.

And finally, Asian Paints has a genuinely independent board. As one of India's most seasoned fund managers told me in October 2015, 'Unlike many other companies, independent directors on the board of Asian Paints are not invited based on their relationships with the promoters, but because of the contributions they can make as board members. The board gets very seriously involved in the appointment of the CEO and of all senior management personnel one level below the CEO. This avoids any bias that the promoter family or other executive directors might have'.

Many Indian companies fill their boards with friends and cronies in order to pay lip service to the legal requirement that mandates that 50 per cent of the board should comprise independent directors. Asian Paints is among that rare breed of companies whose boards are truly independent. Their board is composed of fourteen directors. Of these, six are a part of the promoter families, two from each of the three families. Anand sits on the board as the MD and CEO. The remaining seven independent directors are credible individuals with relevant backgrounds, as highlighted in Exhibit 18.

Exhibit 18: Independent directors on the board of Asian Paints—high-quality professionals with relevant experience

Name	On Board since	Background
Dipankar Basu	15 April 2000	Was chairman of State Bank of India till August 1995. Member of government's Divestment Commission (1996–99). Advisor to the government on banking sector reforms (1997).
Dr S. Sivaram	4 July 2001	Bestowed with Padma Shri in 2006. More than thirty years' experience in research on polymer synthesis. Serves on the editorial board of several journals in chemistry and polymer science.
Mahendra Shah	6 June 2001	Was managing director of The Indian Card Clothing Co. Limited (1985–2001). Was chairman of panels of Textile Machinery Manufacturers' Association. Holds a BE degree in electrical engineering and a master's degree in industrial engineering.
S. Ramadorai	16 September 2009	Recipient of Padma Bhushan in 2006 and CBE (Commander of the Order of the British Empire) in 2009. Was CEO and MD of TCS (2004–09); thirty-two years of total work experience at TCS. Advisor to the prime minister in the National Skill Development Council.

(*Contd*)

Name	On Board since	Background
M. K. Sharma	25 October 2012	Inducted into the board of Hindustan Unilever Ltd (HUL) in 1995 as a whole-time director.
		Vice chairman of HUL (2000–07).
		Completed PGDPM (postgraduate diploma in personnel management) and diploma in labour laws from Indian Law Institute, Delhi.
Vibha Paul Rishi	14 May 2014	Was part of the founding team of Titan Watches, and founding team employee of PepsiCo India.
		Was director, marketing and customer strategy, at the Future Group.
		Seventeen years' experience at PepsiCo in marketing and innovation roles in India, the US and the UK.
Deepak Satwalekar	30 May 2000	Was MD of HDFC Ltd from 1993 to 2002.
		MD and CEO of HDFC Standard Life Insurance Co. Ltd (2000–08).
		Chaired and had been a member of expert groups related to industry, government and the RBI.

Source: Industry, Ambit Capital research.

Strategic assets

Asian Paints's key strategic assets are: a) wide geographical spread of its supply chain network including manufacturing plants and depots, which helps service its dealers efficiently; and b) deep-rooted relationships with paint dealers in the industry. Both of these assets have been built over the past seven decades and are near-impossible to replicate by its competition.

(a) Network of manufacturing plants and depots: Asian Paints has one of the largest number of manufacturing units and depots across the country in its supply chain network. More importantly, the firm leverages on a wider network of manufacturing plants and depots to operate at the highest ratio of revenues per depot or revenues per manufacturing plant, thereby helping improve inventory turnover and working capital turnover for the overall business. For instance, over the past decade, Asian Paints has been setting up distribution centres (DCs) next to the manufacturing units. These DCs will serve as large-format hubs for inventory storage of both fast- as well as slow-moving SKUs. Whilst for slow-moving SKUs, the DC network will aim at replacing the RDC network in its entirety, for the fast-moving SKUs, the DC network will aim at reducing the transfer of surplus stock from one depot to another within the distribution network. The company's size and efficiency is visible in the fact that it has the largest number of dealers (35,000 vs 21,000 for Berger). With only around 125 depots in its supply chain, its revenue per depot is approximately Rs 100 crore, more than twice that of the next highest, which is around Rs 40 crore per depot for Kansai Nerolac. Similarly, its revenue per factory is approximately Rs 1500 crore, twice that of the next highest (just over Rs 700 crore for Kansai Nerolac).

(b) Relationships with dealers built through non-transactional initiatives: The company's relationships with its dealers have been built over decades. These deep-rooted relationships go beyond its stellar IT systems that make dealers' lives easier. Several dealers have told us that Asian Paints has gone beyond its call of duty to help its channel partners should they face any unexpected problems. As Jalaj Dani told me, 'Dealers are part of our family. If we find that they are affected due to unforeseen events such as riots, floods, earthquakes, etc., we ensure that the best support is provided to them in every possible manner, including extending the credit period, so as to help them get back on their feet.'

Anand added to this, 'Fifty per cent of the dealers don't check their accounts, despite having access to a web portal which gives them real-time updates on their accounts. They say they have faith in our fairness in dealing with them. But they check their accounts with other paint companies thoroughly and regularly.' And finally, the founding chief investment officer of a leading equity mutual fund told me in October 2015, 'Distributors are the bedrock of Asian Paints's success, and their relationship is mutual. They look after Asian Paints and Asian Paints looks after them.'

Section 3: Capital allocation

Exhibit 19: Sources of capital during FY96–05

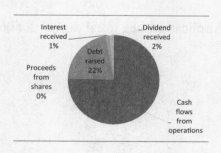

Source: Ambit Capital research.

Exhibit 20: Application of capital during FY96–05

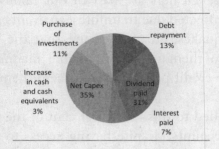

Source: Ambit Capital research.

Exhibit 21: Sources of capital during FY06–15

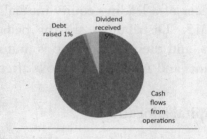

Source: Ambit Capital research.

Exhibit 22: Application of capital during FY06–15

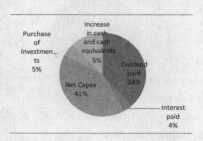

Source: Ambit Capital research.

The company's capital allocation decisions have, by and large, been focused on its core business. Cash generated has been judiciously ploughed back in the business and used for expansion. Even for its daily operations, Asian Paints has regularly invested in technology that has strengthened its competitive position and improved operating efficiencies, irrespective of the payback periods. Some examples of such investments include investments in mainframes in the early 1970s, colour computers in 1979, tinting machines in the 1990s, i2 technologies software in 1999 and ERP software in 2000. The expansion of its manufacturing facilities has been timely and has included backward integration to manufacture important intermediates in the paint-manufacturing process like phthalic anhydride and pentaerythritol.

Its international forays, however, have seen mixed results. Starting from Fiji in 1978, Asian Paints now has a presence in the Caribbean, the Middle East, South East Asia, the South Pacific and Africa. The strategy underlying these international expansion initiatives has been: a) leveraging on the company's skills and capabilities in India to capitalize on growth opportunities in other emerging countries; b) gaining exposure to the rest of the world as the firm prepares for its long-term future; and c) sticking to the paints industry as much as possible since that is what the firm knows best.

Speaking about the acquisition of Berger International (Singapore) and SCIB (Egypt) back in 2002, Jalaj Dani, then head of international operations of Asian Paints and newly appointed chairman of Berger International, said, 'The emerging markets have 50 per cent of the world's population and this is where we see the potential upside as we seek to draw more efficiencies out of the acquisitions we have just completed. Further, the company will implement cost structures in Berger's operations worldwide for increased plant efficiencies and increased asset productivity. It will focus on improving working capital management through various initiatives and introduce IT in areas of operations where essential.'

While the strategy to expand overseas was well founded, these ventures have been a drag on the company's balance sheet. The company's capital allocation in overseas business has not borne fruit even after more than twenty years of consistent investment. To its credit, Asian Paints has resisted the temptation of pumping in more money and stretching its balance sheet to make the international businesses profitable. As a result, the share of overseas business in capital employed has reduced over a period of time, although it still remains significant.

Over the past decade, Asian Paints seems to be preparing for the future by investing in: a) businesses related to homes, such as kitchenware and bathroom fittings, and b) services that could disrupt the traditional Indian model of hiring painters to paint their homes.

In 2013, Asian Paints acquired the Sleek Group which caters to the organized modern kitchen space. In FY15, Asian Paints acquired the front-end business of Ess Ess, a high-quality player in the bathroom fittings segment. Albeit small in size (only Rs 230 crore of total assets), these acquisitions come across as a deviation from the strategy to remain focused on paints. However, the rationale behind these acquisitions is to protect the distribution channel of mom-and-pop stores in the paints industry from disruptive evolution of the industry. This disruption could emerge as the paints industry evolves either into a service-oriented model or a DIY (do-it-yourself) model, thereby enabling large global MNCs to open large-format stores with value addition to customers, which could dilute the importance of the traditional mom-and-pop store network.

To explain this in numbers, consider this: The cost of labour involved in painting a home has increased to approximately 65 per cent of the project cost for a household from around 10 per cent in 1980. This is because labour costs have grown at 9–10 per cent CAGR over FY06–15 versus a mere 3 per cent CAGR in paint prices. With this trend likely to continue, there is a high likelihood that fifteen to twenty years from now, labour costs will be around 90 per cent of the overall paint project cost. Thus, in the future, it might make more sense to buy paint from a store and paint a home yourself rather than employ painters and labourers. Indeed, this is the practice in developed economies. Once this happens, two consumption patterns are likely to emerge.

First, customers will be willing to pay for labour involvement if there is a service-oriented value addition attached to it. This could include decor consultancy services either on the shop floor or at your doorstep, or faster/ cleaner/ highly organized ways of executing the paint project. To this end, Asian Paints has tried several service-oriented models over the past decade like:

a) opening of experience stores in Mumbai, Delhi and Kolkata;

b) Colour Ideas stores (just under 300 in number currently) which provide colour consultancy in the mom-and-pop stores;

c) Home Solutions painting service, which currently executes 20,000–25,000 projects each year;

d) introduction of Royale play, high-end textured paints; and

e) colour consultancy services at home for a price of around Rs 2000 (1,60,000 colour consultancies were provided in FY15).

Two years ago, I got my house painted by my self-appointed painter. After the completion of that project, I appointed Asian Paints Home Solutions for textured paint to be done on one of the walls. Although Asian Paints Home Solutions charged me a rate 15–20 per cent higher than my self-appointed painter, I enjoyed the experience where there was a team of painters led by an Asian Paints employee who was very professional in his conduct, took great care of my existing furniture, and got the work done without any delay. Next time I get my house painted, I will just appoint Asian Paints Home Solutions for an end-to-end service.

Second, a DIY model will emerge. Currently, households do not adopt a DIY approach because: a) without sophisticated tools being available, DIY painting process is tiring, dirty, cumbersome, and lacks uniformity in quality; and b) at 60–65 per cent of the project cost, labour involvement is affordable for many households. However, with the introduction of sophisticated tools like the ones being introduced by Berger in its Express Painting service, and with over 90 per cent of the paint project cost being labour, both these factors are likely to change in favour of the emergence of DIY model over the next couple of decades.

The experience in developed countries like the US and the UK shows that several small-sized exclusive stores, like Sherwin Williams in the US which controls 3500 such exclusive retail stores, replaced the traditional mom-and-pop stores (whose share in industry or aggregate sales has dropped to 10–11 per cent or less in the US and the UK). New entrants into the industry establish their presence through large-format DIY stores which are on the city's outskirts. These stores largely offer private label paint products at

5–10 per cent lower prices compared to the incumbents, and also offer value-added services to consumers.

The company's management is aware that potentially disruptive changes lie ahead. Hence, through the launch of value-added services like Asian Paints Home Solutions, colour consultancies, Colour Ideas stores and its entry into the home improvement solutions business, Asian Paints intends to convert its existing mom-and-pop store network into a one-stop shop for all the needs of the evolving paint customer.

In our discussions, Anand highlighted, 'In a few months, we plan to open our first home improvement solutions store in Coimbatore. It will have all of our products, as well other products, as we don't have the entire product range right now that can be offered through such a store. In every business we have to learn. It will take us time to learn and perfect the business. That's our strategic game plan.' When asked about how the firm views the risk of dilution of ROCE through such a move, the management said, 'At the moment, home improvement business is too small to have any significant impact on the overall ROCE of the firm. But if you are talking about building long-term strength with your channel partners, whatever ROCE we lose in the new business will be more than offset by an increase in ROCE of the paints business.'

Asian Paints's astonishing share price outperformance

A rupee invested in Asian Paints in January 1991 is worth Rs 299 in April 2016, implying a compounded annual return of 25 per cent. That same rupee would be worth just Rs 26 if invested in the Sensex, implying a CAGR of

14 per cent. Thus Asian Paints has outperformed the Sensex by 11.6 times over the past twenty-five years. This outstanding performance has been driven by the promoters' deep focus over the last seventy years on the paints business. This focus has been backed by systematic deepening of its competitive moats via a focus on hiring good people and getting the best out of them, alongside investing in IT systems which improve demand forecasting and supply chain management. Finally, Asian Paints has taken prudent capital allocation decisions which, whilst taking controlled risks, maintain a focus on ROCE.

CHAPTER 3

Berger Paints: 250 Years in the Making

'When you are the anvil, bear—when you are the hammer, strike.'

—Edwin Markham

Little did Lewis Berger know in 1760 that two-and-a-half centuries after he began a manufacturing company in Europe, his surname would live on as the second-largest paints company in India. The Berger Paints of today has a fascinating history of changing ownerships.

According to the British National Archives,[13] Lewis Steigenberger came to London from Frankfurt, Germany, in 1760 as a nineteen-year-old colour chemist to manufacture Prussian blue, using the name of Lewis Berger. After Berger died in 1800, his sons took over the business and converted the paints firm into a limited company, Lewis Berger and

---

[13] http://discovery.nationalarchives.gov.uk/details/rd/19b53177-a2de-4e6e-af52-3e87870d6deb.

Sons Limited. In 1960, the company merged with Jenson and Nicholson, a manufacturer of coach paints, to form Berger, Jenson and Nicholson (BJN). In 1969, BJN acquired British Paints, making BJN the world's second-largest paints producer, after ICI's paints division. British Paints, a part of Celanese Corp (USA) at that time, had an Indian operation based at Kolkata. This Indian operation had been acquired in 1947 from Hadfield's, a small colonial-era company set up in 1923. And so, the routes of Lewis Berger from Germany and British Paints from India intersected as BJN took over British Paints India.

In 1970, BJN was acquired by Hoechst AG, then the world's largest chemical company, based in Germany. In India, Hoechst was associated with liquor baron, Vittal Mallya. In 1956, Mallya and two other Indian partners had tied up with Hoechst AG to promote Hoechst Pharmaceuticals, where he held 48 per cent of the company and was the chairman of the company. In 1978, Mallya became the chairman of British Paints India, and in 1983, British Paints was renamed as Berger Paints India Limited. Following Vittal Mallya's death, his son, Vijay Mallya, took over the group's reins in the 1980s. In 1988, Hoechst AG sold BJN to Williams Holding. Fuelled by his ambitions to build a global conglomerate, Vijay Mallya acquired Berger's overseas operations (except Australia, Europe and the UK) through a leveraged buyout.

Thus, by the late 1980s, the United Breweries (UB) Group emerged as the controlling shareholder in Berger Paints. Then, in 1991, Vijay Mallya sold the UB Group's stake to the current owners, the Dhingra brothers—Kuldip Singh and Gurbachan Singh.

Even as ownership changed hands thrice—from British Paints to BJN (1969), from BJN to the Mallyas (1978) and finally from the Mallyas to the Dhingras in 1991—Berger Paints moved up the rankings in the Indian paints industry. In my discussions with paint industry veterans, I found that Berger moved up the ranks from number seven in 1980 (following a factory lockout) to number four by 1991 and number three by 1998. Currently, Berger is the second-largest paints company in India, after Asian Paints.

This remarkable journey follows in three distinct phases across forty-five years:

The Madhukar/Biji Kurien Era—Transforming into a Decorative Paints Company

Phase 1: 1972–91

'The most difficult thing to change at a company is to change its people. For instance, when I joined Berger as the head of sales and marketing, I was thirty-one years old, supervising around thirteen branches of the company, and most branch managers reporting in me had more than thirty-one years of experience!' So says Biji Kurien, former managing director, Berger Paints (erstwhile British Paints).

Things would have been different at Berger Paints if Biji Kurien, a gold medallist from the prestigious IIM-A, had joined a multinational company instead of Asian Paints in the late 1960s. In 1972, he was roped into Berger Paints by his previous boss, Dongargaokar Madhukar. Madhukar, also from Asian Paints, was Berger's first Indian managing director and already leading the charge in terms of transforming British Paints, as Berger was then called. Kurien joined Berger as their head, sales and marketing, and eventually succeeded Madhukar as CEO in 1980.

Reminiscing in his office in Nungambakkam, one of Chennai's oldest neighbourhoods, Kurien told us that he and Madhukar inherited a company that made paints for marine and rail applications. He estimated that 60 per cent of the colours that Berger produced in the 1970s were not even on the shade cards of distributors. As Kurien says, the biggest challenge was to change the work culture within Berger. This, along with a shift in focus towards decorative paints, was the transformation that Kurien led through the 1980s.

Kurien hired high-quality talent and worked on building a culture that encouraged and retained such talent by giving full autonomy to employees. This improvement in culture gave the employees a sense of togetherness. Alongside this, Kurien shifted Berger's orientation towards a consumer-facing home decor business, focusing on delivering products and services based on the requirements of retail customers. To begin with, several new products were launched in the decorative paints segment—Butterfly Enamel (a solvent-based paint for interior use that gives the surface a glossy look) was launched during the mid-1970s and Luxol Silk was launched in 1979 as the company's first acrylic emulsion.

Kurien ensured that these products were supported by innovative high-profile advertising. This task was given to the Lintas Media Group, which at the time was one of India's largest advertising agencies. The biggest of these marketing campaigns was around Luxol Silk, a brand that was launched at a premium price as compared to the then incumbents like Dulux Velvet Touch, Asian Paints Apcolite, Shalimar Paints Superlac, and Jenson and Nicholson's Special Effects. Through these marketing campaigns, Luxol Silk was successfully established as a premium emulsion associated with households that own luxurious objects like Persian carpets and Waterford crystals. Berger also pioneered the concept of outsourced manufacturing in the paints industry to improve operating efficiencies.

Kurien's strategy worked. Berger's shift towards decorative paints and the success of brands such as Luxol Silk helped Berger rise up the ranks through the 1980s and '90s. Berger Paints grew from the seventh-largest paints company in India in 1980 (smaller than peers like Asian Paints, Kansai Nerolac, Garware, Jenson and Nicholson, Shalimar Paints and Imperial Chemical Industries [ICI]) to become the fourth-largest paints company in the country in the early 1990s, with a strong orientation towards decorative paints.

As Anoop Hoon (national sales manager [decoratives] of Asian Paints during 1991–94) recalls, 'Madhukar and Kurien brought brilliance into Berger Paints. During their era, supply chain, productivity, operational excellence, brands and the focus on the decorative market was initiated—everything they had learnt, experienced and perfected at Asian Paints was carried forth. Berger had been transitioned.'

Even as Berger transformed itself by the late 1980s, its ownership was due for a change with the Mallyas of UB Group looking to sell their controlling stake. Further north, in Amritsar, Punjab, the Dhingra brothers—Kuldip Singh and Gurbachan Singh—were searching for a paints company to diversify their business of paint exports to Russia.

The Dhingra brothers have a family history of continuity in the paints business since 1898 when their great-grandfather and grandfather started a paint shop in Amritsar. In the mid-1960s, they started manufacturing paints under the brand name Rajdoot, and scaled up the business significantly in north India during the 1970s. Thereafter, during the 1980s, the Dhingras established a strong exports platform in the paints industry and became the largest providers of paint to the former Soviet Union. Berger Paints was the perfect fit for the Dhingras, and in 1991, Vijay Mallya sold his controlling stake in Berger Paints to them. The cash flows generated from the Dhingras' exports to the Soviet Union were eventually used to acquire Berger Paints a few months before the USSR disintegrated.

The Dhingra/Subir Bose Era—Rising Up the Ranks to the Second Spot

Phase 2: 1992–2010

The Dhingras acquired a company which was facing considerable financial strain. Berger's aggressive expansion into the decorative paints segment had strained its balance sheet. The company was reeling under capital constraints until 1991, which resulted in delayed payments of salaries to the professional management team and supply chain issues, given its single manufacturing location at Howrah, West Bengal. Kuldip Singh Dhingra was convinced of Kurien's capabilities as well as the strength of Kurien's team. After all, Kurien had ensured that Berger's operations weren't affected by changing ownerships when BJN sold out to the Mallyas. The Dhingras identified liquidity-related bottlenecks early in the game and pumped in funds in multiple stages through short-term loans, debentures with associated share warrants, which were converted into shares, a rights issue in the mid-1990s and a preferential issue in 2008, all of which helped Berger unleash its potential.

During 1995–96, Berger introduced colour tinting machines at dealers' shops. This mission was headed by none other than Abhijit Roy who would go on to lead the company in 2012. Colour tinting machines tint multiple neutral bases each designed to cover a range of colours, i.e., dark, medium or pastel. This machine automatically tints the shade desired by the customer once the shade's code is punched in. As a result, the number of colour shades offered by the dealer at his shop increased dramatically from 125 colours to more than 5000 colours. After leading Berger for fourteen years as its CEO, Kurien retired in 1994, handing over the reins to Subir Bose, who at that stage had already spent a decade in the firm. Bose would lead Berger for the next eighteen years.

Bose led Berger's expansion in the decorative paints segment, reducing their focus on the industrial segment. As India's economy opened up, following the liberalization-led reforms of 1991, Bose led Berger's expansion outside the firm's traditional market in the eastern region of India through new paint units in Puducherry and Jammu. By the late 1990s, Berger was the number three player in both the decorative segment (11 per cent share after Asian Paints and Kansai Nerolac) and the industrial paints segment (14 per cent share after Kansai Nerolac and Asian Paints).

Exhibit 23: Berger Paints's share price chart during 1994–99

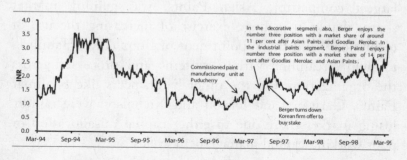

Source: Bloomberg, Company, Ambit Capital research.

Exhibit 24: Berger Paints's share price chart during 1999–2004

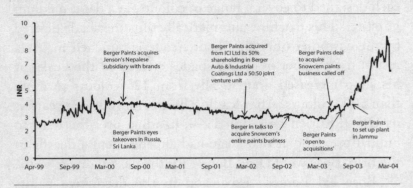

Source: Bloomberg, Company, Ambit Capital research.

Bose also ramped up Berger's presence across rural areas by emphasizing on products such as Jadoo Cem, Jadoo Emulsion and Jadoo Synthetic. On the supply chain front, Bose expanded the Color Bank tinting system to more than 1000 outlets by the end of FY01. The company pursued acquisitions to increase production, especially in Nepal, and to increase its presence in new segments, for example, by acquiring ICI's motor paints business and manufacturing unit in Rishra, West Bengal. During this phase, Berger's largest competitor, Asian Paints, was gaining market share, thanks to a huge exercise of increasing the use of technology, and the appointment of Booz Allen Hamilton to help streamline various systems and processes across the organization. On the other hand, peers like Shalimar Paints, Garware, and Jenson and Nicholson were rapidly losing market share due to either capital misallocation or poor working capital management cycles.

Exhibit 25: Berger Paints's share price chart during 2004–09

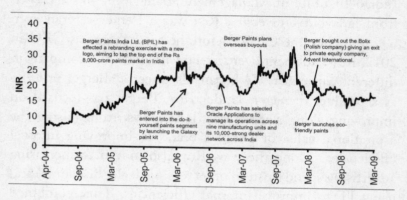

Source: Bloomberg, Ambit Capital research.

The Abhijit Roy Era—Catching Up with the Market Leader

Phase 3: 2011–15

To their credit, the Dhingras have shied away from micromanaging Berger Paints. In the third decade of their ownership, the Dhingras saw the third change in Berger's leadership. Like Kurien and Bose before him, Abhijit Roy also worked at Asian Paints before joining Berger in 1996. In February 2011, Berger announced Roy's elevation from senior vice president, sales and marketing, to director and chief operating officer of the company. In the same announcement, it was also stated that Roy would succeed Bose as the CEO of the company from 1 July 2012. This change in the management team also coincided with the acceleration in Berger's revenue growth relative to the market leader, Asian Paints (see Exhibits 26, 27).

A marketing graduate from the batch of 1989–91 at the Indian Institute of Management, Bangalore, and a BTech from Jadavpur University, Roy was a Berger veteran even before he became CEO. Before he took charge as CEO in 2012, Roy had spent over sixteen years with the company in different capacities. He began his career at Berger in 1996 as a product manager. Under Roy, Berger has focused on improving along a variety of dimensions, from raising the aspirational value of Berger's brand to improving internal efficiencies. Along the way, Roy also moved to increasing advertising spend (instead of increasing dealer discounts) and using IT to improve internal efficiencies. This, combined with a constant focus on cost reduction, has resulted in operating margin expansion. I now discuss each of these points in detail.

Exhibit 26: Revenue growth rebased to 100 in FY06—Asian Paints grew much faster than Berger during FY06–11

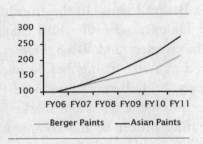

Source: Ambit Capital research. Rebased to 100 means comparing both companies' revenues from the same point (FY06) starting as 100. For example, if Asian Paints's FY07 revenue growth is 10% over FY06, the data point in the above chart for FY07 will be 110 (10% growth over 100). If FY08 is 15% over FY07, then the data point will be 126.5 (15% growth over 110).

Exhibit 27: Revenue growth rebased to 100 in FY11—Berger matched pace with Asian Paints during FY11–15

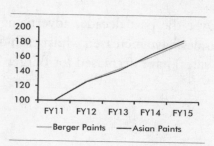

Source: Ambit Capital research. Rebased to 100 means comparing both companies' revenues from the same point (FY06) starting as 100. For example, if Asian Paints's FY07 revenue growth is 10% over FY06, the data point in the above chart for FY07 will be 110 (10% growth over 100). If FY08 is 15% over FY07, then the data point will be 126.5 (15% growth over 110).

Change in Brand Positioning: In an effort to build aspirational connect with the end consumer, Roy has raised advertising spend over the past five years. This has gone towards:

(a) Using Bollywood to connect with the audience: Until 2013, Berger was a relatively unknown player in the premium paints segment which was dominated by Dulux's Velvet Touch (Akzo Nobel) and Asian Paints's Royale. By appointing superstar Katrina Kaif (in 2013) as the brand ambassador of Berger Silk, the firm's premium luxury emulsion, Berger has improved the brand's awareness amongst customers. Whilst this meant that advertising spends to sales ratio increased for Berger over the past five years (see Exhibit 28), this was offset by a reduction in rebates given to dealers. The strategy has worked well for Berger as it has been able to gain share in the premium segment through customer pull for its premium products rather than just incentivizing dealers to push the products to customers.

Exhibit 28: Over the past decade, advertising spends (as a percentage to sales have increased whilst cash discounts (as a percentage to sales) have decreased for Berger

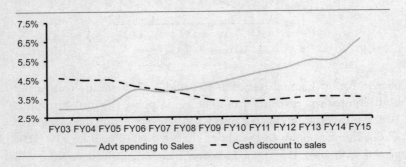

Source: Ambit Capital research.

(b) Advertising the launch of Express Painting Solutions in 2015: A faster and cleaner painting service, Express Painting Solutions enables painters to use advanced equipment to execute the paint project in almost half the usual time with increased convenience for the occupants of the house. As the proportion of labour cost within a paint project increases over time (up from around 10 per cent in 1980 to over 60 per cent currently), over the next 15–20 years, the nature of paint projects is likely to evolve into a combination of DIY and value-added labour services. Berger's Express Painting service aims to not only give a highly value-added approach to services, but may also prove to be a key step towards the launch of DIY paint projects in India. Amongst its competitors, Asian Paints is the only other firm which has initiated similar steps like its Home Solutions and Color Consultancy services.

Improving supply chain management: In the absence of centralized supply chain management infrastructure, managing inventory levels becomes a tough task. Data analytics can be used to improve forecasting demand at a pan-India level; however, without proper supply chain infrastructure, even data analytics cannot achieve much. Whilst Asian Paints took the lead in installing a technologically advanced centralized supply chain management and ERP system over 1999–2002, Berger implemented a similar technological advancement in its distribution channel in 2012 in collaboration with Oracle. Its management believes that the new ERP platform can improve the accuracy of demand forecasting for the group in the years to come. In a press interview in December 2012, Roy said: 'It is the supply side that we need to improve. We lose some amount of sales on account of our inability to supply the right kind of material on time. It's one area which we are working on.'

New approach in hiring, retaining and incentivizing the sales team: Roy has standardized the process for hiring sales personnel across the country to bring consistency in the quality of people being hired. The distribution network has also seen improvement due to these changes. Recruitment of management trainees has been changed to include graduates from IIMs and the quality of training provided has also been improved. Incentive structures of the sales team have been changed to make them more aligned with the firm's focus on network expansion.

Gross margin expansion driven by improved efficiencies around procurement and manufacturing processes: Berger has reported a 450 bps increase in gross margin over FY10–15. This gross margin expansion has come despite no major input cost tailwind over this period. In fact, this margin expansion has come during a period in which Asian Paints has reported no gross margin improvement. Even more interestingly, this gross margin improvement for Berger has come despite putting its product portfolio at a premium having accounted for only a small fraction of this gross margin expansion. As summarized in the firm's FY14 annual report: 'This has been possible through improvement in product mix, generating higher volumes with better economies of scale through wider reach and better servicing, reduction of rebates on the back of improved brand equity, and structured and well-monitored measures for reduction in cost. The last one includes strong management of working capital, improvement of productivity at all plants, continuous development of alternative raw materials, new sources for raw materials, improved formulations for better quality and lower costs, and innovative procuring and application. A new vendor management system was implemented for the purpose of seamless coordination and quicker decisions.'

Reduction in discounts to dealers: Ambit's consumer sector team's channel checks suggest that Berger has historically been the most aggressive amongst the top-five players in the industry in terms of providing discounts and rebates especially to dealers. Also, Berger provides a longer credit option (twenty-eight days vs twenty-one days for Asian Paints) and higher average cash discounts to its dealers. As shown in Exhibit 28, cash discounts and rebates given to dealers as a proportion of sales have been declining consistently over the past five years.

Exhibit 29: Berger Paints's share price chart during 2009–15

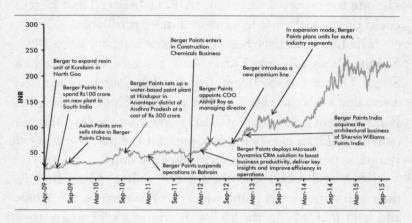

Source: Bloomberg, Ambit Capital research.

What is Berger Paints's secret sauce?

Section 1: Focusing on the Core Business

'We have to focus on paint and grow only in paint. It is a very competitive business. One small mistake can take us back by three to four months or even more compared to our peers. We have to tread safely. Whilst competitors wait for Berger to make a mistake, we too wait for competitors to make a mistake, so that we can cover the gap against them, faster,' said K.S. Dhingra, promoter, Berger Paints during my meeting with him.

Why would any promoter pay for a brand that is strained financially and operates in a tough business? When I asked Kuldip Singh Dhingra this question in the context of the company he acquired from Vijay Mallya in 1991, his reply was that he believed in the quality of the Berger brand and was impressed that the company was professionally managed. Despite the reported financial strain, he believed that Berger could be gradually made more and more profitable.

The Dhingras have been in the paint industry since 1898. Kuldip Singh Dhingra (KSD) and his brother Gurbachan Singh Dhingra (GSD) are the family's fourth generation associated with the paints industry. The fifth generation, i.e. Rishma Kaur (daughter of KSD) and Kanwardip Dhingra (son of GSD), is also being groomed for the past few years at Berger as part of the firm's succession planning.

KSD and GSD cut their teeth selling paint first in their paint shops and paint factory in Amritsar in the 1960s and later in Delhi in the 1970s. It was in Delhi where they received paint orders for exports to the former Soviet Union for the Moscow Olympics of 1980. Their Russian business grew exponentially during the 1980s, thanks to huge orders. However, the Dhingras wanted a backup in case there was a change of circumstances in the former Soviet Union—which did take place in the early 1990s. The Dhingras thus shifted their focus to Berger, entrenching themselves in the one business they understood better than others. To their credit, this laser-like focus has neither wavered nor shifted since 1991.

The paints industry is a ruthless and complex business. Unlike other fast moving consumer goods (FMCG) industries, the paints business faces unique challenges such as limited scope for product differentiation, low involvement of end customers in deciding which paint product to choose, the voluminous nature of the paint product (in terms of price per unit volume), and the large number of SKUs, given varied paint preferences across geographies in terms of colours, type of paints and size of the SKUs. Hence, competitive pressures in the paints industry are high and have resulted in slim trade margins of only 3–6 per cent in the distribution channel for the paints industry as compared to 13–20 per cent for consumer staples categories (like food, beverages, etc.) and 20–30 per cent for most other discretionary consumer categories (like automobiles, durables, leisure, etc.). Higher competitive pressures also result in increased bargaining power of the channel (dealers and painters) as compared to other consumption categories, given their ability to push a particular paint product to the end-consumers.

In such a tough business, with low margins for distributors, how does one gain leadership? What are the critical success factors to beat competition? I believe there are six of them. First, a strong supply chain which keeps a company's inventory costs under control and keeps the dealer happy (with high inventory turnover). Second, a wide enough product range, and third, having products with special characteristics (such as Luxol Silk and Breathe Easy mentioned in the next section). Fourth, effective marketing initiatives that help create demand amongst customers, especially for premium products. For example, Asian Paints invests heavily on experience centres like Asian Paints Signature stores and Asian Paints Colour Ideas stores, which help customers experience the look and feel of products prior to purchase. Fifth, benefits to dealers, given their important role in selling the final product. Rebates, favourable credit terms, and rewards and gifts like international holidays are some of the most commonly used benefits. And finally, top-quality management talent. Given the importance of operational execution in the paints industry, the quality of managerial professionals in the organization is one of the biggest long-term competitive advantages for a paint manufacturer. Most paint manufacturers focus on high-quality management recruits, but only Asian Paints recruits from the top B-schools of India for junior and mid-level managerial roles.

Ambit's consumer sector team believes that on these above mentioned six parameters, Asian Paints scores best on supply chain management, product range, marketing initiatives and quality of management professionals. Berger scores best on product range (alongside Asian Paints) and benefits to dealers/painters. Berger is just a shade behind Asian on some parameters (like supply chain management and quality of management professionals), but on almost all parameters, it is significantly ahead of the remaining large Indian paints companies, namely Kansai Nerolac and Akzo Nobel.

Berger is one of only two companies (alongside Asian Paints) in the industry which has focused consistently on building supply chain efficiencies, consistently widening the distribution network, and effectively investing in branding and marketing initiatives. As Kuldip Dhingra told me, 'Paints are the only business I know and I also know how competitive it is. Hence, I have maintained a philosophy of not taking the risk of allocating capital towards any business which is not related to the paints industry.'

Dhingra also shows a deep respect for professional management. In the past four decades, all four CEOs (D. Madhukar, Biji Kurien, Subir Bose and Abhijit Roy) were professionals with no kinship to the oft-changing owners of Berger. When I met Abhijit Roy (MD and CEO, Berger Paints) and Srijit Dasgupta (director, finance, Berger Paints) in November 2015, they came across as having very high regard for the Dhingras. The only qualification the Dhingras insist on is that Berger's leaders should be from the paints industry. 'I feel that even if people in the senior management of my company are not home-grown, they should have come from within the paint industry. If I bring in a CEO from, say, the automotive industry or FMCG industry, it will take them years to understand the paints industry. I cannot take that risk,' Dhingra added.

It is no surprise then that Berger steadily rose up the ranks from the seventh-largest paint company in India in 1980 to becoming the second-largest decorative paints company by 2000. Since 2000, Berger has widened the gap against the number three and number four players (Kansai Nerolac and Akzo Nobel, respectively). But Berger's strategies are neither unique nor secretly held. If Berger could implement them with such focus, why did Berger's competitors not emulate Berger?

My discussions with paint industry veterans indicate that other than Asian Paints and Berger Paints, the other firms in the paints industry lacked focus, were complacent and refused to learn from their mistakes. Examples include the following: (a) one competitor started a policy where it would give elongated credit periods to its dealers in order to grow its distribution network. This put severe pressure on the company in the 1980s, impairing its competitive positioning; and (b) another competitor ventured into unrelated sectors like financial services, weighbridges and hotels. These forays, along with other factors (floods in 1998–99 affecting factories and depots, poor implementation of strategy towards the launch of tinting machines) negatively impacted the company in the 1990s.

Mistakes made by other larger paint players include: (a) frequent changes to their ownership and management teams which brought discontinuity to the focus on execution at the ground level; and (b) more focus on the industrial side of the paints business rather than its decorative side. Thus, an intense, single-minded focus on the core business is among the key reasons behind both Asian Paints and Berger Paints maintaining their competitive positions in the Indian paints industry.

Section 2: Deepening the competitive moat

Berger Paints has also steadily built its competitive advantages across the four criteria of John Kay's IBAS framework, namely innovation, brands and reputation, architecture, and strategic assets (for more details of this framework, please refer to Appendix 1). Let's focus on each aspect of the framework.

Innovation

Berger's innovations are on three fronts—how the promoters managed the firm, how the firm introduced innovation in the form of tinting machines for dealers, and how the firm introduced innovative products.

Firstly, the promoters: As per Forbes, the Dhingras are among India's fifty richest families. And yet the Dhingras come across as different from the average Indian billionaire. They maintain a low profile and are rarely spotted in the press. They are neither in the business pages of the *Economic Times* nor on page 3 of 'Bombay Times'. For a family of their stature, the office of the Dhingras in Delhi is a sparsely furnished, back-of-the-shopping-precinct affair in an unpretentious downmarket commercial complex adjoining Zamrudpur village. Berger itself is headquartered in Kolkata and runs its operations from a nondescript office building located at the low-profile end of Park Street. In my meetings over the past few years with the Dhingras, I have found them to be refreshingly grounded.

The Dhingras also stand apart in their resolute trust in professional management, a refreshing change from the power-hungry, riven-with-insecurity mentality of Indian promoters. Berger is run entirely by professionals, with the promoters maintaining a hands-off approach. This tradition has continued through decades, despite changes in ownerships. The Dhingras have refrained from interfering in the day-to-day management of the company. A member of Berger's senior management told me, 'One of the biggest contributions of the promoters is that they have always given us a lot of freedom and flexibility to operate. Beyond the support provided in strategic initiatives, and discussions on the annual business plan held in the beginning of the year, the promoters allow complete independence to the management based out of Kolkata to handle and deliver the budget that they have committed to.'

Secondly, the introduction of tinting machines: A tinting machine is the same size as a bank's ATM and is responsible for revolutionary changes in the lives of paints dealers and distributors. When I visited one of the largest dealers of paints in the western suburbs of Mumbai, the tinting machine was neatly tucked away in a corner of the shop. For dealers, tinting machines did away with the necessity of stocking large number of SKUs. This reduced the requirement space for dealers and improved their inventory management. More importantly, dealers could offer many more colour options to customers who, typically, want to experiment with different shades. Jenson and Nicholson introduced these machines in the mid-1990s. Berger came second in 1996, introducing tinting machines to dealer stores at a time when the emulsion category of paints in India was solely controlled by ICI (with its Dulux brand) and Asian Paints (with its Apcolite and Royale brands).

Tinting machines use three main colour bases (dark, medium and pastel) and sixteen colourants to produce 5000 colours instantly. However, the challenge for Berger was that the price of a tinting machine for a dealer was as high as Rs 8,31,000—a large outlay for a dealer in the 1990s—and the Berger brand was unheard of in the emulsions space. To overcome this challenge, Berger used innovative marketing and sales tactics to aggressively push tinting machines to their dealers as an efficient cost-saving and space-saving device. By September 1999, Berger had installed 400 tinting machines, out of a total of 1200 machines in the industry, thus establishing the firm's presence in the emulsions category.

Thirdly, and finally, on products: Berger has focused on introducing products with special characteristics which have allowed it to create a strong brand recall for such products. A few Berger products and their characteristics are listed in Exhibit 30. These products have enabled Berger to sustain its competitive positioning in the industry.

Exhibit 30: Berger's key products and their qualities

Brand Name	Characteristic
Luxol Silk	Upmarket emulsion launched in 1979 with a prestigious feel akin to that of silk. This was launched at a price higher than that of the market leader ICI's Dulux.
Breathe Easy	Made from low volatile organic chemicals and is suitable for schools and hospitals and for the elderly and those who suffer from breathing problems.

(Contd)

Brand Name	Characteristic
WeatherCoat AllGuard	Silicon-based exterior water-based paint with enhanced water resistance.
Easy Clean	Most washable interior paint in India with a pleasant sheen finish.
Designer Finishes	'Illusions' brand that provides metallic/marble-type finishes to walls.

Source: FY13 Annual Report, Ambit Capital research.

Brands and reputation

Over the past fifty years, Berger has consistently invested in creating a strong brand recall in all categories of paints from the economy segment to the premium segment. Kurien, who joined the firm in 1973 as the head of sales and marketing, spearheaded Berger's orientation towards brand creation. After the launch of brands such as Butterfly (1975) and Luxol Silk (1979), through its tie-up with Lintas Media Group, British Paints, as Berger was known then, became the first company that advertised on the cover page of a weekly English news magazine.

One of the most successful advertising campaigns was around Luxol Silk. This campaign helped position Berger in the premium paints category by emphasizing the association of premium paint customers with prestigious objects. The tag lines of the advertisement campaign included, 'When the miniature is Moghul, the walls are Luxol Silk,' 'When the carpet is Persian, the walls are Luxol Silk,' 'When the Piano is Steinway, the walls are Luxol Silk,' 'When the bronze is Chola, the walls are Luxol Silk,' and 'Luxol Silk— It is the only emulsion paint you can tell with your eyes closed.'

In the designer finish segment, Berger was the first off the block with the launch of the brand, Illusions, in 2001. Since then, most of its peers have introduced designer finish paints in their product portfolio.

Since Abhijit Roy took over as the MD and CEO of Berger, the firm has seen a significant increase in its brand salience thanks to the launch of the Berger Silk advertising campaign featuring Bollywood star Katrina Kaif, supported by the launch of the Berger Express Painting Service and the aggressive advertising campaign backing it.

These product launches and marketing initiatives strengthened Berger's relationship with dealers and enhanced brand recall among customers. Berger has aggressively raised its advertisement spend over the years (from 3 per cent of sales in FY05 to around 5 per cent in FY11). By FY15, Berger's advertising and promotion spend stood at 6.6 per cent of sales, the highest among competitors, including Asian Paints (5.2 per cent of sales).

Architecture

Berger has well-entrenched relationships with employees. In this particular aspect, Berger has learnt from the industry leader, Asian Paints, which is well known for its top-of-the-line management. This learning began as early as the 1970s under the leadership of Madhukar and Kurien. As a veteran of the paints industry put it, 'Biji Kurien was a very fine brain and he had a knack for selecting good people. He was the first leader at British Paints to put very young people in charge of very large portfolios. Maybe, one criticism of him was that he delegated too much; but this delegation also meant that the people set the pace for the company to become what Subir Bose could leverage on from the 1990s onwards. So Berger had very capable people in key positions including Research and Development (R&D). R&D was a neglected area before him.'

As Kurien told me, 'In the consumer industry, there are only two things that make a company successful—its customers and its people. These are the only two areas where decision-making and enthusiasm means something. When I was the CEO of British Paints, I ensured that two people in the whole organization—the personnel manager and the marketing manager—had to get my clearance on everything that they do.'

However, to get good people, you have to pay great salaries and this was a constraint for Berger. Moreover, being a little-known brand in the 1970s, hiring quality talent was a challenge for us. Kurien went on to say, 'The kind of salaries that we were paying, we couldn't afford the Asian Paints approach of hiring IIM graduates. My philosophy was that you need to give an opportunity to your employees to perform to their full potential. There were two things I used to tell my recruitment manager: Don't recruit someone who is not able to do a job, just to fill a vacancy. Secondly, even if we don't have a job, but you come across the right person, you must recruit him. Most of the things that I did were essentially to stabilize the operations and to give full autonomy to the people within certain boundaries.'

Kurien's successors and the current promoters have supported this approach of hiring and retaining high-quality talent, and providing freedom (alongside accountability) to employees throughout the organizational hierarchy. Roy, the current MD and CEO, told us, 'Our culture has two parts to it. One, there is freedom to innovate and the freedom to make mistakes. You are not berated or scolded; you are not told to follow a straitjacketed approach from the leaders.

This culture helps cultivate an entrepreneurial feeling amongst our employees. The second part is that we have a very open culture. Anybody from the field level to the sales manager can walk into my room without appointment and talk to me to either give me information or to ask for my views. I sometimes call branch managers into a conference room and ask them to present their success story which we put up on SharePoint (a team collaboration software tool) for everyone else to understand and share. This encourages people to think differently and innovate.' Roy has worked hard to improve and strengthen this culture. He told me, 'I have focused on improving the quality of manpower being hired in this organization over the past five years. For instance, previously, the recruitment of a sales officer used to be carried out by various branch managers. This led to a lack of consistency in the quality of people being hired across geographies and hence inter-branch transfers used to create problems. We have standardized that part now. In terms of management trainees, we have moved to the IIMs and hence recruiting quality has been improved, along with increased focus on training these people.'

This focus on employees is also a stated policy, which is implemented rigorously. According to the directors' report in FY13, Berger recognized the fact that talent and skill are increasingly becoming scarce and it requires considerable effort to identify, engage and retain such talents. The average employee training hours in FY13 were fifteen. The report also added that salary alone is not the criteria for satisfaction of deserving employees and that the firm needs to offer a participative work environment and an open culture.

The second part of Berger's architecture is its strong relationships with dealers. Dealers and painters are, in effect, the first customers for any paints company. Under Roy's leadership, Berger has not only improved distributor expansion but also changed its approach towards hiring, training and incentivizing of the sales team, by giving them reasonably stretched targets to deliver. Berger beats its competitors on this metric by offering the most attractive benefits to both the dealers as well as the painters.

Strategic assets

An all-India network of plants, manufacturing facilities and dealer/distribution network is a key strategic asset which serves as a strong entry barrier. A well-positioned manufacturing plant reduces the need to stock surplus inventory at company depots and also reduces the time to supply products to the dealers. Thus, Berger's manufacturing facilities are its key strategic assets. Starting from the eastern region, Berger has expanded rapidly over the years. Exhibit 31 highlights the network size of Berger's manufacturing plants compared to its peers.

Section 3: Controlled Capital Allocation

'We are clear that whatever capital is available with us, we will use it for our paints business and not anywhere else. This is clear. We will not go for diversification,' said K.S. Dhingra, promoter, Berger Paints, in my meeting with him in October 2015.

The Dhingras have brought with them a disciplined approach towards capital allocation that has been carried forth by Berger's leadership. When the Dhingras acquired Berger, its financials were capital-starved. The Dhingras pumped in their funds to improve the situation. As Kuldip

Exhibit 31: Factory locations of India's largest paint companies

Company	Number of factories	Location			
		North	South	East	West
Asian Paints	8	Kasna (UP), Rohtak (Haryana)	Patancheru (AP), Sriperumbudur (TN)		Ankleshwar (Gujarat), Sarigam (Gujarat), Khandala (Maharashtra), Taloja (Maharashtra)
Berger Paints	9	Sikandrabad (UP), Jammu (J&K), Surajpur (Noida)	Hindupur (AP), Puducherry	Howrah (WB), Rishra (WB)	Jejuri (Pune), Goa
Akzo Nobel	6	Kanpur (UP), Mohali (Punjab)	Hyderabad (AP)	Rishra (WB)	Thane (Maharashtra), Gwalior (MP)
Kansai Nerolac	5	Bawal (Haryana), Jaunpur (UP)	Hosur (TN)		Ratnagiri (Maharashtra), Ahmedabad (Gujarat)
Shalimar	4	Sikandrabad (UP)	Chennai (TN)	Howrah (WB)	Nashik (Maharashtra)

Source: Ambit Capital research.

Dhingra puts it, 'When I bought this business in 1991, the situation was so bad that the management was not even getting paid salaries on time.'

Besides paying for the operating expenses, the Dhingras also contributed significantly towards setting up of manufacturing plants across the country. In our discussions, the management team of Berger stated, 'The supply chain in the paint industry is very important. Until the early 1990s, we used to suffer because our factory in Howrah was at one end of India and we had to supply products across the country from there. Moreover, since paint demand was very seasonal (around festivities), this used to further complicate supply chain issues for us. From 1996 onwards, we started expanding our factories, first in Puducherry, then in Jammu, then Gujarat, all coming in at regular intervals.'

As articulated by Anoop Hoon, 'The problem faced by Berger during a major portion of the Kurien era, particularly in the 1980s, was that the owners were not giving enough capital for capacity expansion. Dhingras understood that what Berger needed was capacity expansion or being able to set up new plants, and to be fully supportive of the professional management team.'

Berger's sustained focus on using technology, as explained in the earlier section, to improve internal efficiencies, along with its successful brand campaign sustaining its number two position, has resulted in superior ROCEs. Berger has been generous with shareholders, paying out, on average, 35–40 per cent of its profits as dividends. Thus, as highlighted in Exhibit 32, Berger's ROCEs have been consistently between 16 per cent and 28 per cent over the past twenty years. This controlled capital allocation by Berger is a result of Kuldip Dhingra's view about allocating capital only to businesses in the paints industry, without diluting the firm's focus on the core domestic decorative business. Dhingra compares this focus to golf. He says, 'My philosophy on capital allocation is similar to what happens in golf—focus on your stance and keep your eye on the ball (which for me is my business). When hitting the shot, don't lift your head to look at the direction in which you want to hit; instead look at the ball. Then it will certainly go in the right direction.'

Dhingra is also ready with plans for the future. He says, 'We bought the biggest specialist exterior insulation finishing systems (EIFS) company in Poland in 2008 where we have a technology-related edge. Although we want to bring it to India at some point of time in future, the right time has not come yet. If I do it now, for a long time I will disturb Berger Paints's balance sheet. Hence, I will wait for the right time.'

Exhibit 32: Berger's dividend payout ratio and ROCE have remained fairly steady over the past two decades

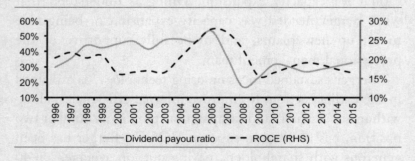

Source: Ambit Capital research.

Berger's Astonishing Outperformance

A rupee invested in Berger in April 1994 is worth Rs 212 presently (in April 2016), implying a compounded annual return of 28 per cent. That same rupee would be worth just Rs 7 if invested in the Sensex, implying a CAGR of 9 per cent. Thus, Berger has outperformed the Sensex by 31.5 times over the past twenty-two years. At the heart of this outstanding performance there have been (a) a deep focus on the paints business and only on the paints business; (b) a deepening of its competitive moats through a focus on hiring good people, training them well and creating a healthy work culture; and (c) prudent capital allocation.

CHAPTER 4

Marico: From a Commodity Trader to an FMCG Giant

'Choose the life that is best and familiarity will make it pleasant.'

—Thomas Aquinas

India has many occupational surnames such as Acharya (teacher), Dalal (broker), Vakil (lawyer), Kulkarni (accounts keeper), etc. Marico is named after its founder, Harsh Mariwala, whose grandfather—Vallabhdas Vasanji—came to be known as Mariwala because of his proficiency in trading pepper, which in Gujarati is known as *mari*.

Vasanji was the nephew of Kanji Moorarji, who came to Mumbai from Kutch in 1862 to trade in spices and agricultural commodities like pepper and ginger. Vasanji joined Moorarji and came to be known as Mariwala later.

Mariwala had four sons—Charandas, Jaysinh, Hansraj and Kishore—who formed Bombay Oil Industries Limited

(BOIL) in 1948 and quickly graduated from trading spices to manufacturing coconut oil, vegetable oil and chemicals in Mumbai and spice extracts in Kerala. Charandas's son, Harsh Mariwala, at age twenty, joined BOIL in 1971. From there, Harsh Mariwala built India's largest coconut oil and edible oil brand. His exciting story is now a well-known part of Indian corporate lore.

Exhibit 33: The Mariwala family tree

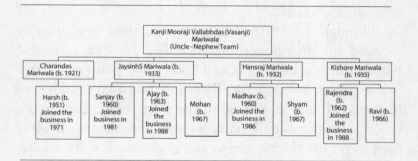

Source: Industry, Ambit Capital research.

Phase 1: 1972–91

Establishing Parachute and Saffola as Consumer Brands

A graduate from south Mumbai's prestigious Sydenham College, Harsh Mariwala found his calling in the consumer products division—which included coconut oil (Parachute) and edible oil (Saffola)—of the various businesses under BOIL. When he joined BOIL, both the brands were doing reasonably well, but remained business-to-business (B2B). Mariwala wanted to switch to a higher-margin, business-to-consumer (B2C) model. He started with small steps such as switching packaging from bulky tin cans of 15 litres to smaller packs of 100 millilitres. He followed this up with seeking professional help in four critical areas: advertising (hired Clarion Advertising agency for the Parachute advertising campaign), marketing (sought advice from renowned professor Labdhi Bhandari of IIM-A), human resources (sought advice from his friend Homi Mulla, HR head at Monsanto) and distribution (recruited Basutkar, a veteran from Hindustan Unilever). Consulting professionals would become a defining trait for Mariwala and a founding principle for Marico.

Through the 1970s, Mariwala used these professionals to build the distribution and branding for Parachute and Saffola. India's diversity is well known and poses challenges in marketing. For example, Parachute was used as edible oil in the south and as hair oil in the west. Thus, Parachute's brand identity was built on universally appealing sentiments such as purity, clarity, aroma and tradition. For Parachute, Mariwala hired another professional—Bindumadhavan, a plastic packaging expert who worked with Ranbaxy before joining BOIL—in the 1980s. Under Bindumadhavan, Parachute moved from tin containers to selling hair oil in plastic bottles—a consumer-friendly move since plastic bottles were lighter and aesthetically better looking than tin containers. All these factors contributed in making Parachute coconut oil a market leader in the north, south and west. In these regions, Parachute had a market share of 50 per cent in 1991, compared to 14 per cent for Shalimar, the next largest brand. Similarly, in the eastern region, Parachute was a formidable number two by 1991, with a market share of 32 per cent, after Shalimar, which had a market share of 43 per cent.

Saffola, on the other hand, was a niche brand in Mumbai. However, research showed that safflower oil reduced cholesterol levels. So, Mariwala hired an advertising agency to build Saffola's brand on the health platform. He also built advocacy from doctors for the brand, which further helped Saffola command a premium in the cluttered edible oil market. While Saffola was a premium edible oil brand, Harsh also eyed the burgeoning sunflower oil market which led to the launch of Sweekar in 1989. By 1991, Marico became the market leader in edible oils commanding about 14 per cent market share. ITC came a close second with a market share of 12 per cent.

By the late 1970s, Mariwala's consumer products division had outgrown all the other businesses under BOIL. And yet, the family style of doing business was a constraint, since Mariwala had limited autonomy in defining his own policies. Once again, Mariwala took the help of professionals. He consulted CEOs of other family-run businesses and analysed organization structures globally. After doing this, he proposed, in 1981, the creation of three profit centres—consumer products for himself; fatty acids and chemicals, and spice extracts divisions for his cousins. However, even this proved to be a temporary solution.

As there was no clear policy on how the profits generated by the three profit centres would be deployed, Mariwala's consumer products division saw gross underinvestment in its production facilities. Over 1975–90, while the consumer products division contributed over 80 per cent to the sales/profits for BOIL, less than 10 per cent of the total capital deployment of BOIL was directed towards this division (out of Rs 4.4 crore spent on plant and machinery by BOIL over 1975–90, only Rs 40 lakh was deployed towards the consumer products division). This led to a situation in the late 1980s where demand was ahead of the production capacity. As a result, BOIL had to outsource manufacturing, which compromised the quality of its products.

By the early 1990s, Mariwala had successfully transformed both Parachute and Saffola into pure consumer brands. But these were still hidden inside the larger business entity of BOIL. Thus, he could not shake off the family-business tag that prevented him from attracting top-notch talent that would go, instead, to a Hindustan Unilever, or a Proctor & Gamble or even domestic, professional companies like Asian Paints. And this gap showed in the failures of Mariwala's other consumer launches in the 1980s such as Whistle tooth powder, Parachute filtered groundnut oil and Parachute branded packaged pulses. By the end of this phase, it seemed inevitable that Mariwala would have to spin his consumer business away from BOIL.

Exhibit 34: Bombay Oil Industries Ltd's division into five different businesses

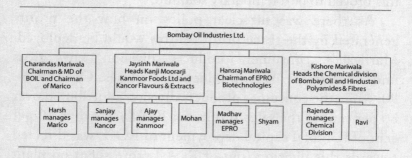

Source: Ambit Capital research.

Phase 2: 1990–96

Laying the Foundation for a Sustainably Profitable Edifice
Harsh Mariwala realized that there was no synergy between his B2C and the other BOIL businesses, which were pure B2B. As his cousins took control of the other businesses, he suggested separation of the family businesses, thus giving each business unit complete autonomy. Accordingly, in 1990, the BOIL board decided to break the business into five separate businesses, all of which were wholly or partially owned subsidiaries of BOIL. The separation of the business allowed Mariwala complete autonomy to build a sustainable profitable business.

The BOIL board finally hived off its various businesses into subsidiaries in 1990. While this separation gave much-needed autonomy to Mariwala, it also left him starved of capital. For a business with an annual turnover of Rs 80 crore, Mariwala was left with a paltry share capital of Rs 90 lakh, reserves of Rs 2.4 crore and a debt of Rs 4.7 crore with which Marico needed to fund its working capital requirements. This meant that Mariwala would have to take his foot off the pedal in terms of new launches, and focus, instead, on building a professional organization that would attract the best of management talent to fuel its growth. For this, he would need nothing short of a transformation.

This transformation began on 2 April 1990 with two dramatic recruitment advertisements, which were headlined '200 employees walk out of Bombay Oil' and 'Mass Killer Nabbed' (see Exhibit 35). The advertisements worked to grab attention. But behind the scenes, Mariwala was also working hard to build a professional structure that would attract talent.

Exhibit 35: Innovative print advertisements followed the incorporation of Marico in 1990

Source: Company, Ambit Capital research.

In late 1989, Mariwala hired Jeswant Nair, a veteran human resource professional, who had previously worked with Asian Paints—a firm which had a reputation of attracting the best management talent. Nair built a new organization structure which comprised five functional heads (see Exhibit 36). By emphasizing Marico's unique culture and the numerous possibilities for growth, Marico recruited thirty-five to forty managers within two years of the organizational changes.

Exhibit 36: The top management team at Marico in 1990 (post restructuring)

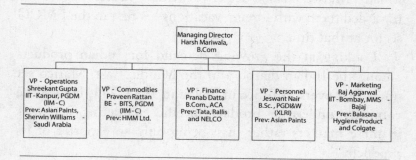

Source: Industry, Ambit Capital research.

Mariwala literally moved away from the family business. He relocated Marico's headquarters from the trading area of Masjid Bunder in south Mumbai to Rang Sharda Hotel, Bandra, in the western suburbs. To reinforce the culture of openness, it was designed as an open office—one of the first such offices in corporate India.

Beyond the corporate office, Marico also revamped and expanded its manufacturing facilities. Marico invested in a new oil mill for copra crushing in Kerala, refurbished its Sewree coconut oil plant and acquired a vegetable oil refinery in Jalgaon, which was fitted with the latest refining technology. A new centre for research and development, product quality, and packaging development was set up in Mumbai. To avoid the shortfall in safflower seeds, Marico started contract farming.

Among the new products created during this period, Marico launched Hair & Care (non-sticky hair oil) and

Revive (cold water starch). In addition, higher advertising and promotional spends were undertaken in Sweekar. Finally, Marico pushed dealers to achieve stretch targets and rewarded them with foreign vacations—a first in the FMCG sector at that time.

Looking at the growing demand for Indian products among the Indian diaspora in the Middle East, Marico set up its first overseas office in Dubai in 1992. This helped the company undertake product-specific marketing activities in these markets rather than being only an exporter of its products.

All of these initiatives helped Marico deliver a healthy 28 per cent CAGR in sales, taking its sales to Rs 350 crore by 1996 from Rs 80 crore in 1990. During this period, Parachute coconut oil increased its market share from 50 per cent in 1990 to 55 per cent in 1996, Saffola and Sweekar maintained their number two position in edible oils while Hair & Care captured 22 per cent share of the light hair oil market since its launch in 1991.

During this period, Marico's ownership changed as Harsh Mariwala increased his stake in the business to 50 per cent in 1996, from 25 per cent until 1990. The remaining 50 per cent was owned by his uncle, Kishore Mariwala. Marico also got the SIL brand of fruit jams in the family settlement, acquired from BOIL's subsidiary, Kanmoor Foods Ltd. Marico went public in 1996, pricing its shares at Rs 175 per share and raising Rs 63.4 crore. This reduced Marico's debt to equity ratio, from 1.4 (FY91) at the time of the split with BOIL to 0.5 post-IPO. Besides, both net sales and profit after tax (PAT) started rising steadily from FY91 onward.

Exhibit 37: Revenue and PAT margin from FY91–96

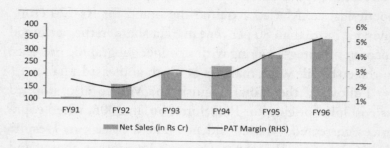

Source: Ambit Capital research.

Phase 3: 1997–2006

David (Marico) vs Goliath (HUL)

By this time, Marico's success in Parachute had put the firm on the radar of consumer giant Hindustan Unilever Limited (HUL). Thanks to its acquisition of Tata Oil Mills in 1993, HUL owned Nihar, which had 17 per cent market share in coconut hair oil and competed with Parachute. In a story that Mariwala loves to narrate, Keki Dadiseth, the then chairman of HUL, called Mariwala in the late 1990s to buy out Marico, saying, 'Mr Mariwala, I will give you enough resources to take care of you and all your future generations.' Mariwala spurned the offer and dug in his heels. Thus began an epic brand war which would come to define Mariwala and Marico.

HUL started with aggressive advertising and sales promotions for Nihar and Cococare. Parachute responded by increasing distribution and improving the packaging and product quality to avoid any loss of market share. In 1999, Marico also acquired Oil of Malabar and relaunched it with a lower price tag to compete with HUL. After failing to make inroads into the category despite several product relaunches, HUL finally gave up and put Nihar up for sale in 2005. As poetic justice, Marico acquired the brand for Rs 220 crore, giving it more than 80 per cent market share in the perfumed coconut oil category along with stronger geographic presence in the erstwhile weak markets of north and east India.

Following the Nihar acquisition, Marico also stopped its cost-plus pricing for Parachute. So, in 2006, when copra prices corrected, Marico did not take a price cut. Despite the high price, Parachute retained its market share, and this helped Marico improve its EBITDA margin from 9 per cent in FY05 to 13 per cent in FY06. The EBITDA margin is earnings before interest, tax, depreciation and amortization (EBITDA) divided by total revenue. It is a measure of a company's operating profitability. The operating profitability of a company is the profit earned from its core business.

The war with HUL spurred many changes within Marico. To reduce dependency on Parachute, Marico acquired the Mediker shampoo brand from Procter & Gamble (P&G) in 1999 and relaunched the shampoo in an anti-lice oil format. Marico also pursued new business opportunities under a new business incubation cell. This led to the launch of Kaya skincare business and the acquisition of Sundari (a brand of luxury Ayurvedic skincare products) in the US in 2003. As shown later in this chapter, Marico introduced several new brands over 2000–05. Not all the new launches were successful. However, these launches helped the company reduce its dependence on its existing portfolio of Parachute coconut oil and Saffola edible oil. The contribution of new launches to total sales increased to 21 per cent in FY05 from 5 per cent in FY01.

During this phase, Marico also strengthened its internal processes and integrated its HR strategy with the overall business strategy. In 2000, Marico also revised the remuneration structure and introduced a new incentive scheme where managers were eligible to a share in the profits beyond an agreed threshold. This helped the firm attract and retain high-quality talent. In 2000, Marico increased its focus on IT and decided to implement the Enterprise Resource Planning (ERP) and Supply Chain Management (SCM) suites from SAP, one of the first FMCG companies in India to implement both the packages. Multinational FMCG companies, like HUL, are known for their generous dividends to shareholders. Marico stepped up its game from 2002 onwards and started announcing quarterly dividends. Finally, Marico improved relations with its dealers by stopping the commonly followed practice of loading sales at the end of the month.

Exhibit 38: Marico's share price chart during 1996–07

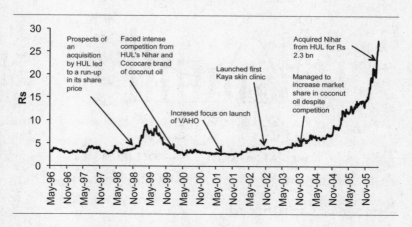

Source: Bloomberg, Ambit Capital research.

Exhibit 39: Revenue growth hampered due to the price war with HUL

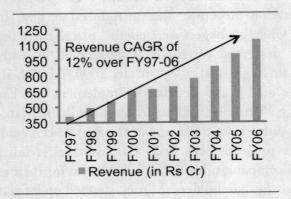

Source: Ambit Capital research.

Exhibit 40: PAT growth was robust; ROCE dampened due to competition with HUL and Nihar acquisition in FY06

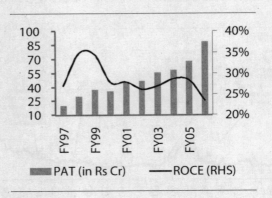

Source: Ambit Capital research.

Phase 4: 2007–12

Pursuing Inorganic Growth

Marico's victory against HUL and its sustained leadership with Parachute and Saffola had firmly established the firm in the league of Indian FMCG majors such as Dabur and Godrej Consumer. The next phase of growth would, thus, be driven by acquisitions and new product launches. On the international business front, Marico had become a significant player. In Bangladesh, it had 67 per cent market share of coconut oil. To fuel its ambition of becoming an emerging market FMCG player, Marico made several acquisitions over FY07–13 (see Exhibit 41). These acquisitions raised the share of international sales as a percentage of total sales to 22 per cent in FY13 from 10 per cent in FY05. Sweekar and SIL were divested in line with Marico's strategy to exit businesses which have low profit margin and which are not part of Marico's core categories (haircare, personal care and functional foods).

Exhibit 41: Acquisitions and divestments by Marico during FY05–13

Year	Acquisition / Divestment	Product Category	Market
2006	Acquires Camelia and Aromatic	Toilet soaps	Bangladesh
2006	Acquires Nihar	Hair oil	India
2006	Acquires Manjal	Toilet soaps	India
2007	Acquires Fiancee, HairCode	Haircare	Egypt

(Contd)

Year	Acquisition / Divestment	Product Category	Market
2008	Acquires Black Chic, Hercules (Enali Pharma)	Personal care	South Africa
2008	Divested SIL	Packed foods	India
2010	Acquires Code 10	Male grooming	Malaysia
2010	Acquires Derma Rx	Skincare	Singapore
2011	Acquires International Consumer Products (ICP)	Male grooming	Vietnam
2011	Divested Sweekar	Edible oil	India
2012	Acquires Paras	Personal care	India

Source: Company, Ambit Capital research.

Back home, Marico acquired Paras's personal care brands in 2012, which gave the firm entry into Indian men's grooming categories such as deodorants, hair gels and other personal care categories like hair serums and skin creams. Over 2007–12, Marico launched several new products in the haircare, personal care, home care and foods category. Out of these, Saffola masala oats, Parachute Ayurvedic hair oil and Parachute Advansed body lotion have been successful.

Marico brought Shanti Amla hair oil under the Nihar fold in 2010 and started selling it at a 50 per cent discount to Dabur Amla. This helped improve Marico's market share in the Amla hair oil category to 33 per cent in FY15 from 19 per cent in FY12. Finally, Marico exited the processed food (SIL brand sold to a Danish business house, Good

Food Group, in 2008) and refined sunflower oil segments (Sweekar sold to Cargill India in 2011).

Over FY05–13, revenue grew at 21 per cent CAGR propelled by domestic and overseas acquisitions. However, these acquisitions compressed ROCEs from around 50 per cent in FY08 to 24 per cent in FY13. The company also cut its dividend payout from 52 per cent in FY05 to 21 per cent in FY13 to conserve capital for acquisitions. The share price grew at 31 per cent CAGR over FY05–13.

Exhibit 42: Marico's share price chart during 2007–13

Exhibit 43: Series of acquisitions bumped up revenues . . .

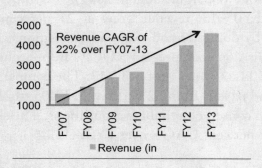

Source: Company, Ambit Capital research.

Exhibit 44: . . . but weighed on Marico's ROCE as well

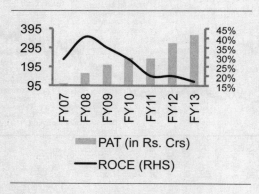

Source: Company, Ambit Capital research.

Phase 5: 2013 onwards

Change of Guard and Focus Back on ROCE

The string of acquisitions and new product launches in Phase 4 were slowly transforming Marico into a diversified, multi-product, multi-geography, FMCG company from a hair and edible oil company. In order to cross-pollinate products and know-how between Marico's Indian and international businesses, Marico undertook a restructuring of its businesses in January 2013. The management also decided to focus on capital allocation given that its ROCEs had halved to 24 per cent in FY13 from 50 per cent in FY08.

As Mariwala said in a June 2014 interview to the trade press, 'Our investors raised the issue that our Return on Capital Employed was falling primarily due to price paid for acquisitions. So we consciously decided that for a couple of years, we will just digest these acquisitions and let the ratios improve. . . . There are some other issues like dividend payout, which, in our case, was lower than some other FMCG companies as a percentage of profit. We have taken one jump and, maybe, over a period of time, we will take one more.'

Marico's domestic and international businesses were merged to create one FMCG business while Kaya was demerged from the FMCG business in order to allow it to run in an entrepreneurial manner as a retail business. Saugata Gupta, who until then headed the domestic consumer products business (CPB), was elevated to chief executive officer for the entire FMCG business. Vijay Subramaniam, who headed the international FMCG business, was appointed as Kaya CEO after its demerger.

A year later, in 2014, Mariwala stepped down as managing director, relinquishing the post to Gupta—a rare move among Indian promoters, most of whom struggle to contemplate ceding control to professional management. Gupta, an IIM-Bangalore and IIT-Kharagpur alumnus, started his career at Cadbury and was part of the team that began ICICI Prudential Life Insurance. Gupta left ICICI

Prudential as chief marketing officer to join Marico as head of marketing in 2004. Thus, in less than a decade, Gupta has risen first to CEO in 2013 and then to MD in 2014. Mariwala remains on the board as non-executive chairman of Marico.

Exhibit 45: Marico's share price chart during 2013–15

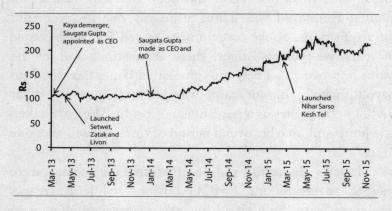

Source: Company, Ambit Capital research.

Exhibit 46: Revenue growth has been healthy over FY13–15 . . .

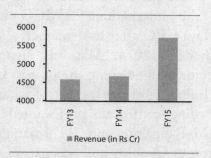

Source: Ambit Capital research.

Exhibit 47: . . . and ROCE has started recovering

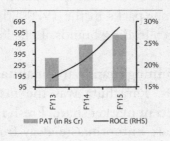

Source: Ambit Capital research.

What is Marico's Secret Sauce?

Section 1: Focusing on the Core Business

> 'I strongly feel that focus will lead to depth and depth will lead to excellence.'
>
> — Harsh Mariwala

'The reason for success of companies like HDFC Bank, ITC and Marico is due to the focus and consistency that they bring to their business,' said B.S. Nagesh, independent director on the board of Marico in my meeting with him in December 2015.

Since the firm's incorporation, Marico has consistently focused on three key factors which drive a consumer staples company's growth rates: (i) maintaining brand leadership; (ii) extending winning brands; and (iii) divesting low-margin brands. This focus is as a matter of policy. Marico's top managers crystallize the company's vision into a two-page strategy document, which is shared with the board of directors. This document articulates features like the categories and geographies that Marico would operate in and also captures what Marico will not do. Since the launch of Parachute and Saffola in consumer packs in the 1970s, the focus has been on creating market-leading brands. Let's look at these three factors in detail:

Protecting winning brands and maintaining leadership: In the late 1990s, Parachute was the market leader with more than 50 per cent market share. Fresh from its success in taking market share in toothpaste away from Colgate using Pepsodent, HUL entered the coconut oil category to take on Marico. Dadiseth, the then chairman of HUL, had warned Mariwala to sell Marico to HUL or face dire consequences. Mariwala decided to take on the challenge. Even the capital markets believed that Marico stood no chance against the might of HUL which resulted in Marico's price-to-earnings ratio dipping to as low as 7x, as against 13x during its listing in 1996.

As part of its plans to take on Marico, HUL relaunched Nihar in 1998, acquired Cococare from Redcon and positioned both brands as price challengers to Parachute. In addition, HUL also increased advertising and promotion spends for its brands. In one quarter in FY2000, HUL's advertising and promotional (A&P) spend on coconut oil alone was an amount which was almost equivalent to Marico's full year A&P budget (around Rs 30 crore).

As Milind Sarwate, former CFO of Marico, recalls, 'Marico's response was typically entrepreneurial and desi. We quickly realized that we have our key resource engine under threat. So, we re-prioritized and focused entirely on Parachute. We gave the project a war flavour. For example, the business conference on this issue saw Mariconians dressed as soldiers. The project was called operation Parachute ki

Kasam. The leadership galvanized the whole team. It was exhilarating as the team realized the gravity of the situation and sprang into action. We were able to recover lost ground and turn the tables, so much so that eventually Marico acquired the aggressor brand, Nihar.'

Marico retaliated by relaunching Parachute:

(a) with a new packaging;
(b) with a new tag line highlighting its purity (Shuddhata ki Seal—or the seal of purity);
(c) by widening its distribution; and
(d) by launching an internal sales force initiative.

Within twelve months, Parachute regained its lost share, thus limiting HUL's growth. Despite several relaunches, Nihar failed against Parachute. Eventually, HUL dropped the brand Nihar off its power brand list before selling it off to Marico in 2006. Since then, Parachute has been the undisputed leader in the coconut oil category. This leadership has ensured that when one visits the hair oil section in a retail store, about 80 per cent of the shelves are occupied by Marico-branded hair oil.

Divesting low-margin brands: In the late 1980s, Marico saw that demand for sunflower oil was rising and launched its Sweekar brand. Sweekar helped as a placeholder brand for Marico through the 1990s while Saffola grappled with supply issues (irregular supply of safflower seeds due to crop failures). Despite Sweekar's success, it had low margins. Once supply issues for Saffola were resolved, Marico reduced focus on Sweekar, thus freeing up resources for Saffola as part of its strategy of focusing on high-margin brands where it was much stronger. Subsequently, Sweekar was divested in 2011 to Cargill India. Marico's single-minded focus on

Saffola has made it the market leader in premium edible oils (FY15 market share of 58 per cent).

Extending winning brands across categories and geographies: Marico has chosen its turf carefully for extending its winning brands. As Mariwala put it during my meeting with him in November 2015, 'People move up the value chain in hair nourishment and grooming. So, our focus is on hair nourishment and grooming and to be the market leader in these categories. We have chosen portfolios where we want to be market leaders and where we think we can be market leaders. We believe in focus combined with right portfolio choice and, by design, not going into some area where we just cannot be the market leader.'

Given Parachute's success, Marico has focused on hair nourishment where it believes it has the 'right to win'—a term frequently used by Marico employees. Similarly, Marico saw Bangladesh as a right-to-win market since consumer habits in Bangladesh are similar to those in India. As a result of its focused efforts on driving market share gains, Marico is the market leader in coconut oil in Bangladesh with a whopping 80 per cent market share. Focused efforts on growing value-added hair oils (VAHO) has resulted in Marico having the highest volume share in this category through three brands—Nihar Shanti Amla, Parachute Advansed and Hair & Care with sales of more than Rs 200 crore. In post-wash haircare, organic growth supplemented with acquisitions has led to leadership in serums (80 per cent volume share) and hair creams/gels (49 per cent value share). Mariwala told us, 'When we entered Bangladesh in 1999, the coconut oil market was dominated by local brands. But with our experience in India, we were actually very clear that we can gain market share in Bangladesh. We could have easily earned profit, but for the first five years, the direction given to our team was to focus on market share. This strategy paid off. Now we are market leaders and profitability in Bangladesh is higher than Marico's consolidated business.'

In another example of Marico's focus, the company demerged Kaya from the FMCG business in April 2013 in order to allow dedicated management bandwidth for the two businesses. Kaya, as a result, got more focused attention to be run as an entrepreneurial retail business without diluting management attention from the FMCG business.

Exhibit 48: Bangladesh sales and EBITDA margin

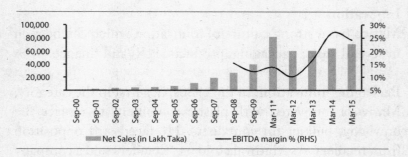

Source: Company. Ambit Capital research.

Note: Net sales for March 2011 is eighteen months.

Section 2: Deepening the competitive moat

Marico, like Asian Paints and Berger, has steadily built its competitive advantages across the four criteria of John Kay's IBAS framework—innovation, brands and reputation, architecture, and strategic assets. Each of these aspects helps a company build sustainable competitive advantages that help keep the company ahead of competition. Innovation is, as commonly understand, developing new methods, processes and ideas. Similarly, brands and reputation are the company's investments in maintaining and sustaining its identity (often built with the strength of its products and services) with customers. Architecture is the network of relationships between various stakeholders such as a company's employees, suppliers, dealers, and customers. Finally, strategic assets are specific to the company, such as licences, intellectual property rights, etc. (For more details on the IBAS framework, please refer to Appendix 1). Let's discuss each aspect of Marico's moat building.

Innovation

Marico has a strong culture of innovation which can be seen in several areas: packaging, products, HR, and finance.

Packaging innovation: In the 1980s, in a first in the category, Mariwala innovated with plastic containers, to replace the unwieldy, bulkier tin containers. He faced stiff opposition from retailers. As Mariwala told us, 'Retailers said a company had tried square-shaped plastic packaging for hair oils and failed as the oil would leak from bottles. This plastic and oil combination attracted rats and they would bite the bottles leading to oil spill in the entire shop. We decided to go with round-shaped bottles as that wouldn't give the rats a grip to bite. Also, we ensured that no oil leaked from the bottle. As a trial, we kept a bottle in a rat trap for a few days and there was no damage to the bottle. We circulated the photos of this experiment amongst retailers and convinced them to stock these bottles. Within fifteen years, 100 per cent of the market changed to plastic packaging.'

The savings generated from the low-cost plastic packaging were invested by Marico into higher advertising and publicity spends to drive market share gains. Later, Marico came out with a wide-mouthed Parachute bottle with a spout to counter the problem of coconut oil freezing in winter in north India. During the early years of the twenty-first century, to counter the growing threat of Parachute duplicates, Marico imported a foreign mould for the bottles. It took almost four to five years for the copycats to replicate Parachute's mould which helped the company curb duplicates in the market.

Product innovation: To ensure that Marico continuously pursues innovation, it follows the concept of strategic funding where a portion (around 10 per cent) of the annual profits is invested in pursuing product innovation. New products are tested through prototyping, where the particular product is test-marketed in a specific geography and then scaled up nationally if it meets internal benchmarks during prototyping.

Although Saffola was a popular brand known for its healthcare credentials, the irregular supply and high price of safflower seeds inhibited its growth. In an innovative step, introduced in the 1990s, Marico launched safflower oil blends such as Saffola Tasty and Saffola Gold which were priced lower than safflower oil, to attract new customers. Success in blended edible oil has resulted in Saffola becoming the market leader in premium edible oils with a 58 per cent market share in 2015.

Marico entered the oats category in 2010 and innovated by focusing on flavoured oats instead of plain oats, which was a category dominated by PepsiCo's Quaker oats. Seeing Indians' preference for savoury snacks, Marico innovated and launched savoury (masala) oats instead of competing in the plain oats category. This was soon copied by competitors such as Quaker and Kellogs, but Marico continues to be the market leader in masala oats category with sales of more than Rs 100 crore. When I tried eating Marico's masala oats, I found that the flavours offered by them were far better than those of its competitors.

Seeing the growing trend of light hair oils in the 1990s, Marico innovated and launched Hair & Care, Parachute Jasmine and Shanti Amla. Each of these brands is at least Rs 200 crore in size and has helped Marico become the market leader in value-added hair oils, ahead of other credible manufacturers such as Dabur, Emami and Bajaj Corp.

HR innovation at the Kerala factory: In the early 1990s, when Marico decided to set up its copra-crushing plant in Kerala to save on freight cost, they realized that other factories in Kerala were facing frequent disruptions due to the presence of strong trade unions. Marico's HR team, led by Jeswant Nair, detected that a culture of alcoholism and excessive free time after work was one of the main reasons for worker unionization. As a result, when Marico decided to set up its coconut oil factory at Kanjikode, Kerala, they divided the workers into four houses similar to the practice followed in schools. After work, cultural and sports competitions were organized to keep the workers occupied. This HR innovation ensured that Marico never faced disruptions at its factory.

Financial innovations: Commodity companies are perceived by investors as cyclical, given their vulnerability to global commodity cycles. Compared to them, FMCG companies' stocks enjoy higher valuations because an FMCG company's profits are more predictable, enabling these companies to reward shareholders with regular dividends. Despite having strong brands, Marico was still perceived as a commodity company, given its vulnerability to copra—a key raw material whose prices were cyclical in nature.

In FY2000, in order to get rid of this 'commodity company' tag, Marico undertook measures such as: (a) improving its financial planning wherein advertising and promotional spends were planned in advance and spread across quarters; (b) keeping buffers in order to safeguard against unexpected costs; and (c) improved demand forecasting which helped it plan its copra purchases better.

These measures helped Marico reduce the volatility in its quarterly profits. As a result, Marico reported fifty-five consecutive quarters of growth over FY2000–14. This also allowed the firm to start declaring quarterly dividends—making it the first company in India to do so. Quarterly dividends helped assure investors that Marico's business was profitable and capable of returning cash to shareholders every quarter. This is also evident from the line of questioning followed by analysts over conference calls over the last two to three years. About a decade ago, analysts would harp on about the price hike/cut taken by the company on Parachute and its subsequent impact on margins, whereas now, given Parachute's consistent volume growth track record, this concern has abated significantly. The investment community's discussions vis-à-vis Marico now are more around the company's long-term growth drivers.

Brands/Reputation

Marico's leadership in both Parachute and Saffola over the past four decades is backed by significant investments. As a result, in FY15, Parachute had sales of more than Rs 2,000 crore and controlled more than 55 per cent of the coconut oil market and more than 25 per cent of the value-added hair oil market. Similarly, Saffola's FY15 sales were Rs 880 crore, with the brand controlling 58 per cent market share in the premium edible oils market and more than 65 per cent of the flavoured oats market.

Parachute: In the mid-1970s, in a first for a coconut oil brand, Mariwala appointed the advertising agency, Clarion, to handle Parachute's advertising. Through expansion of distribution, higher advertising and publicity spends (which focused on the traditional purity and nutritional values of coconut oil), and change in packaging (from tin to plastic), Parachute was able to corner around 50 per cent of the urban coconut oil market by 1992. This strong brand equity, aided by innovative brand positioning, held Marico in good stead when it faced a threat from HUL during 1999–2002.

In one of my discussions with Marico's distributors in November 2015, I was told: 'Even in rural areas, if after purchasing, the consumer realizes that the bottle of coconut oil purchased isn't the original Parachute, they come and return the product asking for the genuine bottle.' In my discussions with regular Parachute coconut oil users, they said, 'We use Parachute coconut oil due to the trust of 100 per cent pure coconut oil built over decades and across generations. The difference in quality between Parachute and a duplicate/competitor's coconut oil is clearly evident when one uses it. The fragrance, longevity and feel of Parachute coconut oil are far superior to that of the competing products.'

Exhibit 49: Parachute's market share of the coconut oil market

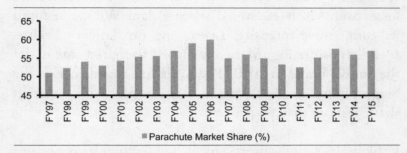

Source: Marico, Ambit Capital research.

Note: The panel used by Nielsen to determine market share undergoes changes every 2–3 years. As a result, the market shares are not exactly comparable year on year. Through the above exhibit we are trying to convey the fact that Parachute has been a dominant player in the coconut oil market over the last twenty years.

Saffola: Following the success of Parachute in the 1970s, an advertising agency was hired for Saffola as well in the late 1970s. To distinguish itself from other brands, Saffola was positioned as a health-oriented edible oil. In the early commercials, the advertisements played on consumers' fear by showing the visual of a man being wheeled into the ICU, as his wife looked on anxiously. The message was clear: Use Saffola and protect the health of your family. Over the years, Marico launched blends in Saffola in order to get around the shortage of safflower seeds and also to improve affordability of the oils. These blends have helped Saffola widen its target audience as the brand was positioned not only as a preventive for heart care but also targeted potential heart patients. With continuous investment, Saffola developed strong brand equity. This was evident when market share losses for Saffola were limited despite a disruptive advertising campaign by Adani Wilmar's Fortune rice bran oil, and these losses were easily recovered when Adani Wilmar reduced its competitive intensity. Leveraging on Saffola's health-friendly positioning, Marico launched flavoured oats under the Saffola brand in 2010. Today, Saffola masala oats is the biggest brand in the flavoured oats category with a market share of more than 65 per cent.

Exhibit 50: Saffola advertisement highlighting its preventive heart-care positioning

Source: Marico website.

A housewife who made the switch to Saffola edible oil a few years ago told me, 'We made the switch to Saffola oil when our family doctor suggested using it in order to control my husband's rising cholesterol levels. Although it's 30–40 per cent expensive versus the oil we were using previously, it is a small price to pay for avoiding heart ailments.'

Exhibit 51: Saffola market share in super-premium edible oil category

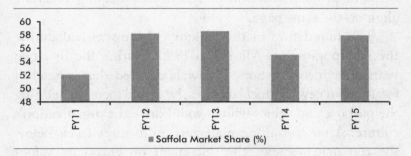

Source: Marico, Ambit Capital research.

Note: The panel used by Nielsen to determine market share undergoes changes every 2–3 years. As a result, the market shares are not exactly comparable year on year. Through the above exhibit we are trying to convey the fact that since separate market share was reported for premium edible oils, Saffola has been a dominant player in this segment.

Architecture

Multinational FMCG companies in India are known for their professional management and a positive, pro-employee work culture. Over the years, Marico has matched and perhaps beaten these MNCs on this aspect of work culture which is critical to attract good talent. It has used its powerful board of directors for effective guidance. Let's look at these aspects in detail:

Work Culture—Marico's key competitive advantage: The role of culture in building a sustainable profitable business is underappreciated by investors, particularly in the case of promoter-led businesses. As Mariwala said during my meeting with him, 'I strongly believe that culture can be a source of competitive advantage in an organization and it is impossible to copy. The organization's culture is a major driving force in the execution of strategy. Correct culture helps in proper execution of strategy by helping everyone align on the same page.'

The foundation of this unique culture was laid during the incorporation of Marico in 1990. During the first two years after incorporation, Mariwala decided that instead of focusing on new product launches, he would focus on defining the purpose and values which would drive the organization's culture. After consulting managers up to three levels below the top management, the document on corporate values was drafted. It envisaged a work culture based on values such as openness, informality, participation, empowerment, meritocracy, apolitical behaviour, job rotation and learning. In order to translate these values into culture, Mariwala interacted with all Marico employees, from managers to factory workmen, to stress the importance of these values. HR policies were formulated which reinforced these values and helped create Marico's unique culture.

Specific measures that Marico emphasized on in this culture include:

- Openness: When Marico moved into its new office after its incorporation in 1990, in a first for an Indian company, an open office was created where the top management didn't sit in cabins. First names were used to reinforce informality.
- Empowerment of responsibility: There are no attendance registers (or musters as they are commonly known in

factories) to be signed for daily attendance, and employee leave is not monitored;

- Integrity: In order to reinforce integrity, employees authorize their own expense claims up to a preset limit, instead of authorization from seniors;
- Meritocracy: A significant portion of an employee's variable remuneration is based on the individual's performance rather than on the company's overall performance. This helps stress the concept of meritocracy.

The uniqueness of Marico's culture is evident from some of the discussions we have had with Marico's former employees. Milind Sarwate, former CFO of Marico, told us, 'When I came to Marico, I quickly sensed that it had an environment different from my earlier organization, Godrej Consumer. In Marico, hierarchy was based, not on age or seniority, but on the criticality of the role and the potential and effectiveness of the individual.'

Referring to his relationship with his boss, Sarwate added, 'Harsh would empower one totally and not in bits and pieces. Unlike other Indian companies of that time where approval of the promoter would be needed for most decisions, in Marico, I needed to take approval for very few critical things. Harsh's logic was—if he has assigned a role to a professional and the professional has a sound logic underpinning his actions, Harsh should not interfere. These empowerment principles flowed down in the organization, right from Harsh to the senior management team and then to the levels below.'

B.S. Nagesh, the former MD of Shoppers Stop and an independent director on Marico's board, said in my meeting with him in December 2015, 'How do you transfer ownership to a management team without making them owners? This is one of the keys to success. Otherwise, one owner cannot be the Brahma, Vishnu and Mahesh (the holy trinity of Hindu gods). Because of Marico's culture of empowerment, I see more owner-managers than just managers. This has enabled them to counter threats from Wilmar and HUL.' One of India's most seasoned fund managers, in my discussions with him in October 2015, described Marico's work culture as 'massive freedom in your job, huge amount of responsibilities, and no interference'.

Marico's professional and meritocratic culture places it on par with its MNC competitors like HUL and Nestle and ahead of domestic majors like Dabur and Godrej Consumer. This makes Marico an employer of choice. I spoke to a recruitment consultant on how jobseekers perceived Marico as a place to work for, and her response was, 'Amongst the domestic FMCG companies, Marico and Asian Paints are considered top tier, whilst Dabur and Godrej Consumer Private Limited (GCPL) are a notch below. Employees of multinational FMCGs like Mondelez and HUL seek opportunities with domestic FMCGs like Marico, where, although the remuneration is lower, due to its unique culture, employees get more responsibilities and hence wider exposure than in an MNC. This has allowed Marico to attract some of the best talents in the market. Marico has been able to create substantial brand equity, making it the employer of choice among its domestic FMCG peers.'

A top-notch board of directors provides a wealth of knowledge: Indian promoters often pay lip service to the legal requirement of having at least 50 per cent of the total number of directors as independent directors. Often, independent directors have no work experience relevant to the boards they sit on and play no role in helping and guiding the company in key strategic decisions. Their main role is to be a golf course buddy for the promoter and look the other way if he is dipping his hand into the till. Marico has broken away from this paradigm.

Mariwala explained this to me: 'What we need to understand is that the board is a source of competitive advantage and is there not just to meet statutory requirements. At Marico, we identify the competencies we need in the business and accordingly build the board.' Marico's board is composed of nine directors. Of these, only two—Harsh and Rajen Mariwala—belong to the promoter family. Saugata Gupta sits on the board as the MD and CEO. The remaining six independent directors are highly credible and have relevant backgrounds, as highlighted in Exhibit 52.

Exhibit 52: Background of independent directors on the board—high-quality professionals with relevant experience

Name	On board since	Background
Anand Kripalu	2007	MD and CEO of United Spirits; was MD and president of India and South Asia with Mondelez International until Sept 2013; was MD for Unilever's East Africa operations; 22 years' experience in HUL.
Atul Choksey	2001	Chairman of Apcotex Industries Ltd and Apco Enterprises Ltd; was MD of Asian Paints from 1984 to 1997; 24 years' experience in Asian Paints; was president of the Bombay Chamber of Commerce and Industry of India 1993–94.

Name	On board since	Background
B. S. Nagesh	2010	Vice chairman and non-executive director of Shoppers Stop Ltd; chairman of Retailers Association of India; 24 years' experience in retail industry; first Asian to be inducted into the World Retail Hall of Fame, 2008.
Hema Ravichandar	2005	Was vice-president and global head of HR for Infosys Group; was the chairperson for The Conference Board's HR Council of India and member of the National HRD Network of India; 28 years of experience in HR.
Nikhil Khattau	2001	MD of MF Advisors Pvt. Ltd; was founding CEO of SUN F&C Asset Management which was sold to Principal Financial Group, USA, in 2004; on the board of the national board of advisors of AIESEC in India.
Rajeev Bakshi	2003	MD of Metro Cash & Carry India Pvt. Ltd; was joint MD of ICICI Venture Funds Management Company Limited; was MD of India operations and South African business in Mondelez India Foods.

Source: Industry, Ambit Capital research.

B.S. Nagesh explained to us how Marico extracted maximum value from its board and turned it into a competitive advantage. He said, 'Boards build the effectiveness of management. So a promoter supporting and listening to the board, although he is a 60 per cent shareholder, makes us independent directors feel proud because we think that we are able to contribute to Marico. All major decisions impacting shareholders are discussed thoroughly with the board. The board is also involved in recruiting the CEO and one level below the CEO. An effective board gives Marico a combined experience of other big companies like Diageo and Mondelez, which adds tremendous value to the organization. These things don't reflect directly on the balance sheet, profit and loss statement (P&L) or share price, but these are inputs which go into creation of long-term shareholder wealth.'

Marico's board has also played an important role in guiding the company in its inorganic growth plans, helping it decide which targets to acquire and when to go slow on acquisitions.

Strategic Assets

For any FMCG company, width and depth of its dealer–distributor network and its relationship with distributors are key strategic assets. Marico has a distribution reach of more than four million outlets and a direct distribution reach of a million outlets. Marico's network of loyal distributors has been built around strong personal ties that date to the BOIL days of the 1970s and '80s.

To improve its trade equity (relationship with trade partners), in the early noughties, Marico stopped the tradition of pushing stock to dealers towards the end of the month in order to achieve the sales target for the month. This, coupled with better sales planning, smoothened the monthly sales pattern to 27/32/41 per cent across the first/second/third set of ten days from an uneven distribution of 10/28/62 per cent. The entire supply chain from raw material sourcing to distributors was linked using supply chain management (SCM) software.

Ambit's consumer sector team's discussions over the years with Marico's distributors indicate that they feel a sense of pride in doing business with the company. One Marico distributor described to my colleagues how Marico takes care of its distributors, 'Marico was one of the first FMCG companies to take the top-performing distributors on a foreign trip in the mid-1990s. When they took us to Singapore along with our families, we were given luxury treatment. In the early part of the last decade, when they implemented IT solutions for improving our ease of business, we were way ahead of our distributor peers in the capability of using IT for distribution, thus giving us a sense of pride.'

This allows Marico to experiment with new launches without fearing distribution attrition in case of failure. Some initiatives taken by Marico that improved its relations with its associates include:

(a) Company-agnostic order management software provided to distributors: Marico installed order management software at the distributor end, which allowed the distributor to use it to manage not only Marico's orders but also those of other companies as well. Initiatives such as these enabled distributors to improve their overall efficiency.

(b) Predefined processes for timely replacement of damaged and expired goods: Marico set up systems and processes which helped distributors claim losses for damaged or expired goods in a timely manner compared with the tedious process laid out by peers. As a result, several large FMCG distributors regard Marico as the most preferred partner for a long-term business relationship.

Marico has also used IT and analytics to stay ahead of the curve, especially in its sales and distribution function. In 2000, Marico was one of the first FMCG companies to implement the ERP–SCM suite from SAP. These IT investments helped Marico in better inventory and demand forecasting and helped avoid stock-outs. Marico sales executives were also given handheld terminals (HHT) for order booking which helped them cover more retailers as time taken for order booking was reduced. Since then, Marico has continuously upgraded its IT platform to improve the ease of doing business for its distributors. In December 2014, Marico implemented automated primary ordering system which significantly reduced manual intervention of Marico's sales team in pushing products on to distributors' balance sheet. This software, used by only a select few large consumer organizations in India, helps Marico's sales team to focus more on secondary sales (i.e. sales to dealers and end customers) rather than spending too much time with the distributors. It has also widened the range of products sold by distributors and has helped Marico achieve faster order closures, which allows better and timely dispatch planning by the depot.

Section 3: Controlled capital allocation

FMCG companies are well known for their high ROCE due to:

(a) Low capital intensity: Manufacturing of FMCG products isn't capital-intensive and can be outsourced. This result in high asset turnovers—typically, one rupee of fixed asset investment results in four rupees of sales.
(b) Low working capital requirement: Most FMCG companies have negative working capital as their creditors exceed debtors.
(c) High operating profit margins: Market-leading brands command a price premium which results in higher margins.

Thus, the core businesses of most FMCG companies do not need incremental capital to grow due to this highly cash-generative nature. By their very nature, fast-moving goods are paid for immediately. They do not enjoy a long period of credit (like, say, a company buying a boiler for its plant pays over a period of time). But the FMCG company enjoys a longer period of credit from its suppliers. To put this simply, an FMCG company receives money from sales quickly, while it has to pay for its raw materials over a long period of time. This is called a negative working capital (or, in financial analysis terms, when creditors exceed debtors) and this means that an FMCG company's cash balance remains high (hence the cash-generative nature of operations). However, as companies mature and growth levels off, FMCG companies must pursue new growth opportunities that will not offer high ROCEs from day one. At the very least, these new opportunities need to generate ROCEs equivalent to at least the cost of capital to provide capital for the next opportunity and hence ensure longevity of growth. These opportunities can be organic, such as new product launches—which are mostly funded by cash generated from operations or inorganic, which involve decision on large capital allocation. Marico scores reasonably well on both fronts. The Parachute and Saffola brands have funded their brand extensions until these extensions became capable of sustaining themselves. However, the verdict on Marico's acquisitions is a mixed one. As mentioned earlier, Marico executed a series of large acquisitions like Paras in India and a slew of overseas acquisitions.

Due to this, Marico's ROCE more than halved to 17 per cent in FY13 from 41 per cent in FY08. As a result, Marico has decided to go slow on acquisitions over the last two years and instead give itself time to assimilate the existing acquisitions. Some of its acquisitions in Egypt, Vietnam and South Africa have taken a bit longer than expected to stabilize.

Not all the news on acquisitions is bad though. Marico has gained from these acquisitions in terms of the wealth of knowledge and opportunities gained. For example, the Vietnam acquisition gave Marico an understanding of the male grooming category which it is using for its Indian male grooming brands, Set Wet and Zatak. More importantly, Marico's employees get an opportunity to gain an international perspective, thereby helping them grow further. These international postings also act as a good way of retaining talent for Marico. Mariwala told me, 'With profit centres now in four different countries, I can train managers on the entire P&L in these countries. If I had only the India business, I would have had only functional heads. This is also part of our thinking on international acquisitions.'

Cognizant of the damage done to its ROCEs, Marico has taken several steps to improve them. These include:

(a) **Raising the dividend payout ratio:** In FY14, the dividend payout was raised to 48 per cent (24 per cent, excluding a one-time dividend payment of Rs 1.75/share) as against 19 per cent in FY13. Mariwala acknowledged this in an interview[14] with Forbes India in 2014: 'There are some other issues like dividend payout which, in our case, was lower than some other FMCG companies as a percentage of profit. We have taken one jump and, maybe, over a period of time, we will take one more.'

(b) **Acquisitions to no longer be the escape button for inability to grow organically:** Given the large-scale acquisitions done over 2006–12, Marico has paused for a few years to digest the existing acquisitions. Instead, it has focused on improving the profitability and realizing more synergies from these acquisitions. Having seen an improvement in its ROCE (29 per cent in FY15 vs 17 per cent in FY13), the company is now willing to look at smaller acquisitions/ tie-ups only if there is a strategic fit and if valuations are right. In addition to strategic fit, the company would now also evaluate if there is management capability in driving the acquisitions. In our recent discussions with the management, Saugata Gupta stated, 'Acquisitions had become an escape button for not growing the domestic portfolio. We are changing that. We need to grow organically.'

Marico's share price outperformance

A rupee invested in Marico at its IPO in May 1996 is worth Rs 117 presently (in April 2016), implying a compounded

---

[14] http://forbesindia.com/article/boardroom/marico-3.0-from-singlebrand-to-diversified-consumer-goods/37958/0.

Exhibit 53: A series of acquisitions bumped up revenues . . .

Source: Company, Ambit Capital research.

Exhibit 54: . . . but at the cost of declining ROCEs

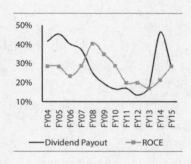

Source: Company, Ambit Capital research.

annual return of 27 per cent. That same rupee would be worth just Rs 7 if invested in the Sensex, implying a CAGR of 10 per cent. Thus, Marico has outperformed the Sensex by over 17.8 times over the past twenty years. At the heart of this outstanding performance there has been a relentless focus on maintaining brand leadership (even amidst the tremendous odds as seen during the turn-of-the-century battle for supremacy in the coconut hair oil market with HUL), extending winning brands (such as Saffola) across categories and divesting low-margin brands (such as Sweekar) which struggle to deliver adequate levels of ROCE.

CHAPTER 5

Page Industries: Jockeying from Manila to Bengaluru

'Nothing contributes so much to tranquillize the mind as a steady purpose—a point on which the soul may fix its intellectual eye.'

—Mary Wollstonecraft Shelley, nineteenth-century English novelist

The origins of Page Industries are split across two cities located around 13,000 kilometres apart. In St Joseph, a small city in Wisconsin in the USA, Samuel Cooper and his sons began making socks and undergarments. In the context of undergarments, the term 'jockey' goes back to 1874,[15] when jockstraps (the closest comparison in India is the loincloth known as *langot* in Hindi) were invented to provide support

---

[15] http://www.independent.co.uk/life-style/fashion/features/a-brief-history-of-pants-why-mens-smalls-have-always-been-a-subject-of-concern-771772.html.

and protection for cyclists who rode on cobblestone streets. In 1934, Cooper hit gold with the Jockey shorts, featuring the famous Y-shaped fly. At a time when jumpsuits and shorts were the norm, Jockey briefs (which removed the long legs and inserted a Y-shaped fly at the front) created a sensation, selling 30,000 units in three months—a hit in that era.

Meanwhile, around 13,000 kilometres west of Wisconsin, in the city of Angeles, Philippines, a Sindhi businessman, Verhomal Lilaram, and his son, Genomal Verhomal, had established V. Lilaram and Co. to import garments from neighbouring countries and sell them in the Philippines. In 1930, when Lilaram passed away, the twenty-one-year-old son, Verhomal, took control of the business. Business boomed after World War II since Manila was at the centre of the war in the Pacific between the Japanese and the American forces. In the 1950s, V. Lilaram & Co. was the first company to charter a Pan American airlines cargo flight with a full load of textiles from New York to the Philippines. The top-selling item, Verhomal noticed, was Jockey undergarments, which catered to the American military which was still present in the Philippines in large numbers after the war. The largest American air and naval bases outside the US mainland were in the Philippines—Verhomal's main market. From these military bases, Jockey's market expanded to the local population in the Philippines.

Forty years later, in the 1990s, Jockey International (USA) gave the exclusive licence to the Genomals to form a company that would launch and expand Jockey's presence in India. Within two decades, this company—Page Industries—would go on to become the biggest licensee of Jockey in the world.

Phase 1: 1959–92

Establishing Jockey's leadership in the Philippines

Verhomal's booming business in the Philippines didn't go unnoticed by Coopers (renamed as Jockey International in 1972). Impressed with his success, they offered him the licence to manufacture Jockey in the Philippines in 1959. Recalling that pivotal moment in the family, Sunder Genomal, the promoter of Page Industries, told me, 'I visited the Jockey factory for the first time at the age of nine. I remember finding it extremely exciting to see all those machines buzzing and sitting through sales and advertising meetings with my older brothers, Nari and Ramesh.'

Sunder's brothers, Nari and Ramesh, joined the business in the 1960s and 1970s. Being a small family-run business, managerial responsibilities were controlled mainly by members of the promoter family; the few professionals who were there were at the lower managerial levels. The Genomal brothers learnt the trade working at the shop-floor level and visiting retailers with samples. The business continued to expand across the Philippines, growing as Jockey launched new products (coloured fashion innerwear in 1973, Jockey for Her in 1986) and kept innovating (box packaging in 1975).

Meanwhile, in the US, Jockey had a string of firsts to its names: prominent display of underwear on retailer's sales floors in 1910 (until then, underwear was kept in boxes behind the counter), the first men's briefs in 1934, Y-front design and cellophane packaging in 1935, the first underwear fashion show in 1938, stitching the brand name on the waistbands of the underwear in 1947, the first bikini brief for men in 1958, etc. The Genomals had access to all these innovations, thanks to their licence. The Genomals were also willing to experiment. In 1989, they started the concession model of retailing (shop-in-shop) within the top department stores in the Philippines. Prior to this, all products were sold on outright basis to the department stores.

Interestingly, Jockey's first attempt to enter India wasn't with the Genomals. It was with Associated Apparels in 1962. Through the 1960s, many foreign innerwear brands were launched in India. Associated Apparels introduced the then world-famous Maidenform bras (owned today by Hanes) and tied up with Jockey to launch Jockey underwear in 1962. The international brand, Lovable, entered India in 1966 through a licensing deal and became a huge success. Along with it entered the brand Daisy Dee, through a subsidiary of Lovable, followed by Feelings. In 1971, Maxwell Industries launched VIP-branded innerwear for men in the economy segment, catching the attention of the discerning public with an advertisement featuring a Bollywood actor. In 1973, however, Jockey decided to leave India after the Indian government used the Foreign Exchange Regulation Act (FERA) to force multinational companies to dilute their ownership in their Indian ventures to 40 per cent.

After Jockey exited India, its competitors flourished. Associated Apparels continued to focus on mid-premium innerwear during the 1980s and was successful in establishing themselves as a dominant player in the mid-premium innerwear segment through Liberty (men) and Libertina (women). Maxwell Industries, during the 1980s, launched the brand, Frenchie, to cater to the mid-premium innerwear segment. In 1985, Rupa & Co. emerged in the innerwear market, offering products across categories, including men, women and kids, and became one of the biggest manufacturers and sellers of innerwear in India. The success of Rupa was followed by many other domestic brands in the 1980s and '90s, including Amul, Lux Cozi and Dollar in the men's category, while Neva, Bodycare, Softy, Lady Care, Little Lacy, Red Rose, Sonari, Feather Line, etc., were the key players in the lingerie market.

Then came the liberalization of 1991. With the regulatory hurdles to enter India removed, Jockey decided to return to India. And this time, it chose the right partners.

Phase 2: 1993–97

Jockey re-enters India through Page

In 1991, when India opened up its economy, Jockey International was approached by some well-known large Indian companies for a tie-up. This time, Jockey urged the Genomals to expand beyond Philippines. Genomal told me, 'We said we've never lived in India or done business there. They said they are okay with that as long as they have partners whom they can trust and who share the same vision and values. The words of the then president of Jockey, Rick Hosley, come back to me every now and then. He actually said to me in 1993, 'Should you guys decide to take up the licence, you will one day become the biggest licensee of Jockey in the world.'

With those words ringing in his ears, Genomal toured India in 1993. He saw that innerwear was a generic clothing category, relegated to mass selling. He was sure there was a market for a premium, foreign brand. He hired market research firm MARG to scour several cities and towns for a detailed study. The researchers were armed with hundreds of samples (with and without packaging) to carry and show to the respondents. The response was positive and encouraging enough for Genomal to plan a serious foray in India. Genomal also knew the biggest challenge would be setting up a distribution network across a vast, diverse country with unorganized, fragmented retail infrastructure. Genomal decided it was worth the risk. He named the Indian company Page after the initials of his mother, Parpati Genomal. Page Apparel Manufacturing was incorporated in November 1994, and the name was changed to Page Industries in 2006, just before its IPO.

Genomal shortlisted Mumbai and Bengaluru as cities where he might set up a manufacturing facility and met several people, ranging from professionals working at some of the largest garment manufacturing firms of the country to accountants and real estate developers. Between the two cities, Genomal chose Bengaluru. Genomal recollects, 'Manufacturing was always going to be the backbone of our organization. Bengaluru made a lot more sense in terms of real estate and labour. I started to feel that, unlike Mumbai, Bengaluru did not have a cultural baggage attached to labour-intensive manufacturing facilities and, hence, I could see myself setting up the culture in my own way in this city.'

On the distribution front, unlike competitors like Liberty, Rupa and VIP, which had set up wholesale-driven distribution networks, Page expanded solely through individual distributors. Genomal wanted to regulate the sales channel so that he could ensure uniformity of selling price across all stores. He wanted consumers to interact with the product directly, rather than the products being showcased by retailers. With that in mind, Genomal introduced a new method of in-store marketing of innerwear products where the product would have exclusive display fixtures and bold in-store advertisements. Genomal then hand-picked his distributors, choosing only those with the right attitude towards marketing and brand building. He invited 100 top retailers from four metros (Delhi, Mumbai, Chennai and Kolkata) and three large cities to five-star hotels and presented his products, display fixtures, point-of-sales features and marketing plans. 'The response was overwhelming. Almost like a stampede. Retailers actually rushed to queue and sign up. Even larger multi-brand retailers, which rarely carried innerwear, rushed to join. When I witnessed this, I knew right away that our future was made,' he said.

Madhu Mansukhani, owner of Jockey's first exclusive brand outlet in India, told me, 'Mr Sunder Genomal invited me with my whole family for the fashion show at ITC Windsor Hotel during the launch of Jockey in 1995, where 100 retailers were invited. They also invited Sushmita Sen, who was then the recently crowned Miss Universe. After the fashion show, Page's management team and Sushmita Sen came to my store for its inauguration.'

The early 1990s was a good time to set up a consumer brand in India. In the first few years, post-liberalization, consumer confidence and aspirations were high. Coke launched in 1993 and slugged it out with Pepsi. New private airlines were being launched (Jet Airways in 1993) as were new private sector banks (HDFC Bank in 1994). In 1994, Sushmita Sen won the Miss Universe crown, soon followed by Aishwarya Rai wining the Miss World title—an achievement celebrated in India almost like a cricket World Cup victory. On 15 August 1995, Videsh Sanchar Nigam Limited (VSNL) launched

Internet services, only a few weeks after the first mobile telephone call had been placed. Thus, change was in the air when Page launched the Jockey brand of men's innerwear in November 1995, coincidentally a month after the release of the Bollywood blockbuster, *Dilwale Dulhania Le Jayenge*. Genomal's vision was bold. He set Page's mission statement: 'To be the brand of choice for innerwear and leisurewear in our target market'. The vision statement was: 'To continue to dominate the innerwear market in India for the next one hundred years and beyond'.

Between 1995 and 1997, Genomal built his core team to scale up execution. Pius Thomas, from telecom operator BPL, joined the company to look after finance. Shekhar Tiwari joined from Eureka Forbes to take charge of marketing and sales, and Vedji Ticku, also from Eureka Forbes, joined in 1997 as sales manager for the south zone. Thomas went on to become the CFO in 2012, while Ticku took over as CEO in 2016.

Later, Tiwari went on to head Hanes Brands Inc. and is currently CEO of Enamor (which had joined hands with Gokaldas Exports in 2003). It is a testimony to Genomal's willingness to let professionals run the show that two of his senior-most employees today are also among the first hires of his company.

Phase 3: 1997–2003

Gearing up for competition

Not everything went according to plan for Page in its first years. Given that most innerwear brands were low-end, mass-produced and mass-distributed, Page found a distinct lack of quality in the Indian textile manufacturing environment. For example, establishing relationships with high-quality raw material suppliers was a challenge.

Despite initial enthusiasm from Page's distributors, as an overall category, innerwear remained a low-profile product in retail stores. This would ultimately necessitate a high-pitched, pan-India advertising campaign from Page, but the costs were prohibitive. Competitive intensity from incumbents had already increased substantially during 1995–2000. When the company reached sales of Rs 21 crore in FY2000, Rupa and Maxwell were already at Rs 150 crore each. One level above them, in the mid-premium segment, brands like Liberty, Libertina and Tantex (TTK Tantex) were firmly ensconced. Associated Apparels (Liberty and Libertina) reported sales of Rs 100 crore during the same period.

In a stroke of luck for Page, both TTK Tantex and Associated Apparels fell prey to labour strikes. TTK Tantex saw labour-related plant shutdowns in 1997 that lasted for two years, sending the company's revenues into a steady descent (see Exhibit 55). The TTK Group had twenty companies across many sectors and, due to lack of management bandwidth to handle the crisis, sold the innerwear brand in FY02. In the same year, Associated Apparels had a labour strike in one of its factories that disrupted its supply chain. The exit of both TTK Tantex and the crippling of Associated Apparels played into Page's hands as all the large innerwear retailers (dealers) in northern and western India shifted to Jockey.

Exhibit 55: Annualized revenues of TTK Tantex over 1996–03

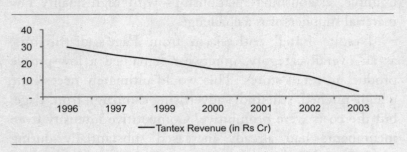

Source: Capitaline, Ambit Capital research.

In three years, Page doubled its sales, hitting Rs 50 crore in FY03 with a retail network of 10,000 outlets and in-house production of one million pieces a month. It was time to take on the competition.

Phase 4: 2004–15

Beating the competition

Page raced ahead of its competition in this phase. In FY15, Page clocked revenues of Rs 1543 crore—far ahead of Rupa and Maxwell. In eleven years, Page had grown its revenues twenty-five times—at an impressive CAGR of 35 per cent. This growth was propelled by new launches at the rate of at least one new product every year from 2004 until 2015. Between 2004 and 2006, Page introduced several new products like the sub-brand, Jockey Zone, in 2004, brassieres in 2005, and the No Panty Line Promise range of products in 2006. These product launches were supported by consistent expansion in manufacturing capacity, increase in automation of manufacturing processes, and the use of technology and data analytics to improve supply chain efficiencies. As a result, sales per employee improved consistently, as shown in Exhibit 56.

Exhibit 56: Page's sales per employee has been increasing with stable volumes per employee

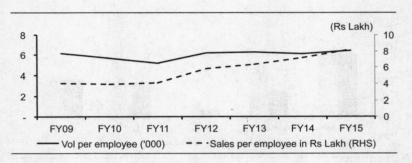

Source: Ambit Capital research.

What makes Page's achievement more impressive is that it staved off competition from almost every foreign brand that entered India. After the turn of the century, many more international brands entered the Indian innerwear market. Enamor joined hands with Gokaldas Exports in 2003. Triumph, which now has presence in fifty-two cities, entered in 2002. In 2006–07, several brands entered the Indian innerwear market, including La Senza, La Perla, Amante, Undercolors by United Colours of Benetton, Fruit of the Loom, Calvin Klein, etc. Advertising played a key role for Page, as we will see in the next section, as it held its own against growing competition with several highly successful advertising campaigns including Just Jockeying (2010) and Jockey or Nothing (2015). In 2007, Page raised Rs 100 crore via an IPO which reduced the promoters' stake in the firm to below 75 per cent. This corpus was used for brand building, manufacturing capacity expansion and IT infrastructure upgrades.

Exhibit 57: Revenue and earnings CAGR of key undergarment brands in India over FY06-15

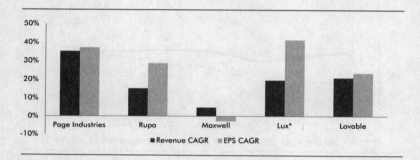

Source: Ambit Capital research.

Note: *Lux data pertains to FY09-15. Athough Lux's EPS CAGR has been higher than Page's; its cash conversion has been poor with cumulative post tax CFO/EBITDA of -27% for FY09-15.

The biggest testimony of the strength of the relationship between Jockey USA and Page is the fact that in 2010, Jockey extended their licensing agreement with Page for a twenty-year period, instead of the standard practice of five years. Moreover, in the new agreement, the UAE was added as a new territory of exclusive licence and, in 2011, Page made its first shipment to the UAE. The Genomals added another brand to Page when they signed a licence and distribution agreement with swimwear brand Speedo for an exclusive right to manufacture and distribute Speedo products in India. Similar to Jockey, this agreement was signed due to the existing relationship between Speedo International and the Genomals, with the latter having expanded Speedo's presence in the Philippines since 1988.

Page's growth is commendable considering that it came without any compromise to its balance sheet. Many companies justify risking balance sheet and profits for fuelling growth. However, as can be seen in the Exhibit 58 and 59, Page has maintained steadfast financial discipline whilst expanding its operations, and at the same time its share prices have also kept up an upward trend.

Exhibit 58: Consistent sales growth, steady ROE and net profit growth over FY01–15

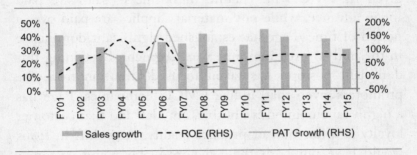

Source: Company, Ambit Capital research.

Exhibit 59: Share price chart

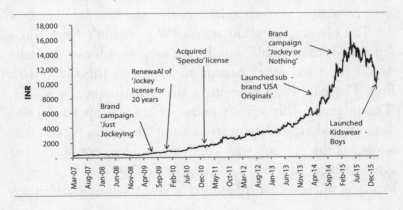

Source: Bloomberg, Ambit Capital research.

What is Page Industries' secret sauce?

Focusing on the core business

Page's journey with Jockey goes back to 1959 and continues to date. Four generations of the Genomal family have run the business and have no intention of diverting their attention to anything else. As Genomal told me, 'This is a business and a brand that's been in our blood and etched in our hearts and minds from a very early age.'

Page's business model generates large amounts of cash, given its FMCG-like nature of business—sales are paid for in advance, while raw material supplies are paid over a period of time. Page has established significant dominance in the mid-to-premium innerwear segment. Sustaining this dominant position has taken focused attention from the promoters given that, unlike FMCG companies, Page has a highly labour-intensive business model, and that customer loyalty is a function of product quality. Any shift in focus would have put both these factors—labour and customer loyalty—at threat. Therefore, the fact that Page's promoters stuck to innerwear and associated categories like leisurewear, and with Jockey as the only brand, is a significant driver of their consistent performance over the past two decades.

The obvious question arises: Why couldn't Page add a few brands to its stable? Surely, the success of Jockey in India would have led other brands to approach the Genomals. Pius Thomas, Page's executive director (finance) told me, 'The promoters historically know Jockey and Speedo in and out and understand the intricacies of the business, and that is one of the reasons why competitors have not succeeded against Page.' Indeed, a testimony to Page's dedication to Jockey is the fact that it handled labour relations better than its competitors did; TTK and Associated Apparels were left behind due to labour-related problems.

Deepening its competitive moats

In its twenty years in India, Page has consistently widened the gap between itself and its competition. It has mastered manufacturing processes and used operational efficiencies and R&D to help it produce a high-quality product.

Page didn't just stop there. It built a very strong front end, with innovative marketing, retail and distribution. One would think that making innerwear isn't rocket science. And given that innerwear is neither on display (at least not in India) when worn by users nor widely spoken about in everyday conversation, the presumption would be that brand can't possibly be that important. But think about this: Comfort in innerwear is much more important than the clothes we wear above them. Innerwear also has to be strong and durable. To add to this, difference in physique, weather-related factors and consumer preferences of comfort in India are not entirely similar to those abroad. Consequently, the product design, fit and fabric composition have to be indigenized in order to be successful in India. This is a curse if you get it wrong and a boon if you get it right.

If a consumer accepts a particular style and brand, it is highly likely that he will stick to it. Therefore, consistency of product quality and design over a period of time across geographies is critical for a brand to avoid losing a satisfied consumer. Finally, a steady stream of new products keeps distributors and retailers active and interested. Selling the same product year after year does get boring. The feel-good factor of consumer purchase in innerwear is driven by a combination of fresh introduction of designs across various sub-segments of innerwear and fresh introduction of colours within existing styles. Very few clothing brands have got all of these factors right in India.

Innovation

Page has been ahead of its competition with regard to the pace of new launches (at least one new product range every year in each of its categories), the quality of products as well as innovations in these products. The licence agreement with Jockey ensures that Page has access to Jockey's innovations.

Page, Jockey USA's team and Jockey's other licensees in different countries meet twice a year to discuss the technology related to product development. Some examples include Jockey's 3D-Innovation collection, which is based on eight-way stretch technology, and Sports Performance collection, which has mesh inserts for increased moisture management.

Page also has a twenty-member R&D team headed by Shamir Genomal, executive director, chief strategy officer, and the promoter's son. The R&D team's focus is to identify local consumer preferences and introduce new styles regularly. Page's management has highlighted that at any given time, at least 110 SKUs are on the shelf with the R&D team to help deliver 'fresh and good' products to consumers. This keeps distributor loyalty alive since not only does Page launch new products, it also removes products that don't work. Distributor feedback is heard and acted upon.

The owner of Jockey's exclusive brand outlets (EBO) in Bengaluru told me, 'One good thing about Jockey is that every three months they keep refreshing the product range, be it underwear, track pants or T-shirts. For instance, they will remove five colours which are slow-moving and replace them with new colours. That gives a different look to the product and customers want to try new colours.'

Page has also leveraged off the customer loyalty that it has built with its premium products. After establishing itself in men's innerwear, it moved to the women's innerwear category (in 2005), followed by expansion into leisurewear in 2009.

Apart from innovation in product development, Page has also been innovative in many aspects of labour/workforce management. For instance, more than ten years ago, Page pioneered the practice of offering free lunch to its workers. This practice subsequently became popular in the garment-manufacturing industry. This, along with several other initiatives highlighted in the sections below, has helped Page manage scalability of a labour-intensive manufacturing process without disruptions related to labour unrest over the past twenty years.

Page has employed another unique strategy. It makes its own elastic, compared to the industry practice of outsourcing this from small cottage industries. Over the years, Page has steadily expanded these elastic manufacturing capacities (see Exhibit 60).

Exhibit 60: Page has increased its elastic capacity exponentially

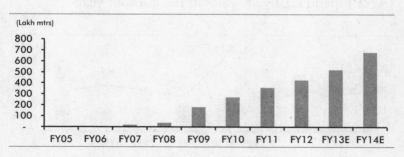

Source: Company, Ambit Capital research.

Note: Actual numbers are available in annual reports until FY12 only. Data for FY13, 14 are estimated.

Brand

Among the biggest challenges for any entry-level consumer company in segments like watches, footwear, garments and kitchenware is how to maintain an aspirational value over long periods of time. There have been several instances of brands which were once significantly dominant in India in their respective product categories, and saw a reduction in their market share with a dilution in their aspirational value. Some key examples include brands like Titan in watches (2005–12), VIP Frenchie (1995–2005) in men's innerwear, and Bata in footwear (2000–10). Clearly, this loss of aspirational value is a big risk for any brand. This is because the definition of aspirational consumption in every category changes over time, and hence, the brand recall of leaders needs to evolve accordingly in terms of price points, type and mode of branding initiatives, and product characteristics. How has Page beaten its peers in this regard? Part of Page's success arises from consistently spending around 5 per cent of its revenues on advertising (see Exhibit 61). More

Exhibit 61: Page has maintained its advertising and promotional (A&P) spend relative to sales in the last four years

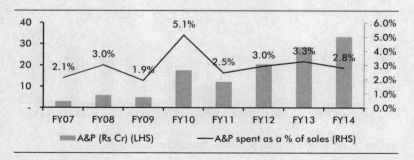

Source: Company, Ambit Capital research.

importantly, Page's approach towards advertising and brand building has been unique compared to peers in two key aspects:

Nature of advertising/media initiatives: Page's approach towards advertising has been unique on several fronts. Firstly, its advertising campaigns have consistently been high-impact affairs like Just Jockeying in FY10–14 (se Exhibit 62) and Jockey or Nothing launched in FY15 (see Exhibit 63). Secondly, Page has placed significant emphasis on in-store advertising to the extent that in most Multi-brand Outlets (MBOs), Jockey's advertisements cover the bulk of in-store advertising space. Thirdly, in a neat play on Indians' world view, Page has made consistent use of Caucasian models in its advertisements (see Exhibits 64–67) and thus firmly entrenched its brand recall as an international brand. This unique approach in advertising has helped Jockey emerge as the sole aspirational brand in the mid-premium innerwear segment.

Exhibit 62: Brand campaign in FY10–14: 'Just Jockeying'

Source: Company, Ambit Capital research.

Exhibit 63: Brand campaign in FY15: 'Jockey or Nothing'

Source: Company, Ambit Capital research.

Exhibit 64: Advertisement of Caucasian models in an EBO in Bangalore

Source: Ambit Capital research.

Exhibit 65: Racks displaying Jockey products in a large departmental store in Bangalore

Source: Company, Ambit Capital research.

Exhibit 66: Caucasian models for a recent launch of kids' wear

Source: Ambit Capital research.

Exhibit 67: Caucasian models for a recent advertisement for Active Bra

Source: Company, Ambit Capital research.

Maintaining pricing discipline across India through the year: Page refuses to offer any discounts on its products. In a country obsessed with discounts, deals and offers, this obstinacy is unique. In my discussions with Page as well as with Jockey dealers, I found that there are no end-of-season sales in any Jockey store. As a policy, retailers and MBOs do not even offer on-the-spot discounts to persistent customers (inveterate Indian shoppers have a habit of begging dealers for discounts with a variety of imaginative reasons such as auspicious day, buying in bulk, first purchase of the day, etc.).

To ensure that distributors follow this no-discount policy, Jockey's sales team keeps policing the entire network of retailers to ensure the product is not being sold below the maximum retail price (MRP). As a result, the management believes that at least 90 per cent of annual sales from retailers to the customers are carried out at MRP consistently every year. Unsuccessful SKUs/unsold products in the firm's inventory are sold at a flat 40 per cent discount through seconds sales twice each year.

Even in this case, Jockey's approach is unique. Normally, dealers and distributors are given these garments for sale at their stores. In fact, many shops on Ambedkar Road in Mumbai's Dadar and Parel areas specialize in the sale of garments, footwear, etc., that are seconds or export-rejects. However, Jockey's seconds sales are done through agents who directly buy the products from the company, receive a 3–4 per cent mark-up on their purchase price, and sell through stalls outside hotels and on high streets. Thus, Page maintains a strict discipline even on unsold products.

Architecture

'Our managers understand that it's not about having power but about how you empower your subordinates and bring about the best results from your team members. Hence, we have a team where each member behaves like a leader. This gives us a winning culture,' said Sunder Genomal during our discussions with him in February 2016.

Page's strong relations with its labour force stands out as a huge competitive advantage. Consider this: Textile manufacturing is one of the most labour-intensive industries globally. In India, those companies that manufactured in-house (TTK Tantex and Associated Apparels) found it tough to maintain cordial labour relations. Both companies were adversely affected by labour-related disruption.

Others like Maxwell and Rupa sell low-end, economy products that are mass-produced and do not require any major attention to detail. No wonder then that both companies have maintained an outsourced manufacturing set-up over the past three decades and, therefore, have been successful only in the economy segment of the innerwear industry.

The owner of a chain of six EBOs of Jockey in Bengaluru told us, 'Quality of product and supply chain management are the two strongest aspects of Jockey compared to its peers. When you order Jockey's product, it comes within two days. Other brands outsource manufacturing. If you have outsourced factories, there is no confirmed timeline to make product delivery at stores.'

However, Page's products are driven by high product quality, customer loyalty and frequent product innovation. To sustain all of this, Page has no choice but to rely on a well-trained workforce with high retention rates and, hence, an in-house manufacturing process. Page has done an excellent job on this front so far. It has scaled up operations in a labour-intensive manufacturing process while maintaining attrition rates at levels as low as 12–13 per cent (remember that Page has no competitor to compare these rates to). How has Page managed this seemingly impossible task?

One of the main reasons is sticking to Karnataka as a manufacturing base where Page has consistently expanded capacities in a modular fashion (i.e. not too much concentration of capacity in one unit) across various plants and locations, which further reduces the possibility of labour unrest (see Exhibit 68).

Exhibit 68: Page has expanded manufacturing capacities in and around Bengaluru, in a modular fashion

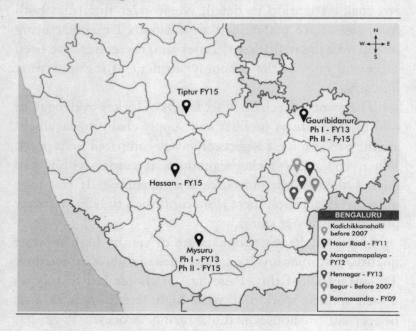

Source: Company, Ambit Capital research.

When I visited Page's manufacturing facilities, I noticed a high number of women workers. This was something new to me since in all my visits to shop floors in India, I found that the labour force is dominated by men. As I learnt later, women account for as high as 88 per cent of Page's labour force. The primary benefit of this is reduced probability of labour unrest as compared to a male-dominated workforce.

The company also spends a lot of effort in training their workers. Once hired, Page's workforce is put through a structured training process in the company's own training centres. Initially, thirty days of training is given, following which, based on performance, labourers are trained in multiskilled operations. On average, the company trains 900–1000 workers in these training centres annually. Page's employee policy also ensures that workers are treated with respect and dignity. Sunder Genomal told me, 'To me it is important that our workforce should feel as happy and excited coming to work in the morning as they are to go home at the end of the day.'

Page's management has a strict policy against supervisors shouting at workers in its manufacturing plants. There are a number of welfare officers in their factories whose job is to make sure that workers are not unhappy about their working conditions. Page also provides various benefits and facilities to their workers like good-quality free food in the factory canteen, transportation for shift workers, crèche for children of workers, proper sanitation and health centres in the factories. Page has also employed qualified doctors and nurses who provide free medical aid to the workers. The company also provides medicines free of cost to their workers, a unique feature compared to many other textile manufacturing set-ups.

Page focuses on recruiting fresh employees to its labour force as the management believes this reduces the chance of negative cultural baggage from other factories entering Page's ecosystem. This has also helped the company hasten its training and induction process.

After labour relations, the second pillar of Page's architecture is its strong ties with distributors, right down to the massive network of mom-and-pop hosiery stores across India. Unlike its competitors, Page uses a three-tier sales and distribution network (see Exhibit 69).

Exhibit 69: The various channels through which Jockey products are sold

	Channel I	Channel II	Channel III
Sales channel	Large-format store (LFS)	Exclusive Brand Outlet (EBO)	Multi-brand Outlet (MBO)
Contribution to revenues through this format %	6	11	83
Typical store type	Modern trade, e.g. HyperCity, Lifestyle, Shoppers Stop	Air-conditioned Jockey exclusive store	Hosiery store—44%, Regional LFS—24%, Multi-product outlets—15%
Typical store size	Shop-in-shop format	800–1000 sq. ft	100–800 sq. ft
Source of procurement	Distributors	Distributors	Distributors
Trade margin received (% of MRP)	26–28	26–30	25–26
Discretion to choose SKUs for stocking	Yes	No	Yes
Strength of the channel (as on 3Q FY16)	NA	270 stores	More than 35,000 stores

Source: Company, Ambit Capital research.

Distribution to MBOs across the country can be carried out through two types of channel partners: (a) distributors who are exclusive to a particular brand and, hence, work with the brand to push products to specific types of retailers at specific prices; or (b) wholesalers who do not work with the brand and have the discretion to sell any product at any price to any retailer. While a mass-produced and mass-sold brand like Rupa or VIP can use the wholesale channel for distribution, a quality-conscious, mid-to-premium brand like Page needs to target distributors directly. This enables it to control distributors and maintain pricing discipline, aspirational brand recall, and push the product to increase penetration at new retailers or new regions. Therefore, while it is easy for both a premium brand like French Connection United Kingdom (better known as FCUK) to target modern retail outlets and economy brands like Rupa to target the wholesale channel, it is very difficult for both of these brands to build a presence at the mom-and-pop hosiery stores across the country through authorized distributors.

Page's distribution strategy is unique because it is well entrenched across hosiery stores, LFSs and EBOs as shown in Exhibit 69. For example, if you shop at Linking Road in Bandra (Mumbai)—one of India's busiest high-street shopping areas—you can buy a Jockey product at a small hosiery store (that also stocks, say, Rupa and VIP), at Jockey's own exclusive outlet, and at the Shoppers Stop mall—all of which are within 1–2 km of each other. Each store reaches out to a different clientele and Jockey has covered a wider base than having just one of those three formats.

Page has increased its network to more than 450 distributors across India from 140 in FY07. These distributors cater to more than 35,000 retail outlets currently (vs 14,000 retail outlets in 2007), spread across the three retail formats highlighted in Exhibit 69. Page is currently increasing the number of retail outlets (or dealers) it services through distributors by around 6 per cent CAGR.

In fact, a Jockey dealership is a lucrative proposition. Dealers earn a higher return on their investment than those of competing brands. Given Jockey's high market share, brand image and premium pricing, they are not only selling more products, they are also selling higher-priced products. This improves inventory turnover. One of Bengaluru's largest innerwear multi-brand retailers told me, 'Jockey gives me 25–30 per cent margin compared to around 35 per cent for some other brands. However, if I keep other brands and Jockey in front of new customers; out of ten customers, seven will walk out with Jockey. I can guarantee that.'

EBOs help push new SKUs to MBOs by establishing customer traction of such SKUs. Finally, Jockey's own sales team operates between distributor and retailer, helping push its products and helping distributors to collect their dues from retailers.

The third pillar of Page's architecture is a process-oriented approach to business. Pius Thomas told me, 'From day one, Mr Genomal has pushed us into adopting a process-oriented approach. Almost everything we do at Page is part of an Excel sheet. As a result, he has instilled a strong process-oriented culture.'

This systematic, analytical approach to Page's business has various aspects. As the company's revenues grow in size and the number of SKUs in its product portfolio increases, working capital management for Page as well as its distributors can become challenging. In order to overcome this, it adopts a demand-forecasting methodology. Vedji Ticku, Page's CEO, told me, 'Our sales and marketing team forecasts demand a year in advance based on a very granular Management Information System (MIS) we have for each and every product. This helps create order pipeline for our production team. Based on how sales are progressing against our projections, these plans are revised on a monthly basis. Since we have many years of experience using MIS, accuracy of our demand projections is higher than what it used to be previously.'

Given its size and scale, Page manages to procure high-quality yarn consistently and at favourable rates (3–4 per cent cheaper than those of its larger peers) from around four to five large yarn vendors. Vendors give Page preferential treatment because Page provides at least three to four months of clear visibility on the volume of yarn that it plans to purchase. This helps the vendors plan their purchases, funding and working capital cycles in advance; in turn, they pass on some of these benefits back to Page through lower prices.

Further, Page uses General Sewing Data (GSD), a global benchmarking tool created by a British firm for sewn products, to measure labour productivity. GSD's primary functions are rationalizing the manufacturing methods and producing an accurate evaluation of the time required to perform a specific task or operation. The management wants each worker to reach an efficiency level which is close to 60–65 per cent of GSD at the time of commissioning of the manufacturing facility. 'We have developed an in-house software using a barcoding system that automatically measures each operator's performance and skill level and assigns her a salary grade. There is no manual intervention here, so that they are immune from bias which can sometimes result from manual intervention by supervisors,' Genomal told me.

Finally, Page is enhancing its IT system via two phases. Phase 1 was completed in December 2015 and Phase 2 is under way. The system will track: (a) real-time distributor sales; (b) performance of the sales team; (c) MIS across SKUs; and (d) online stock ordering by distributors/EBOs. These initiatives will reduce inventory days, avoid stock-outs of fast-moving SKUs, and sustain the healthy working capital cycle of the distributors. 'We want to keep our distributors' balance sheets healthy because our business is dependent on their finances. If they have wrong inventory stuck with them, it neither helps us nor them,' says Ticku.

The fourth and final pillar of Page's architecture is personnel management. The incentive structure for Page's senior management team is designed to drive consistency and sustainability of growth momentum. Genomal and the senior leadership at Page have a hands-on approach with its employees. The same culture that is followed at the worker level is replicated at the employee level with leaders frequently interacting with team members and supporting them to meet their targets and achieve Page's overall vision.

Strategic asset

Genomal's relation with Jockey International, USA, is Page's biggest strategic asset. As I mentioned earlier, Jockey renewed its licence with Page in 2010 for twenty-one years, instead of the earlier practice of five years. In effect, until 2030, Page will remain Jockey's exclusive franchise in India and the UAE.

For Jockey USA, Page Industries is now its biggest franchisee. For the Genomals, India remains a large market growing in size (more consumers aspiring to buy Jockey products) and expanding in depth (new segments like leggings for women and underwear for children). Accessing Jockey's innovations in the US and bringing them to a steadily growing market like India is a formula that has worked since 1995 for Page, and should continue in the foreseeable future.

Capital allocation

Page's philosophy on capital allocation is best summarized by Pius Thomas. He said, 'At Page, we are very careful about our capital allocation and will not invest in projects which are not directly related to the core business. Even core projects will not be taken up unless they promise an ROCE of at least 20 per cent.' To Page's credit, they have maintained impressive discipline with regard to capital allocation, best summarized in Exhibit 70. As can be seen, the company has maintained earnings growth without compromising on its ROCE.

Exhibit 70: Page's ROCE increased from 25% in FY08 to 42% in FY15

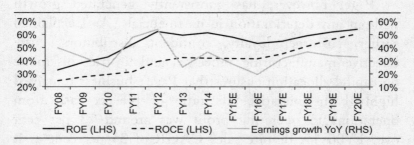

Source: Company, Ambit Capital research.

Note: E indicates estimated, not actual, data.

Page started operations in 1995 with capital employed of only Rs 1 crore. Given the shortage of capital, the management team kept the business asset-light by using various methods such as leasing land instead of outright purchase, outsourcing capital-intensive processes like spinning, knitting and weaving, and incurring capex only for the final garmenting process. Thomas was strict on costs: 'We stayed in our Abbaiah Reddy Industrial Area office for as long as it was possible and moved to a new one only in 2014. All of this adds to your ROCE.'

As a company expands rapidly, its growth can cause deterioration in its financial health. Analysts call this expansion the growth phase. During this phase, companies tend to report lower operating profit margins (as new products are launched, they might flop) and higher working capital (debtors' days are relaxed to allow distributors to push new products, offer discounts, etc.). All of these usually result in lower, or even negative, operating cash flows (i.e. companies have to borrow money because their internal cash generation is insufficient to fund growth). Analysts normally accept this growth phase as inevitable.

Page, however, has consistently generated growth without any deterioration in its financials. As I explained earlier, customer loyalty, confident distributors, cost-effective manufacturing processes and a strict discipline on capital allocation ensures that Page's business remained highly cash-generative. Its ratio of pre-tax cash from operations to operating profit was around 73 per cent over FY06–15, despite sales CAGR of 35 per cent as it has maintained efficient control on working capital (see Exhibit 71). In contrast, for peers such as Lux, the ratio of pre-tax cash from operations to operating profit over FY09–15 was -27 per cent (negative cumulative cash from operations over this period).

Exhibit 71: Page's working capital days (excluding cash) have been broadly stable despite high sales growth

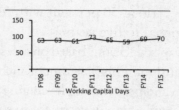

Source: Company, Ambit Capital research.

Exhibit 72: Page has maintained a high pre-tax CFO to EBITDA ratio despite strong revenue growth

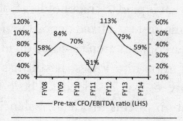

Source: Company, Ambit Capital research.

Note: CFO to EBITDA ratio checks a company's ability to convert EBITDA (which can be relatively easily manipulated) into operating cash flow (which is more difficult to manipulate). A low ratio raises concerns about the company's revenue recognition policy (because this may imply aggressive revenue recognition through methods such as channel stuffing).

Page has been judicious while balancing the source of funding—between equity and debt—for its growth. As Genomal told me, 'Given the returns we have been able to generate on capital employed, it makes sense to leverage with borrowed funds which, depending on government schemes, can also have interest concessions and capital subsidy. However, to mitigate risks, we have an internal policy to limit debt/equity ratio at 50 per cent with repayment of such borrowings restricted to five years.'

Page makes capex decisions based on assessment of business growth and expansion. This assessment includes subjects like market expansion and penetration, leveraging new technologies to reduce cost of production, investment in software, backward integration for cost advantages, etc. Bearing in view such capex requirements and external borrowings available, given prevailing debt-to-equity levels, Page has maintained a dividend payout ratio, which is the percentage of earnings paid to shareholders in dividends, at 55–60 per cent.

Dividend is what is paid to shareholders from net profits of a company; unlike interest on a fixed deposit which is assured to a deposit holder, shareholders aren't assured dividends. Therefore, when a company runs into losses, it still has to pay interest, but it doesn't have to pay dividends. The board of directors decides the quantum of this dividend, balancing the needs of the company and the needs of shareholders. The quantum of dividend is recommended by the board and approved by the shareholders at the annual general meeting. Interim dividends, however, does not require shareholder approval.

A high dividend payout ratio—anything above 50 per cent, as in the case of Page—indicates that the company has sufficient funds for its operations and is confident enough in paying out surplus funds to shareholders. Page's internal accruals account for more than 75 per cent of funds generated in the past decade, with the remaining being external borrowings and IPO proceeds. Page's debt-to-equity ratio and dividend payout ratios have remained steady. Finally, deployment of funds has been a steady mix of core capex and dividend payout.

Exhibit 73: Sources of funds during FY05–15: Large internal accruals

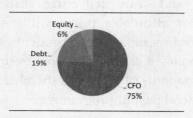

Source: Company, Ambit Capital research.

Exhibit 74: Application of funds during FY05–15: Capex + Dividends

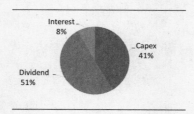

Source: Company, Ambit Capital research.

Page Industries' astonishing share price performance:

A rupee invested in Page Industries' IPO in March 2007 is worth Rs 34 presently (in April 2016), implying a compounded annual return of 47 per cent. That same rupee would be worth just Rs 2 if invested in the Sensex, implying a CAGR of 8 per cent. Thus Page Industries has outperformed the Sensex by 16.6 times over the past nine years. At the heart of this outstanding performance there have been (a) a focus on deploying in India the learnings of over five decades of experience in the undergarment trade; (b) a deepening of competitive moats around in-house manufacturing and thus delivering sustainable product differentiation at affordable prices whilst maintaining an aspirational brand recall; and (c) a prudent capital allocation on modest amounts of capex in the core business, along with returning vast amounts of money to shareholders through an aggressive dividend payout programme.

CHAPTER 6

Axis Bank: Confounding the Sceptics Repeatedly

'Banking is a very good business if you don't do anything dumb.'

—Warren Buffett

'Adventure is the life of commerce, but caution is the life of banking.'

—Walter Bagehot, founder of *The Economist* and author of *Lombard Street: A Description of the Money Market*

Banks are fundamentally different from manufacturing companies. For one, the raw material and finished products for all banks are the same—money. Given their central role in a country's economy, banks are also heavily regulated by the government and the central bank (which in India is the Reserve Bank of India [RBI]). Thus, for a bank, its biggest assets are its people, processes and brand name. Therefore, at least on two fronts, Axis Bank (or UTI Bank as it was known

179

in its earlier avatar) was born with a silver spoon in its mouth. Backed by the Unit Trust of India (UTI), then India's largest mutual fund, and helmed by career bankers from the public sector, Axis Bank had everything going for it when it started in 1994. However, the bank struggled in its first few years of existence. From then until now, its transformation into one of India's leading private sector banks under the successive leadership of Supriya Gupta, P. Jayendra Nayak and Shikha Sharma is a journey containing many riveting stories.

Phase 1: 1994–99

The Early Years: A Shaky Start
The 1990s were heady days with the balance of payments crisis in 1991 leading to the economic liberalization spearheaded by the memorable double act that was Prime Minister P.V. Narasimha Rao and Finance Minister Manmohan Singh. These reforms were followed by the government opening up the banking sector to private players in 1994—the biggest change in the banking sector since the nationalization of large banks in 1969.

In 1994, the RBI issued licences to ten private sector banks. These included four banks backed by large financial institutions (HDFC Bank, ICICI Bank, IDBI Bank, UTI Bank), five backed by individuals and corporate groups (Bank of Punjab, Centurion Bank, Global Trust Bank, Indusind Bank and Times Bank), and one cooperative bank that was converted into a commercial bank (Development Credit Bank). Interestingly enough, of these ten licensees, only six survive today.

Back in 1994, Axis Bank (then UTI Bank) found itself in a unique position. Compared to the other financial institutions (the Housing Development Finance Corporation [HDFC], the Industrial Credit and Investment Corporation of India [ICICI] and the Industrial Development Bank of India [IDBI]), it was backed by a retail giant—the government-owned UTI. Constituted in December 1963, UTI, for a long time, was the only mutual fund available to Indian citizens who wanted to invest in the capital market without the hassle involved in trading in shares directly. The deeply entrenched UTI brand was a key competitive advantage for Axis Bank. For UTI, entering the banking sector was a logical extension of leveraging its brand name in investments in the newly opened banking sector. Using this strong brand name, Axis Bank commenced operations in its earlier avatar as UTI Bank in April 1994.

UTI's strategy was clear—Axis Bank would use UTI's thirty-five million unitholder base and Rs 48,000 crore corpus as a base to sell its products. As UTI chairman S. A. Dave said in 1994, 'While UTI Bank plans to offer the full range of banking activities including retail banking, corporate banking, export-import finance and treasury services, the bias will be towards investment and capital markets.' Axis Bank's dependence on UTI was also evident in the fact that in the first year, it opened merely seven branches, focusing instead on starting its services from forty-one UTI offices over its first five years.

This UTI affiliation did help the bank. The bank got appointments from all big corporates to pitch its banking product as all these corporates were dealing with UTI in one way or other. New banks were not given membership of clearing house due to low volumes and they had to become sub-members of a bigger bank (State Bank of India [SBI], in case of Axis). This was operationally an optimal arrangement for Axis Bank. However, Axis Bank got so much business from UTI in early days that the RBI offered it direct membership of clearing house within a couple of months of starting the operations.

With this strategy set, the next step was hiring the leadership team. UTI's chairman, Dave, roped in Supriya Gupta, then deputy managing director at State Bank of India (SBI), as Axis Bank's first chairman and managing director (back then, both these positions were held by the same person).

Fifty-seven-year-old Supriya Gupta was by career a 'state banker' with thirty-seven years of working experience at SBI, including a stint as managing director of State Bank of Bikaner and Jaipur (SBBJ). Having lost out to Dipankar Basu in the race to become managing director of SBI in 1993, Gupta decided to spend the last few years of his career setting up Axis Bank. Gupta was a part of the prestigious Bengal Club of Bankers (since SBI is headquartered in Kolkata), and he came with a sterling reputation. Where he and UTI chairman Dave differed, however, was on choosing the leadership team at Axis Bank. Dave had appointed management trainees from the prestigious IIMs, and senior bankers from Bank of India and Canara Bank. Gupta would have none of this. He wanted his own team and sent Dave's recruits back to UTI, creating a first of the several fissures that would develop in the relationship between UTI and Axis Bank.

Gupta's reputation meant that he could hire the best talent from SBI and SBBJ purely on account of his personal relationships. As a result, Axis Bank's senior management came from SBI and the middle management came from SBBJ. (Contrast this with HDFC Bank's approach of hiring its leadership from Citibank and Bank of America.) One such recruit for Axis Bank was Hemant Kaul, who went on to become the head of retail banking at Axis Bank.

I met Kaul at his bungalow in the quiet residential area of Shyam Nagar, Jaipur, where the sixty-year-old now resides. Kaul had resigned in 2009, three months after Shikha Sharma took over. Reminiscing about his early days at Axis

Bank, Kaul told me, 'My offer letter from Axis Bank had no details about compensation! But the temptation to start a new bank with Gupta overshadowed all my inhibitions.' Like Kaul, Axis Bank's initial recruits (V.K. Ramani, Partho Mukherjee) were mostly in the age group of 35–45 years, already equipped with 15–25 years of experience and a deep sense of purpose. For these recruits, the motivation to join Axis Bank was twofold: first, the security provided by working for a bank promoted by a behemoth such as UTI; and second, the unique experience of building a new organization from scratch. Gupta's approach to building a team from the SBI group also provided a sense of continuity for the new recruits.

I got a sense of the dedication of Axis Bank's first cadre of recruits when I met V.K. Ramani, who went on to become executive director (ED) for technology and business processes and retired in 2009. Ramani joined Axis Bank in 1995, after working for more than twenty years with SBI. 'In PSUs, people spend half the time answering (to their superiors) rather than doing (their work). In fact, a doer needs to answer more. At Axis Bank, we had a mission and a thrilling attitude. UTI, as a promoter, provided a cushion of safety. Otherwise, PSU (Public Sector Undertaking) bankers would not have joined. The entire recruitment process was done on the basis of personal relationships and there was no negotiation of salary,' he told me.

With such a stellar, motivated team in place, you would imagine that Axis Bank would have a head start over the competition. Ironically enough, the reverse happened. In the first five years of its existence, Axis Bank built a loan book similar in size to HDFC Bank and ICICI Bank with one unfortunate difference—its gross NPAs (Non-Performing Assets, i.e., a loan where the borrower stops repaying his dues) were significantly higher (see Exhibit 75).

Exhibit 75: Loan book and credit quality of new private sector banks at the end of FY2000

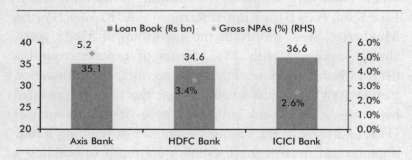

Source: Axis Bank, Ambit Capital research.

The build-up of bad loans was due to Gupta's strategy of lending to mid-corporates, instead of targeting the blue chips. Mid-corporates tend to suffer during an economic slump, like the one seen in the middle to late 1990s (GDP growth in FY98–99 averaged 5.5 per cent versus 7.2 per cent during FY95–97). Loans to these mid-corporates accounted for half of Axis Bank's loan book during these periods. The other half was made up of bill discounting, a low-end way of earning interest by providing financing against bills of exchange (notes raised by sellers of goods against payments due to them by buyers of those goods).

The bank's mid-corporate loan book consisted of companies like the notorious M.S. Shoes (which collapsed in 1995 after its promoters were prosecuted for cheating and criminal conspiracy), the CRB Group (which collapsed in 1997 following a deposit scam), and others like Woolworth, Indo Rama and Western Paques —all of which wilted during the middle to late 1990s. Axis Bank was one of the key lenders to M.S. Shoes and the write-offs against this company resulted in the bank posting losses of Rs 10 crore in its second year of operation, after having reported a profit of Rs 3 crore in its first year of operation.

Axis Bank suffered on the deposits side of its balance sheet too. Banks offer three types of accounts to retail customers: current accounts, savings accounts (better known as CASA) and term deposits. Since banks don't pay interest to current account holders and only pay very low interest rates to savings accounts holders, CASA deposits are a cheap source of funds for banks compared to term deposits. Thus, building up a high CASA ratio is a key component of any bank's strategy and HDFC Bank is the leading exponent of the high-CASA ratio strategy.

However, building a high CASA ratio also requires huge investment in building a branch-cum-ATM network and spending on advertisements. However, Axis Bank did not spend much on its expansion and was lagging behind its peers, HDFC Bank and ICICI Bank, on this front by the end of FY2000 (see Exhibit 76).

Exhibit 76: Network of new private sector banks at end-FY2000

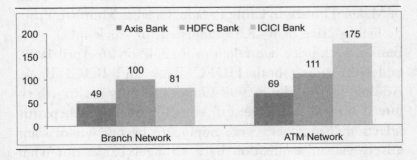

Source: Axis Bank, Ambit Capital research.

An inadequate number of branches and ATMs meant that in the first ten years of its operations, Axis Bank could notch up a CASA ratio of just 15–17 per cent (of total deposits). The rest of its deposits were mainly wholesale term deposits, which are more expensive to maintain compared to CASA deposits. This mix of deposits meant that Axis Bank's cost of funds was higher compared to other private banks. At the end of FY2000, the bank's CASA ratio stood at 17 per cent (compared to 21 per cent for ICICI Bank and 46 per cent for HDFC Bank), while the cost of funds was 8 per cent, similar to ICICI Bank but much higher than HDFC Bank's 6.6 per cent.

This unfavourable mix of deposits dented profitability further, exacerbating the pain arising from the write-offs of bad loans. Axis Bank's net interest margins (NIMs) at 1.8 per cent were the lowest among its peers, namely ICICI Bank (2.1 per cent) and HDFC Bank (4.2 per cent).

Thus, by the end of 2000, morale was at a rock bottom in Axis Bank. Rising NPAs, dubious lending practices, dents in its reputation, low CASA, low salaries (after all, as Ramani and Kaul said—no one negotiated on salaries when they joined Axis Bank) fuelled an impending sense of doom at the headquarters, which in 1991 was at the F-wing of Maker Towers in Cuffe Parade, Colaba, Mumbai. From its listing price of Rs 3.39 (adjusted for stock split), Axis Bank's stock price had fallen to Rs 2.47 on 26 April 1999, underperforming both HDFC Bank and ICICI Bank. Adding to the gloom was Gupta's fading health which forced him to take time off work for treating a hepatitis infection. Employees were hoping to be put out of their misery via an acquisition by a stronger bank. But what happened next was something nobody in the bank could have predicted.

Exhibit 77: Axis Bank's lacklustre post-IPO share price performance

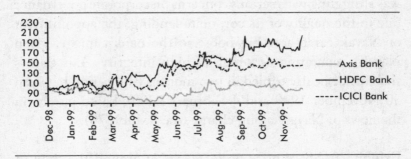

Source: Bloomberg, Ambit Capital research.

Phase 2: 2000–09

The P. Jayendra Nayak era: An unusual and inspirational banker who transformed the bank

'When you're in a commodity business, the only way to thrive is to be a low-cost producer. And when you're selling money, you're in a commodity business.'—Duff McDonald, author of *Last Man Standing: The Ascent of Jamie Dimon and JPMorgan Chase*.

As far as work experience was concerned, Dr P. Jayendra Nayak was the least likely person to take charge of Axis Bank. On the basis of professionalism, integrity and probity, however, he was the best person for the job. Nayak was a civil servant with an MA and a PhD in economics from Cambridge University, UK. He had earlier completed a stint in the Ministry of Finance as joint secretary in the department of economic affairs. He was a government-appointed executive trustee in UTI when he was appointed as chairman and managing director of Axis Bank. As Hemant Kaul told me, 'We were surprised when we initially heard that Nayak is joining as CMD.' On hindsight, Nayak was the right man at the right time for the right job. At a time when Axis Bank was struggling with serious concerns on corporate governance due to the quality of its corporate lending, the appointment of Nayak came as a big boost to the bank's image, given Nayak's reputation as a man of high integrity. Axis Bank's share price nearly tripled in two months (the period between 30 November 1999 and 4 February 2000), based purely on the news of Nayak taking charge (see Exhibit 78).

Exhibit 78: Share price performance at around the time of appointment of Nayak as CMD

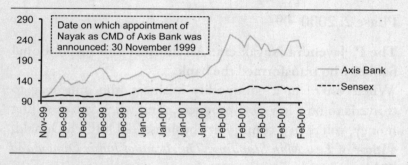

Source: Axis Bank, Ambit Capital research.

However, senior employees of the bank were not as enthused about the management change as the stock market was. Having dealt with civil servants in the Ministry of Finance, bankers did not think highly of a civil servant's financial acumen and managerial ability. In fact, a fair amount of scepticism prevailed amongst senior bankers regarding Nayak's ability to alter the waning fortunes of the bank.

I discussed this with Sujan Sinha who was head of retail assets at Axis Bank during Nayak's tenure and is currently the CEO and MD at Shriram Housing Finance, a non-banking financial company. Talking to me in his office in Mumbai's Bandra Kurla Complex, Sinha said, 'There was trepidation about a CMD who was an IAS officer and a bureaucrat with no banking experience.' The scepticism did not last very long and in his very first address to the employees, Nayak was able to break the ice and win the confidence of many senior employees. 'When we met him, the first thing everyone noticed was the erudition and clarity of thought. He joined on 1 January 2000 and by the end of January, he started talking about, for example, how there is a need for a separate marketing department,' said Sinha. Kaul told me, 'His first meeting with senior bankers was what looked like a mind-blowing extempore speech; I was completely sold. Later, I came to know that he had worked on the speech for two days.'

By FY2000, average salaries at Axis Bank (Rs 2.43 lakh) were far below the prevailing compensation levels in HDFC Bank (Rs 2.85 lakh) and ICICI Bank (Rs 4.63 lakh). Nayak scored an early victory at Axis Bank by bringing the bank's salaries closer to those paid by its competitors (see Exhibit 79).

Expectedly, Nayak faced tremendous resistance from Axis Bank's board of directors, which was dominated by representatives from the UTI. These representatives did not favour the idea of Axis Bank employees getting higher salaries than UTI employees. However, Nayak was adamant and threatened to resign if his demands were not met and eventually the board agreed. First, Nayak negotiated an Employee Stock Ownership Plan (ESOP) for the bank's employees. In 2001, the first ESOP awarded stock options to all the confirmed employees of the bank, with total ESOPs granted coming to around 10 per cent (1.297 million shares were granted) of the capital base. Axis Bank's ESOP was different compared to those of the other banks, wherein only top management received stock options. Nayak also embarked on human resource (HR) rationalization and appointed Mercer, a global management consultant specializing in HR, as consultants for a range of HR rationalization programmes, including salary revisions. On Mercer's recommendations, Nayak raised salaries across the board, except his.

Exhibit 79: Axis Bank salary increase under Nayak's management

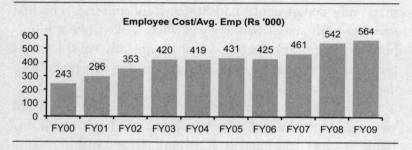

Employee Cost/Avg. Emp (Rs '000)

FY00	FY01	FY02	FY03	FY04	FY05	FY06	FY07	FY08	FY09
243	296	353	420	419	431	425	461	542	564

Source: Axis Bank, Ambit capital research.

'The staff realized Nayak had put his job on the line to increase their salaries by not revising his own salary. This earned him tremendous loyalty and respect,' Kaul told me. Recalling the exhilaration then at Axis Bank, Sinha told me, 'Nayak became a sort of shepherd with the staff. He put us in charge of roles saying, "You guys are the owners and you can make a difference to this organization." So when the roles started coming, each of us took it upon ourselves; we had to prove that we were the best.'

Another major transformation that happened at the start of the Nayak era was the IT upgradation of the bank. 'Axis Bank had forty-nine branches in 1999 which used different software versions, thereby lacking a uniform banking software across the country at any given point in time. This constrained the bank in launching nationwide loan and deposit products with the same product features and service levels. Hence, marketing was a challenge for the bank,' recalls Ramani, who spearheaded the IT transformation of the bank at the beginning of the century.

Based on his interactions with Ramani before joining the bank, Nayak knew that networked online real-time banking was required for a fundamental change in the bank. So, immediately after joining the bank in January 2000, Nayak entrusted Ramani to network all branches by March 2000.

'However, people who could help me achieve this were deployed for manning IT systems in various branches,' recalls Ramani. The bank issued transfer letters to all these employees and called them to the headquarters. The new IT system was in place by April 2000.

Now that the IT system was set, duties given and salaries established, the next priority was to inculcate professionalism across the bank. This involved breaking the region-based coteries that had developed within the bank—the most powerful being the Bengal Club, due to the large number of new hires who came from SBI's Bengal circle (one of the most prominent circles within SBI) and SBBJ. In fact, there was a time when Axis Bank was called the 'State Bank of Bengal' among bankers. Nayak did away with these groups by realigning employees' priorities with the bank, instead of the regions of their origin.

Having boosted the morale of the organization, Nayak moved to cleaning up Axis Bank's balance sheet. In his first big step, Nayak convinced the board to infuse foreign capital. In FY02, Axis Bank raised Rs 157.5 crore via a preferential allotment of shares to private equity investor, Actis Capital (then known as Commonwealth Development Corporation, or CDC Group, which eventually spun off its emerging markets' private equity funds, including its stake in Axis Bank, into Actis Capital) and South Asia Regional Fund. Back then, Actis's investment was the only case of a private equity firm being allowed to acquire that high a stake in an Indian bank; later, rules pertaining to banks' shareholdings were changed.

As a result of the capital infusion, Axis Bank's tier-one capital ratio improved to 6.4 per cent (FY02) from 5.8 per cent (FY01). A high tier-one capital ratio is broadly seen as a measure of a bank's strength and is the ratio of equity capital divided by its total risk-weighted assets.

Fortuitously, Nayak was helped by a big fall in the yields of Government securities (G-sec) to 5 per cent by the end of FY03 from 11.7 per cent in FY2000. A fall in G-sec yields boosts the treasury incomes of banks by increasing the value of the bond portfolio. High treasury income and capital infusion provided buffers at a time when Axis Bank wrote off its NPAs, leading to net NPAs as a percentage of loans declining from 6.3 per cent of loans at the end of FY99 to 2.7 per cent by the end of FY02.

With its investment, Actis took two seats on Axis Bank's board, thereby reducing UTI's influence. This was extremely helpful for Axis Bank since UTI found itself at the centre of a stock market scam in 2001 following its investments in stocks whose prices had been artificially rigged by stock market scam accused, Ketan Parekh. The introduction of Actis's representatives on the board bolstered Nayak's efforts at professionalizing the bank.

Having won the trust of the employees and infused capital into the bank, Nayak set forth on an aggressive growth journey of opening Axis Bank's branches across a wider geographical reach. At the end of FY2000, Axis Bank had forty-nine branches, compared to 110 for HDFC Bank and eighty-one for ICICI Bank. In the next nine years, by the end of FY09, Axis Bank's branch network expanded at a CAGR of 38 per cent to reach 835 as compared to HDFC's 34 per cent and ICICI Bank's 19 per cent.

To ensure that the rapid branch expansion also resulted in higher productivity, speedy mobilization of low-cost liabilities and other business opportunities, several other initiatives were taken up. This included various activities like branch roll-outs that were accompanied by an aggressive ATM (automated teller machine) roll-out, segmentation and targeting of customers, a change in the sales model, and centralization of processes (discussed in later sections). By the end of FY09, Axis Bank had the highest ratio of ATMs per branch—4.3 ATMs per branch, compared to 3.3 for ICICI Bank and 2.3 for HDFC Bank.

Nayak's efforts had a tangible impact on Axis Bank's performance. The numbers speak for themselves and show a huge expansion in business, along with a rise in profitability. From FY2000 to FY09, Axis Bank's CASA deposits grew at a CAGR of 61 per cent, which was much higher than its peers'. This resulted in its CASA ratio rising to 44 per cent at end-FY09 from 15 per cent at the end of FY01. During this period, Axis Bank's loan book grew at a CAGR of 43 per cent and net profit climbed to a CAGR of 50 per cent. The bank delivered a stellar average ROE of 23 per cent during this period (see Exhibit 80). Notably, Nayak also led the change in name to

Axis Bank, from UTI Bank, in 2007. I will discuss more on that later in the chapter.

Exhibit 80: Axis Bank outshone HDFC Bank and ICICI Bank over FY01–08

	Axis Bank	HDFC Bank	ICICI Bank
Loan Book CAGR	43%	45%	64%
EPS CAGR	24%	27%	9%
Average ROEs	24%	20%	18%
CASA CAGR	61%	42%	46%
CASA ratio, FY01	15%	41%	27%
CASA ratio, FY08	46%	54%	26%

Source: Company, Ambit Capital research.

Note: Adjusted for acquisitions made by HDFC Bank and ICICI Bank during FY01–08.

Axis Bank's stunning run from FY01–08 spoke volumes about Nayak's leadership. Nayak was to retire on 31 July 2009 at the age of 62. On 20 April 2009, there was a board meeting held to choose his successor. This was the last board meeting that Nayak attended at Axis Bank. In all my meetings with Axis Bank's employees and even board members present at that fateful meeting in 2009, the common thread shared with me was that there was a high level of acrimony between Nayak and the other members of the board. Most of these members were professional, independent directors. Nayak had two obvious choices for a successor: Hemant Kaul (ED, retail banking) and Manmohan Agarwal (ED, corporate banking). Depending on whom you speak to, there are varying versions regarding who was Nayak's favourite. However, for reasons that remain unclear, the board refused to consider either of Nayak's protégés as a worthy successor. This was strange considering that both Kaul and Agrawal were veterans at Axis Bank and responsible, in their own way, for its success story.

It is equally unclear why Nayak, with all his brand equity, charm and probity, could not convince the board to accept either Kaul or Agrawal. To put it mildly, a number of questions surrounding that board meeting remain unanswered. As veteran financial journalist Sucheta Dalal wrote,[16] 'Couldn't the board have found a way to ensure that Dr Nayak's exit was more graceful? Why does that last meeting have all the signs of a boardroom coup? Were the board members really unaware of Dr Nayak's extraordinarily strong preference for an internal candidate—especially when he has earned the right to have such a preference, since he has virtually rebuilt this bank twice over?'

As that fateful meeting ended late in the evening, Nayak walked out of the boardroom of Axis Bank, never to return. The rest of the board was unanimous in their choice of Axis Bank's next leader—Shikha Sharma, at the time the MD and CEO of ICICI Prudential Life Insurance.

Phase 3—2009-Present

The Shikha Sharma Era: Seamless Reorientation

'I advise other companies' CEOs not to fall into the trap where you go, "Where's the growth? Where's the growth? Where's the growth?" They feel a tremendous pressure to grow. Well, sometimes you can't grow. Sometimes you don't

---

[16] A Fairy-tale Career Goes Off-Axis (6 May 2009); http://www.suchetadalal.com/?id=36970b1c-08b5-357f-4a0156d4a7b0&base=sections&f&t=A+Fairy-tale+Career+Goes+Off-Axis.

want to grow. In certain businesses, growth means you either take on bad clients, excess risk, or too much leverage.'—Jamie Dimon, chairman and CEO of JPMorgan Chase.

Axis Bank's board chose one of the most experienced private sector bankers in India to lead the bank in 2009. Sharma, then fifty-one years old and an alumna of the prestigious IIM-A, started her career at ICICI Ltd (the original financial institution that was parent to ICICI Bank and which later reverse-merged with ICICI Bank in 2001) in 1980. From 1980 to 2009, Sharma spent nearly three decades setting up diverse businesses at ICICI Bank such as stockbroking (ICICI Securities), investment banking, structured finance and retail finance. In the last stretch of her career at ICICI Bank, Sharma as MD and CEO built ICICI Prudential Life Insurance and made it the largest private sector life insurance company (measured by new premium market share).

Sharma joined Axis Bank in 2009 from ICICI Bank, where she was also one of the contenders for the top post. Her impeccable pedigree, however, did not guarantee that Sharma would win over Axis Bank's employees from day one. On the contrary, her entry was viewed with a degree of scepticism at Axis Bank which, unlike ICICI Bank, had a more sedate, but professional and friendly work culture. Thus, being an outsider from a rival bank, there were no red carpets rolled out for Sharma at the bank's headquarters in Cuffe Parade.

With Nayak not around to help in the transition to a new leadership, Sharma had to depend on the team that Nayak had built over a decade. She was able to rally many senior management officials from the existing team, including Manmohan Agarwal (ED, corporate banking), Somnath

Sengupta (president, finance and accounts) and Snehamoy Bhattacharya (president, human resources) to provide the much-needed leadership continuity. This was particularly significant at that time considering that senior staff like Hemant Kaul, Manju Srivatsa (president, retail banking assets), Rajagopal Srivatsa (president, IT and operations) and Sujan Sinha (head of retail lending) had left the bank.

I met Sharma at Axis Bank's new headquarters based in Worli, located right next to the Hard Rock Cafe. Recalling her game plan in those turbulent days, Sharma told me, 'I inherited a very passionate team. The bank was talked about as public sector, but I think the passion and commitment of the employees surprised me. I think all leaders bring in a little bit of themselves into what happens in an organization. Dr Nayak had the ability to galvanize his staff to go after specific goals. So, I inherited an excellent liability franchise and to take this franchise forward, we changed the operating structure to customer-focused rather than product-focused and laid emphasis on building the retail lending book.'

The move from product-focused to customer-focused entity involved some restructuring within Axis Bank and this was done in a gradual non-disruptive manner. In October 2009, Sharma created four Strategic Business Units (SBUs): (1) retail, small to medium-sized enterprise (SME) and agriculture banking; (2) corporate banking; (3) non-banking retail subsidiaries; and (4) a corporate centre. The objective was to make the organizational structure flatter and remove rigid hierarchies. Along with restructuring, Sharma replaced the outgoing team with professionals she knew from her ICICI Bank days. In 2009, she brought in V. Srinivasan (former employee of ICICI and J.P. Morgan) as executive director, corporate banking, and subsequently in 2010, Jairam Sridharan (former employee of Capital One and ICICI Bank) as head, retail assets business. In one of her more unusual hires, Sharma hired Manisha Lath Gupta from Colgate Palmolive as chief marketing officer (CMO) to lead Axis Bank's brand and communications strategy.

However, Sharma's boldest and controversial move as CEO was the acquisition of Enam Securities in an all-stock deal for Rs 2000 crore (around 8 per cent of Axis Bank's FY10 net worth) in October 2010 (the deal was approved by the RBI in October 2012). Among private sector banks, ICICI Bank had the strongest presence in investment banking and stockbroking (thanks to ICICI Securities, a business that Sharma had built). HDFC Bank has traditionally been weaker in investment banking and institutional stockbroking and a distant second to ICICI Bank in retail equity broking. Axis Bank already had a very strong debt capital markets business from Nayak's days; adding Enam on the equity capital market side completed its product offerings for Indian corporates.

Enam, a well-established brokerage firm formed by Nimesh Shah and Manek Bhansali (hence Enam, or N–M), also had a successful investment banking arm. Whilst critics argue that Axis paid too high a price for Enam, the acquisition helped the bank progress towards an integrated universal banking model for its corporate banking clients.

In less than two years, Sharma changed Axis Bank's team and operational structure, and completed a substantial acquisition. Her next move was to rejig the loan book towards retail and reduce the concentration on corporate lending. This was a logical move considering that Axis Bank's retail loans had plateaued at 20 per cent of the total loans in FY09 compared to 61 per cent for the leader, HDFC Bank. India's consumption growth was also rising and demand for consumer loans was only bound to rise. Hence, after an 'offsite session' with her core strategy team in FY10, Sharma pivoted Axis towards retail.

Exhibit 81: The share of retail assets in Axis Bank's loan-book pie began to stagnate over FY06–10

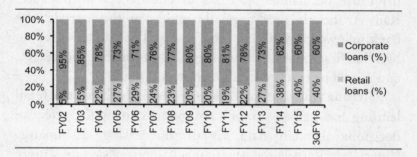

Source: Axis Bank, Ambit Capital research.

Note: *The share of retail loans underwent a reclassification in FY14, with a positive impact of ~700bps.

Sharma's approach towards retail built upon Nayak's work. While Nayak successfully set up a large branch network (835 branches by 2009) and a proportionately large customer base (one million), Sharma used the same base to extend more retail loans and retail term deposits. Every customer who walks into a bank branch to open a savings account is also a potential client for a term deposit, credit card, personal loan and vehicle loan. Axis Bank had yet to master this consumer conversion. Sharma achieved this by overhauling the credit underwriting process, creating an analytics team, and investing in physical technology infrastructure and channel infrastructure.

'One fundamental thing that we have been successful in achieving over the period of the past five to six years is integrating the deposit side and the lending side of the retail business. We leveraged upon the massive infrastructure of branches to grow the lending business and were able to get the branches to own up to selling and servicing loan products. Today, 50 per cent of the lending business that we do comes from the branches—up from practically zero,' elaborates Rajiv Anand, the head of retail banking, on the approach the bank followed in building retail assets. The bank focused on building first the secure side of retail assets, such as mortgages, and mined its own internal customers.

Sharma's move towards data-driven analytics to drive retail lending has helped senior management in taking effective decisions through data visualization using dashboards. Proprietary knowledge was slowly being replaced by a more inclusive data-empowered decision-making at an individual leadership level. This shift from people to processes was critical as the bank was moving away from reliance on corporate banking (a relationship-driven business with higher tolerance for individual-driven judgements) to retail assets (which needs very high use of data and analytics-based decision-making to grow the business whilst maintaining commercial viability).

With initial focus on balance sheet granularity during 2009–10, by 2010–11, the bank began addressing its reliance on wholesale funding and sought to scale up retail deposit balances. For the first time, an advertising campaign focused solely on retail deposits was launched in 2010–11.

Exhibit 82: Starting from FY12, Axis Bank decisively shifted towards retail liabilities

As a % of total liabilities	FY07	FY08	FY09	FY10	FY11	FY12	FY13	FY14	FY15	3QFY16
Current Accounts	17%	21%	19%	20%	17%	16%	16%	15%	14%	12%
Savings Accounts	18%	21%	19%	21%	19%	20%	22%	23%	22%	22%
Retail Term Deposits	11%	12%	13%	17%	16%	19%	20%	25%	26%	28%
Wholesale Term Deposits	42%	37%	38%	31%	36%	32%	27%	21%	18%	17%
Borrowings	13%	9%	12%	11%	12%	13%	15%	15%	20%	21%
Total Interest bearing Liabilities	100%	100%	100%	100%	100%	100%	100%	100%	100%	100%

Source: Company, Ambit Capital research.

Exhibit 83: The same shift towards retail was reflected on the assets side as well

As a % of total loans	FY07	FY08	FY09	FY10	FY11	FY12	FY13	FY14	FY15	3QFY16
Large and Mid-corporate Loans	47%	49%	51%	50%	53%	54%	50%	44%	45%	47%
Retail Loans	24%	23%	20%	20%	19%	22%	27%	32%	33%	34%
Agriculture Loans	11%	9%	10%	12%	12%	10%	8%	8%	7%	6%
SME Loans	18%	19%	20%	18%	15%	14%	15%	15%	14%	13%
Total Loans	100%	100%	100%	100%	100%	100%	100%	100%	100%	100%

Source: Company, Ambit Capital research.

In subsequent years, the bank has continued to address further gaps in its offering. Anand mentions how he found it odd that the bank didn't have any material presence in private banking to cater to affluent customers. This was particularly odd given how some brokers with a limited offering were able to break into the market. Thus, Axis Bank launched its own privilege banking, branded Burgundy, in 2014. Anand underscores the opportunity that foreign banks exiting from the Indian markets provide to Axis Bank. A new team has been built with defined value proposition for offering the entire range of banking services, an area where broker-driven private banking has its challenges. The experiment has met initial success with Assets Under Management (AUM) growing steadily.

Anand highlights the digital wave as the second area of immediate focus in retail banking. Axis Bank was early to recognize the emerging trend and was one of the first banks to launch its app. The targets stay stretched with the intention to continue driving customers' transition to the digital platform as well as to ensure that back-room operations are also similarly strengthened. The question that is continually asked within the organization is, 'Can we do this digitally?' A tablet-based microfinance operation, digital solution for retail assets collection, apps for internal HR processes and raising productivity of the more than 10,000-strong feet-on-street sales force are some examples of how the bank is on its journey towards becoming a 'digital bank'.

Broadly too, technology has had far-reaching impacts. It has allowed the bank to alter its branch model by reducing the size of many of its palatial, yet underutilized, branches by introducing automation at banks. Use of technology, such as biometric Aadhaar-based authentication, has drastically cut the time in opening a new account from 8–10 days to two minutes. Axis Bank was the first bank in India to launch

Aadhaar-based e-KYC (electronic Know Your Client) in India. As Anand puts it succinctly, 'Technology has allowed banks to go for both enhancing client experience, and managing operational challenges and risk.'

Axis Bank's shift towards retail loans also reduced the proportion of its corporate exposure. The timing of this shift was serendipitous. Starting from FY10, the Indian economy was seeing a manufacturing-led slowdown: GDP growth during FY12–15 averaged 5.9 per cent, much lower than the 8.3 per cent growth seen during FY07–10.

As seen in the late 1990s, this economic slowdown could put corporate credit quality under stress and resulted in higher NPAs. Starting from FY12, Axis Bank's strategy to raise the share of retail loans began to gain momentum and its share of corporate loans began to moderate. Thus, at a crucial time when the Indian economy was slowing down, falling exposure to corporate lending lowered the risks to Axis Bank's balance sheet. On other hand, for example, ICICI Bank had started increasing its exposure to corporate loans in FY12, which later resulted in a higher amount of bad loans for ICICI (see Exhibit 84).

Exhibit 84: Corporate loan growth YOY for ICICI Bank and Axis Bank

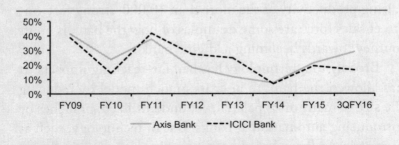

Source: Axis Bank, Ambit Capital research.

But still, Axis Bank wasn't as lucky as HDFC Bank, which escaped largely unscathed from the slowdown. Axis Bank's exposure to corporate lending was still significant and it had been growing the corporate loan book rapidly until FY11. More specifically, the bank's exposure to some sectors like infrastructure and power increased during this period which caused asset-quality stress for the company and still remains an overhang for the bank.

Apart from slowing down its corporate lending post-FY12, the bank also changed its focus on improving the quality of its corporate loan book. Under Nayak, the bank's chief aim was to focus on finding high-quality, mid-sized companies to lend to and service them from different divisions of the bank. Sharma changed this by putting higher emphasis on large marquee corporate clients. I met V. Srinivasan, deputy managing director, who was earlier the managing director and head of markets at JPMorgan. Srinivasan, fifty years old, is a tall, soft-spoken, veteran corporate banker. 'One thing I did on coming here was to consolidate all the coverage into one person who is called the relationship manager. He will funnel all the products to the client. There will be separate functional roles, but delivering value to the client and extracting value from the client is the job of the relationship manager,' he told me.

Under Sharma, Axis Bank further strengthened its corporate banking by ramping up its international banking and equity capabilities—again areas of speciality for ICICI Bank. As corporate India went global with large acquisitions like Tata Steel–Corus (2006) and Tata Motors–Jaguar Land Rover (2008), their borrowing needs expanded. Foreign banks were stronger, given their large presence in overseas markets. Hence, Axis Bank also opened offices at major international money centres like Singapore, Hong Kong, Dubai and London to get its foot into big-ticket corporate banking. The share of international business has gone up from 6 per cent of the balance sheet in FY08 to 11 per cent in FY15.

In terms of profitability, Axis Bank does not declare results separately for its international business. However, Ambit's banking sector team believes that this business has grown strongly. This can be gauged from the fact that in recent times, forex translation gain on repatriation of profits of foreign branches has driven Axis Bank's other income.

On the equities front, thanks to the well-integrated Enam franchise, Axis Bank can now offer to raise IPOs for the same client that it lends to. This is a huge step-up in the perception of the bank. As Srinivasan told me, 'If we look at the hierarchy of a company's needs, equity capital takes topmost position. I might be best in loans, but I would get more of the promoter's time and attention if I can raise equity capital for him, which translates into more business for us.'

Irrespective of the size of the deal, working with a promoter on an equity transaction provides immense connect and mindshare for Axis with its client. If an equity transaction has been conducted successfully for a corporate, it becomes relatively easier to cross-sell plain debt, salary accounts, cash management, etc. Thus, Axis Bank's corporate banking model is unique; all client relationships, be it through Axis Capital or any other group business, flows through Axis Bank and are delivered through a single relationship manager.

Huge wins for Axis Bank in this regard include PVR's acquisition of Cinemax (November 2012), and the IPOs of Syngene (July 2015) and Narayana Hrudayalaya (December

2015). Srinivasan told me, 'A loan is valuable for mid-cap companies, but large companies need more than that. Hence, companies like Axis Finance and Axis Direct are integrated with the bank and help us serve these large clients better.' Axis Bank's unique, integrated, universal banking approach to its corporate and commercial banking clients reflects in superior cross-sell and fee income generation, as shown in Exhibits 85 and 86.

Exhibit 85: High current account balances indicate better cross-sell (average for FY13–15)

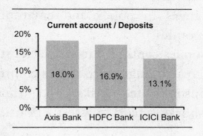

Source: Axis Bank, Ambit Capital research.

Exhibit 86: Better cross-sell reflects in superior fee income (average for FY13–15)

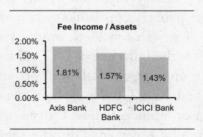

Source: Axis Bank, Ambit Capital research.

It has been less than seven years since Sharma took charge. Despite asset-quality challenges over the last couple of years, Axis Bank's profitability has remained strong with earnings per share (EPS) CAGR of 26 per cent during her tenure, with average ROEs of 18.8 per cent during this period.

Yet the corporate book's asset-quality deterioration in FY16 has been a sobering experience for the bank. Sidharth Rath (president and head, corporate relationship group and transaction banking) sums up the key learnings from current asset-quality cycle as:

- concentration risks in select infrastructure sectors and sudden changes in policy and environment changed project economics;
- global economies continued to stay lacklustre and China's slowdown created huge price risk in commodities; and
- project-sponsor-related risks and their ability to withstand shocks is hard to assess a priori.

What is Axis Bank's secret sauce?

Unlike the other companies mentioned in this book, banks are unique in that their core business cannot change, simply because they are heavily regulated by the government and the RBI. Unlike public sector banks (where the government is typically a majority shareholder), private sector banks like Axis Bank (where the influence of UTI reduced through the years, making it an independently run, private sector bank), HDFC Bank and ICICI Bank are not owned by any one single promoter or business family. Instead, they are led by a chairman and run by a managing director (both are different posts held by different people as per the RBI's directives). This managing director or chief executive officer—unlike a company promoter—does not hold a controlling stake in the company. This structure is unique and makes banking inherently different from manufacturing companies. In particular, this operating structure makes the CEO of a private bank both less powerful than a promoter of a non-bank company, but more influential than the CEO of a non-bank company.

First under Nayak and then under Sharma, Axis Bank has steadily built its competitive advantages across the four criteria of John Kay's IBAS framework—innovation, brands and reputation, architecture and strategic assets (for more details, please refer to Appendix 1).

Deepening the competitive moat

Innovation

Nayak led the bank's shift towards retail liabilities (i.e. ramping up customers via branch and ATM expansion) while, almost a decade later, Sharma led a shift towards retail assets (i.e. ramping up consumer loans), technology and investment banking. Both of these efforts involved multiple innovations that set Axis Bank apart from competitor banks.

Under Nayak's leadership from 2000 to 2009, the retail liability initiatives were led by Hemant Kaul, executive director, retail banking. Kaul's mandate was clear: raise the share of low-cost CASA deposits to total deposits (which, in FY99, was low for Axis Bank at 16.8 per cent, compared to HDFC Bank at 45.6 per cent). How do you attract customers to open an account with the bank and use that relationship to give them loans (also known as cross-selling)? Kaul showed me a slide from an old presentation. It was a simple depiction of what the customer wanted matching with what the bank offered (see Exhibit 87).

Exhibit 87: Axis Bank's approach to customer segmentation during 2001–09

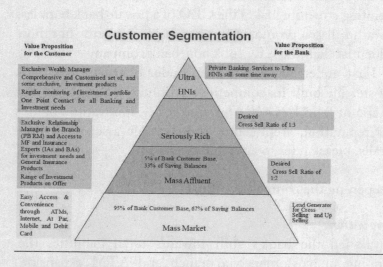

Customer Segmentation

Value Proposition for the Customer

Exclusive Wealth Manager
Comprehensive and Customised set of, and some exclusive, investment products
Regular monitoring of investment portfolio
One Point Contact for all Banking and Investment needs

Exclusive Relationship Manager in the Branch (PB RM) and Access to MF and Insurance Experts (IAs and BAs) for investment needs and General Insurance Products
Range of Investment Products on Offer

Easy Access & Convenience through ATMs, Internet, At Par, Mobile and Debit Card

Ultra
HNIs

Seriously Rich

5% of Bank Customer Base, 33% of Saving Balances
Mass Affluent

95% of Bank Customer Base, 67% of Saving Balances
Mass Market

Value Proposition for the Bank

Private Banking Services to Ultra HNIs still some time away

Desired Cross Sell Ratio of 1:3

Desired Cross Sell Ratio of 1:2

Lead Generator for Cross Selling and Up Selling

Source: Axis Bank, Ambit Capital research.

The slide wasn't rocket science. The challenge was to get branch managers align to the strategy shown in the slide. Until then, branch managers flew blindly, targeting anyone from a non-resident Indian to a senior citizen. Kaul stressed on discipline by insisting that branch managers provide clear strategies to attract customers. For example, a low-cost sales force was used to attract low-income customers who were serviced via call centres (only inbound calls), while high-end, priority customers were given dedicated relationship managers.

However, Kaul's bigger wins were getting the salary accounts of government departments, public sector employees, armed forces, etc. Having missed the private sector salary accounts to HDFC Bank and ICICI Bank, Kaul managed to get the salary accounts from Mumbai Police, Delhi Police and teachers in Ahmedabad's public schools. Another big win for Axis Bank was getting a good share of all the bank accounts of the Indian Army. Incidentally, the record for the world's highest ATM belonged to Axis Bank for a long time for its ATM located at a small village called Thegu en route from Gangtok to Nathu La (on the Indo-China Border) in Sikkim at an altitude of 13,200 feet, to serve army personnel (see Exhibit 88).

Exhibit 88: Axis Bank (then called UTI Bank) ATM at an altitude of 13,200 feet

Source: Axis Bank; sevendiary.com.

Other innovations included adding an accident insurance cover of Rs 2,00,000 to a salary account in 2004. Normally, the cost of providing insurance to employees would get charged to the employer, but Kaul cracked a deal with the National Insurance Corporation to provide this at a very low cost. This was a great selling point to sell salary accounts to corporate companies and government departments. Axis Bank was able to break into Maruti's (India's biggest car manufacturer) account by giving car loans to police personnel which other banks were reluctant to do. Axis Bank later tied up with Maruti to offer car loans to teachers in Ahmedabad and this helped the bank in getting the savings accounts of these teachers.

Exhibit 89: Growth in Axis Bank's cash management business since FY01*

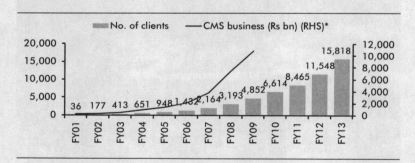

Source: Axis Bank, Ambit Capital research.

Note: *Axis Bank stopped reporting data points relating to CMS business post-FY09.

Kaul employed innovative strategies for ramping up ATMs by locating them close to the bank branch. At the end of FY2000, Axis Bank had sixty-nine ATMs for forty-nine branches (1.4 ATMs/branch). In FY01 alone, the number of

ATMs jumped to 303 (3.5 ATMs for eighty-six branches). Nayak told us over lunch in December 2015 that when in FY01, the head of branch banking in Hyderabad asked him to sign on adding an extra ATM in Hyderabad, Nayak asked, 'Don't you need fifteen more ATMs?' After further dialogue, Nayak persuaded the manager to take fourteen extra ATMs for Hyderabad.

Opening ATMs close to the branch ensured: (a) raising the command area of the branch; (b) outflanking the existing branch network of other banks, mainly PSU Banks; and (c) increasing brand visibility. This focus on ATMs has continued in subsequent years as well. Currently, the number of ATMs per branch stands at 4.5 for Axis Bank (as compared to 2.7 for HDFC Bank and 3.2 for ICICI Bank).

The biggest innovation for Axis Bank, however, was to field its own sales representatives to get business. This was a tough choice among the multiple options available in the early noughties, which ranged from the use of Direct Sales Agents (or DSAs, employed by ICICI Bank and many foreign banks) to the use of a subsidiary (as followed by HDFC Bank), onwards to contractual employment. Among all the options, the full-employment model had the lowest risk, but came at the highest cost of customer acquisition. Kaul's model of contractual employment thus had to have higher productivity per sales executive. Kaul would be vindicated in the years to come, when business procured via DSAs led to asset-quality challenges for ICICI Bank amongst others.

Nayak's aggressive ramp-up in retail liabilities from 2000 to 2009 was followed by Sharma's focus on retail assets from 2010 until date. When Sharma took charge as MD and CEO in September 2009, retail loans formed around 20 per cent of the bank's loan book (as compared to 57 per cent for

HDFC Bank and 45 per cent for ICICI Bank) and the retail assets business was managed mostly as a separate business from retail liabilities. In contrast, both HDFC Bank and ICICI Bank ran integrated retail business.

Sharma thought out of the box for implementing a shift towards retail lending. Instead of poaching from a competitor bank, she hired Jairam Sridharan, who was then working with Capital One in the US. Sharma told me, 'As I had a background in creating various start-ups for ICICI Bank, I knew it was best to go to an organization which had well-developed skills for each of the specialist areas.'

Sridharan built a team for retail credit policy and retail credit underwriting. He strengthened this by adding teams for analytics and business intelligence with large-scale capability for analytics and modelling. What started off in 2010 with a couple of members is now a 100-member team, doing analytics not only for retail lending but also for retail liability, corporate banking and wholesale banking.

In 2012, Sharma focused on the rebranding of Axis Bank with the tag line, *Badhti ka naam zindagi* (life is about progress). The campaign targeted the age group of twenty-five–thirty-five-year-olds who aspired to progress towards a better life.

The results of these focused efforts are clear: Since the end of FY10, retail loans have grown at a CAGR of 33 per cent for Axis, compared to 24 per cent for HDFC Bank and 29 per cent for ICICI Bank. The majority of this growth has been driven by cross-selling retail asset products to existing liability customers from the bank's own branch network. This, in turn, has been enabled by heavy use of technology and analytics, using specialized statistical tools on Big Data.

The bank also shifted the operational structure towards functional groups (like sales group, product group, etc.)

from geography groups (each geography having its own sales head, product head, etc.). It also standardized the layouts and designs for all of Axis Bank's branches and offices across India instead of each branch having its own design.

Brand

UTI Bank became Axis Bank on 30 July 2007 and it is the only example of a large private sector bank completely changing its identity. To put things in perspective, the rebranding involved changing signage across 600 offices and 2457 ATMs in 346 cities, towns and villages; all this in addition to new letterheads, visiting cards, chequebooks, etc.

While the UTI brand name was useful in the earlier years to set up the bank, it had lost most of its brand value by 2007. Firstly, UTI Mutual Fund had lost market share to several private sector players. Secondly, UTI's stake in Axis Bank had dropped to 27.4 per cent by FY07 from 91.7 per cent at the incorporation of the bank. Finally, and most importantly, UTI had been bailed out by the government in 2001 following the infamous Ketan Parekh scam (which involved price rigging in many stocks). The bailout involved splitting UTI into a Special Undertaking of Unit Trust of India (SUUTI—which held investments that the government took over from UTI, including its stake in Axis Bank) and UTI Mutual Fund (all other investments held as mutual fund). As per an old agreement between the government and the UTI, the UTI brand was to be shared free of cost by UTI's nine subsidiaries, including UTI Bank, until 31 December 2007. Starting January 2008, the bank would have to pay royalty to UTI Mutual Fund for use of the name.

Nayak used this opportunity to rid the bank of the UTI association. 'We had to change our name to have our own brand and identity. We had to give up the UTI name after using it for thirteen years as we were not prepared to accept the terms and conditions (including royalty) from UTI AMC to use the name. Now we will be seen without a public sector connotation,' explained Nayak in 2007.[17] The name Axis Bank was chosen from among fifty names. 'We wanted to be a pan-India brand and were developing international ambitions. We avoided some funky names since we were corporate bankers. We shortlisted Capital Bank, but there was a local-area bank called Capital Trust Bank in Punjab and hence we finally selected Axis Bank,' Kaul told me.

Kaul also recalled the lengths to which the bank's board of directors went to ensure the acceptability of the new brand name. Sensitive of the World War II connotations of Axis—the name given in the war to the united forces of Germany, Italy and Japan—the board even reached out to Jewish associations in the US to clear the use of the name. The brand campaign, created by advertising agency Ogilvy & Mather, involving twins, was memorable. It had the tag line, 'Everything is the same, except the name.'

The second major investment in branding was done when Sharma was at the helm in 2010. As mentioned earlier, this began with the *Badhti ka naam zindagi* advertising campaign in 2012. The bank continued with its brand's alignment towards customer's aspirational needs and, to this end, for the first time, Axis Bank signed on a Bollywood superstar— youth icon Deepika Padukone—as a brand ambassador in June 2014 (see Exhibit 90). Anand explained the rationale behind this move.

---

[17] http://archive.financialexpress.com/news/uti-bank-is-now-axis-bank/207688.

'To create a strong brand connect with the youth and the affluent customer segment, we needed a brand ambassador who could connect with this segment and also showcase the essence of the brand, i.e. *Badhti ka Naam Zindagi*. Deepika fitted the bill. She is not only an accomplished actress but also a youth icon of the country. She brings in fresh energy, youthfulness and vitality required for the idea to imbibe our philosophy. She has progressed in her journey from being an accomplished badminton player to a model and then to a very successful actress. She is on her journey of progress, representing the new India which is young, hard-working, in tune and aware of the world around them.'

Exhibit 90: New brand identity of Axis Bank—aspirational yet grounded

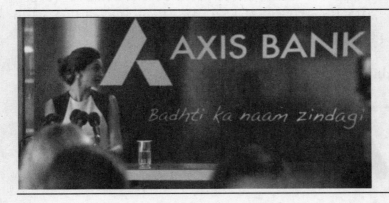

Source: Axis Bank, Ambit Capital research.

This wasn't the first time a private bank had used a Bollywood star. ICICI Bank had used Shah Rukh Khan and Amitabh Bachchan in the past. However, the choice of a youth icon was a deliberate move for Axis Bank to further entrench its positioning as an aspirational brand among the youth. With the emergence of digital banking, Axis Bank is also preparing to take on the new breed of payment banks whose founders, most prominently, Vijay Shekhar of Paytm, are active on social media. Anand, the head of retail banking at Axis Bank, is active on Twitter with more than 5000 followers. I also noticed a QR code for downloading the Axis Bank mobile app strategically placed on the reverse side of employee visiting cards!

In the same vein, the bank's brand strategy in corporate banking has been aligned with the business strategy of projecting the bank as an integrated universal bank. The Axis Bank brand is an overarching brand taking precedence over any other brand within it and all of them have been aligned with a uniform branding linked with Axis Bank. For logos of Axis Bank and its subsidiaries, please see Exhibit 91. As per the 2015 Brand Trust Report, Axis Bank ranked fifth with 10 per cent of the entire trust placed in banks.

Exhibit 91: Logos of Axis Bank and its subsidiaries

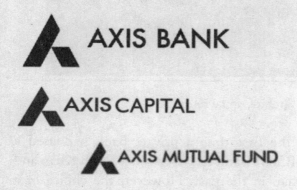

Source: Axis Bank, Ambit Capital research.

Architecture

Axis Bank's consistent financial performance (ROE greater than 15 per cent in fifteen out of the last fifteen years), despite two big management changes, stands testimony to strong internal architecture. There are two aspects to this strong architecture. The first is a strong board of directors. The culture of a strong, professional board was started by Nayak with the inclusion of two directors from Actis when the private equity fund took a stake in the bank in 2001. The strength of the independent directors on Axis Bank's board was evident, ironically enough, when Nayak was replaced by Sharma in 2009. The fact that the board decided to think and act differently from a chairman with titanic reputation was the sign of a superior level of autonomy.

The second aspect of Axis Bank's architecture is an employee-friendly, result-oriented work culture that attracts and retains talent. I have met many employees of Axis Bank, past and present. Across the board, the impression I have always got was of a bank that, despite huge changes in top leadership, has kept the rank and file motivated. While senior leaders like Kaul and Srivatsa left after Nayak's departure, there were many employees who stayed on. As a senior official and a veteran from the Nayak era said, 'There are many employees whose employee codes are still in four digits—dating back to the time when codes were first given; this shows that they've stayed on with us for a long time.' Early examples of this work culture include the introduction of ESOPs in 2000 and substantial salary hikes to align salaries with peers, despite resistance from the board. Banks do not declare attrition data, but I am given to understand that attrition levels are low and there is hardly any attrition for employees at the level of vice president and above.

Equally notable is the presence of a crèche for employees' children at the bank's headquarters in Worli. In a city where prime real estate is amongst the most expensive in the world, this crèche (which has prominent signs requesting people to keep the noise down so that children don't get disturbed) is tangible proof of how far Axis is willing to go for its employees.

Each bank has its own culture and while the official version is printed on websites and annual reports, the culture really manifests when you meet employees, insiders and banking sector veterans. For example, ICICI Bank's aggressive, sink-or-swim culture is legendary. Similarly, HDFC Bank is highly respected for its focus on systems and processes, so much so that one insider called it SOP bank, where SOP stands for Standard Operating Procedure.

Sidharth Rath, president and head, corporate relationship group and transaction banking, attributes the distinct culture of Axis Bank to the fact that, among the major banks, it is the only one to have grown entirely organically. This allowed an organizational culture to take root. An ex-employee, who did not wish to be named, told me, 'Employee policies are very consistent at Axis Bank and there is little ambiguity and subjectivity in the pay hikes and bonuses. All supervisors have to clearly explain the ratings they assign to their subordinates and why employee X got a higher rating than employee Y. Pay rise, promotion and bonus, all have a direct correlation with your rating. You won't find this in other private sector banks, where a lot of randomness prevails in salary hikes, bonuses and promotions, where lower-rated employees have got higher bonuses, etc.' This employee-friendly image of Axis Bank has significantly improved its standing with freshly minted chartered accountants and business school graduates, compared to a decade ago. No wonder then that Axis Bank is rated much higher compared to HDFC Bank and ICICI Bank in the 'Great Places to Work' survey.

Strategic assets

The branch and ATM network, and base of deposit holders, form the core strategic assets for any bank. On this front, Axis Bank compares well with HDFC Bank and ICICI Bank (all three banks received their licences in 1994). Axis Bank has 2805 branches, 12,631 ATMs and 16.6 million savings accounts, as in December 2015 (see Exhibit 92).

Exhibit 92: Strength of distribution network of new private sector banks

As of December 2015	ATMs	Branches
Axis Bank	12,631	2805
HDFC Bank	11,843	4281
ICICI Bank	13,372	4156
Kotak Mahindra Bank	1987	1298
IndusInd Bank	1621	905
Yes Bank	1480	750

Source: Company, Ambit Capital research.

At a time when competition is set to intensify with the arrival of twenty-three new banks, long-term relationships with the existing wide customer base and data-driven insights into their behaviour is a key competitive asset.

Beyond plain-vanilla banking, Axis Bank has a strong franchise in areas of transaction banking, such as cash management, payments, business banking and government businesses. As a result of its strong transaction banking franchise, the bank's current accounts per branch is the highest amongst the larger banks (see Exhibit 93).

Exhibit 93: Axis Bank's current accounts/branch is the highest among its peers

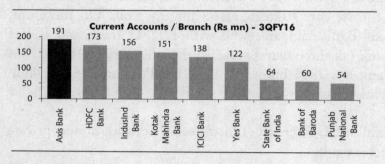

Source: Company, Ambit Capital research.

Axis Bank's share price outperformance

Axis Bank, its management and indeed the management of every other bank in India with a large commercial loan book are under intense scrutiny at present. Such scrutiny is justified given the extent to which commercial loans disbursed in India over the past decade have rotted on the loan books of banks. However, those who write off Axis Bank don't realize that this is not the first time that the bank has found itself in such a predicament. As highlighted in the preceding pages, the bank has come back from lending debacles in the past and ultimately that's why it is in this select league of great companies—companies which can lose several battles and still win the war.

A rupee invested in Axis Bank (or UTI Bank as it was then called) at its IPO on 30 November 1998 is worth Rs

128 presently (in April 2016), implying a CAGR of 32 per cent. That same rupee would be worth Rs 9 if invested in the Sensex, implying a CAGR of 13 per cent. Thus, Axis Bank has outperformed the Sensex by fourteen times over the past seventeen years.

At the heart of this outstanding performance there have been (a) a strong brand—initially the UTI brand and then over the past decade, the Axis brand—that Indian customers, especially savers, trust; (b) the largest ATM network and one of the largest branch networks in the private sector; and (c) consistent innovation over time in segmenting and tackling groups of customers in novel ways.

CHAPTER 7

HDFC Bank: The Power of Textbook Execution

'Any intelligent fool can make things bigger and more complex. It takes a touch of genius—and a lot of courage—to move in the opposite direction.'

—Albert Einstein

'Simplicity is the ultimate sophistication.'

—Leonardo da Vinci

My office in Lower Parel is next to HDFC Bank's headquarters and whilst from one window of my office I can see the cubicles of HDFC Bank's top brass, from the other window I can see Kamala Mills, the place where the bank set up its first large office over twenty years ago. Whilst the geographical distance between Kamala Mills and HDFC Bank's current headquarters is barely a hundred metres, the actual transition that the bank has made—operationally, financially and psychologically—over the past two decades is of a completely different scale.

Started by a group of highly motivated bankers from large foreign banks like Citibank and Bank of America, HDFC Bank is today India's largest private sector bank franchise (by market capitalization). Globally, as of 2 April 2016, HDFC Bank is the only Indian bank to feature in the list of the top fifty largest banks in the world. The bank has achieved all of this under a single CEO, Aditya Puri, and a team that has been with the bank, by and large, from its inception. In my meetings with bankers, industrialists and journalists who cover the banking sector and investors who have bought shares in the bank, the one word that is repeatedly mentioned in the context of HDFC Bank is 'execution'. Relentless execution of its goals and a steady focus on profitability lie at the core of HDFC Bank's story.

As simple as it sounds, execution has made HDFC Bank stand apart from other banks. After all, banking is all about acquiring funds at a low cost and selling them as loans and services to customers. Banking products (such as a savings account, a fixed deposit or a loan) are shorn of glamour and have no aspirational value. In such a generic market, HDFC Bank has excelled at executing both sides of the game—acquiring funds at a low cost and selling them at a lucrative rate of interest. It has done this without any compromise on the quality of its loans and with a focus on profitability, thereby maintaining a high quality of loan book and, at the same time, a high net interest margin. Backed by mortgage financing giant HDFC Limited (HDFC), HDFC Bank started from scratch in 1994. Its subsequent transition towards becoming one of the remarkable success stories of post-1991 India is an engrossing journey that I discuss here in three phases.

Phase 1: 1994–99

A corporate bank with a difference

HDFC Bank's roots go back to the mortgage giant HDFC Limited (which currently owns 21.5 per cent of HDFC Bank). Housing Development Finance Corporation or HDFC was started in 1977 by Hasmukhbhai Parekh, who was the chairman of ICICI Bank in 1972. HDFC was the pioneer in mortgage lending (or home loans, as they are popularly known in India). In fact, one of my first memories of a financial services transaction is accompanying my father as he negotiated a home loan from the HDFC branch in Safdarjung Enclave in New Delhi in the early 1980s. Parekh's nephew, and now one of India's most distinguished corporate leaders, Deepak Parekh took over as managing director of HDFC in 1994. When HDFC received its banking licence from the RBI in 1994, it was Deepak Parekh who zeroed in on Aditya Puri to run this newly formed bank. As veteran journalist Tamal Bandyopadhyay describes in the opening chapter of his book, *A Bank for the Buck: The Story of HDFC Bank*, hiring Puri was no easy task.

Puri was heading Citibank's Malaysia operations when he received an offer from Parekh to join the bank. Puri was a career banker from Citibank, having earlier worked for the American banking behemoth in India, Saudi Arabia and Hong Kong. He was a rising star in Citibank and was among the fifty executives worldwide identified by Citibank's chairman and CEO as being crucial for the bank's future. Hence, he was well paid and had sizeable stock options incentivizing him to remain with the bank. It took a lot of persuasion from Parekh to convince Puri to accept the offer. Sizeable stock options and the opportunity to be with his father finally convinced Puri to accept it.

Puri built most of his team by hiring young bankers from Citibank (Paresh Sukhtankar, Samir Bhatia and Shailendra Bhandari), Bank of America (A. Rajan, C.N. Ram, Harish Engineer and B. Chandramouli) and Hong Kong and Shanghai Banking Corporation (HSBC) (Luis Miranda and Girish Marathe). It was the reputation and pedigree of Puri and Parekh, along with an opportunity to build a bank from scratch, that would eventually convince people like Luis Miranda, Harish Engineer, Shailendra Bhandari and many more to quit their comfortable and glamourous jobs at reputed foreign banks and join a 'start-up' bank.

I met Samir Bhatia, an avid marathoner and now the founder of SMECorner.com, in his office (also in Lower Parel). Bhatia was head of corporate banking at HDFC Bank when he left in 2006. 'Competence and chemistry—that's what the team got right at the start. We came with a similar mindset, some knew each other and hence were aware of our paths.'

Shailendra Bhandari, who joined HDFC Bank in 1994 from Citibank and subsequently went on to lead other banks like Centurion Bank of Punjab and ING Vysya, told me, 'When the bank was first being set up, and before it was known who would form the team, someone from HDFC reached out and asked for a meeting, where the topic of joining the bank was broached. I politely declined, and thought the matter was over, the next day at work, when I got a call from Citibank, Kuala Lumpur. It was Aditya, who, in his usual style, said, "I will be joining in a few months to head the bank, and I want a few key people with me to create and run this." I mentioned that my wife might not want me to move, and again in his typical style, he said that he would call her if required and convince her. That was not needed, and by the end of the phone call, I agreed to join the bank.' HDFC Bank's founding team thus included some of India's finest young bankers. Also part of the founding team was Vinod Yennamedi, a career finance executive who had worked with large corporate groups like Shell International and RPG Group, amongst others. Parekh knew him from his chartered accountancy days in London and trusted him to keep an eye on the young bankers who were joining HDFC Bank from foreign banks.

With most of the bank's initial hires coming from foreign banks, when the bank opened for business in 1994, it was but natural for it to focus on corporate banking. With neither a balance sheet size nor a branch network, HDFC Bank made inroads into corporate banking by offering innovative solutions to corporates and customers.

An early example of the sort of innovative solutions that HDFC Bank would become famous for was the novel cheque settlement system that it rolled out for cooperative banks in 1998. Cooperative banks are restricted to one state and their customers and branches are only in that state. The moment they had to do any interstate transfer, they were dependent on another bank. For example, a customer of a cooperative bank situated in state A issues a cheque to his supplier who is in state B. When the supplier deposits the cheque to his bank in state B, the supplier's bank charges a fee to the supplier as the supplier's bank had to send this cheque to its own branch in state A where the settlement happened. In the 1990s, this entire process took three to four days before the money was credited to the supplier's account. So the supplier was not willing to accept a cooperative bank's cheque. HDFC Bank offered a simple solution to cooperative banks. It issued cheques at par to cooperative bank customers through which they could pay their suppliers anywhere in India. The supplier's bank used to settle the money with the local branch of HDFC Bank. However, cooperative banks had to keep interest-free deposits with HDFC Bank to get this service. This enabled HDFC Bank to get free money.

However, given its acutely risk-aware DNA, HDFC Bank focused its lending activities only on blue-chip corporates, which meant that the bank had to operate in the most competitive segment in Indian banking. Hence, the only way HDFC Bank could make inroads into these corporates was by having lower cost of funds and/or offering innovative services/solutions to corporates. Therefore, from the outset, the focus of the bank was on raising low-cost liabilities (for a bank, a liability is the source of funds; for example, a savings deposit is a liability for a bank since it is obligated to repay the deposit to the customer), on finding gaps in the existing offerings of competing banks and on finding innovative solutions to fill these gaps. As HDFC Bank did not have the balance sheet size to lend to corporates, the initial focus was on capturing transactional and cash management business from these corporates rather than lending money to them.

With the advent of the Internet in the mid-1990s, technology was transforming the way banking was done. HDFC Bank's managers knew that technology had to be at the core of its services. Thus, when it came to selecting its core banking platform, the bank looked for a centralized real-time system and decided in favour of Microbanker, an offering from Iflex Systems. As several members of the bank's founding team told me, in spite of a strong pitch from others, what swung the decision in favour of Iflex's offering was that Microbanker was a fully integrated online banking automation system compared to others which were offline systems. In the years that followed, this system helped HDFC Bank provide several innovative solutions to customers which could not have been offered with an offline system. H. Srikrishnan, then head of transactional banking and operations, gave me an example, 'We looked at funds transfer—which was manual—such as MTs (mail transfers) and TTs (telegraphic transfers). When we implemented a centralized banking solution, the key things we could do were to sweep across multiple locations and get the balances of customers or transfer funds from one location to another using core banking. Those were big problems we solved.'

HDFC Bank was thus the first among Indian banks to have a centralized system. Whilst foreign banks like Citibank had centralized systems, they lacked the branch strength to fully leverage them. It is worth remembering that in the mid-1990s, banking didn't really exist in the form that we know of today. Customers could open bank accounts, but the whole gamut of products (home loan, car loan, etc.) and services (Internet banking) was just not available. Salaries would still be paid by cheque and employees would have to take time off from their jobs to go to the bank, write a deposit slip, hand it over to the teller and then wait for the cheque to get cleared. Also, the employer would have to take time off to sit and sign numerous salary cheques to be given to all the employees. Compare this to the instant, online credit of salary today and a notification by SMS and email at the end of every month! HDFC Bank's centralized technology platform allowed it to kick-off a revolution in how employees were paid their salaries.

We tend to think of corporate visionaries in terms of the high-profile projects they executed, the markets they captured or the companies they acquired. However, in HDFC Bank's case, it is hard to emphasize enough just how important this choice of centralized online banking system proved to be. In an age when very few people had even heard of phrases like the email or the Internet, HDFC Bank's management made an ahead-of-the-curve call regarding its core banking technology platform.

Current account and savings account (CASA), as highlighted in the previous chapter as well, is the biggest and cheapest source of funds for a bank. Banks do not pay interest on current accounts and pay very low interest on savings accounts. In comparison, banks pay a higher rate of interest on other sources of funds such as fixed deposits, wholesale deposits, etc.

In what has become the stuff of banking legend, HDFC Bank used its centralized technology systems to build its business in two different ways: garner low-cost corporate deposits and earn cash management fees (fees earned by collecting cash or cheques and meeting the cash requirement of corporates). I now provide an example which illustrates how cleverly the bank re-engineered the payment processes using IT is the capture of the clearing business for stock exchanges and their members by HDFC Bank.

Paresh Sukhtankar, deputy managing director of HDFC Bank, told me that in the late 1990s, when the business of share settlement was dominated by banks like Bank of India and Canara Bank, Puri and his team thought of an idea to pull away market share from the market leaders. In those days, though the stock settlement was electronic (thanks to dematerialization), the payment cycle was still manual. In 1997, Puri successfully pitched to the exchanges and their members the idea of converting this manual payment process into a real-time electronic processing system. HDFC Bank then targeted the entire supply chain of players in the stock market—investors, brokers, exchanges and custodians— with a highly successful pitch which highlighted that HDFC Bank's automated settlement would not only reduce the quantum of work associated with manual payment but also reduce the operational and financial risk that various players in the supply chain were facing.

Thus, the speed of funds transfer was matched with that of the stock settlement and the turnaround time for cash to move from one account to another was reduced from around four days to real time. This reduced the amount of working capital required for various players in the supply chain; but in order to get this benefit, these players had to open HDFC Bank accounts. Thus, HDFC Bank garnered the low-cost deposits and eventually, the cash management business of an entire ecosystem of capital market participants.

The bank's cash management business registered 40 per cent CAGR revenue between FY01 and FY11. Current account deposits accounted for 33 per cent of its deposits by the end of FY2000—the highest amongst peers (see Exhibits 94–96). The impact of these higher current account deposits was that HDFC Bank's cost of funds was significantly lower than that of its peers like ICICI and Axis Bank. By FY2000, HDFC Bank had a CASA ratio of 46 per cent versus 17–20 per cent for its contemporaries like Axis Bank and ICICI Bank. Thanks to this surge in current account deposits (the 'CA' in CASA), HDFC Bank's cost of funds was 150–200 bps, lower than that of its peers like ICICI and Axis Bank, a significant competitive advantage in the banking business.

Exhibit 94: In FY2000, HDFC Bank had higher CA . . .

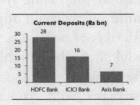

Source: HDFC Bank, Ambit Capital research.

Exhibit 95: . . . as a percentage of deposits and...

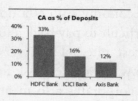

Source: HDFC Bank, Ambit Capital research.

Exhibit 96: . . . per branch

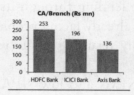

Source: HDFC Bank, Ambit Capital research.

The focus on blue-chip corporates and lower funding helped HDFC Bank derive higher net interest margins (NIMs or the difference between interest earned from income-generating assets like loans and interest paid to the source of funds, such as savings deposits, measured as a percentage of income-generating assets), despite having a lower lending yield than its peers. For example, HDFC Bank's NIMs in FY2000 were around 215 bps higher than those of ICICI Bank, despite the lending yield (interest rate charged on loans) being marginally lower than in ICICI Bank. Remember, a lower lending yield also implied that HDFC Bank was taking less risk than its peers. I met Luis Miranda, who was part of the start-up team at HDFC Bank and went on to become the treasurer. Miranda recalled the early days, 'If you lent at higher rates, you clearly ran into big credit risk in an economic downturn.' What he meant was that when an economy suffers a downturn, low-credit borrowers find it difficult to pay back a loan, especially those made at high interest rates. Thus, very early on, HDFC Bank figured out how to take less risk for higher return. Its focus on blue-chip corporates also meant that when issues of asset quality in corporate lending arose in the banking system in 1998, HDFC Bank was relatively unscathed, with its gross non-performing assets (NPAs) at just 2.54 per cent versus 4.5 per cent for Axis Bank (back then ICICI Bank was doing corporate lending through its parent, the ICICI Limited, which was already facing problems in its corporate loan book, eventually resulting in its reverse merger with ICICI Bank).

With superior NIMs and low NPAs, the return ratios for HDFC Bank were very healthy. Throughout the late 1990s, HDFC Bank's ROA (return on assets, an indicator of a bank's profitability which is calculated by dividing net profit by total assets) was 100 bps higher than that of its peers.

Phase 2: 2000–08

Building the Retail Bank

'The fundamental problem with banks is what it's always been: they're in the business of banking, and banking, whether plain vanilla or incredibly sophisticated is inherently risky.'—James Surowiecki, author of *The Wisdom of Crowds* (2004).

HDFC Bank was acutely aware of the opportunities that lay in retail banking: taking savings deposits from customers and in turn providing them loans like car loans, credit cards, etc. Whilst the bank had started talking about the opportunity in 1997, the focus of the bank was still on building its corporate franchise and there was no separate retail group within the bank. Moreover, the bank did not really have the branch strength before 2000 to do full-fledged branch banking (at the end of FY99, HDFC Bank only had fifty-seven branches). This was in part because branch licensing was not easy in those days as the RBI used to issue only a limited number of licences.

Initially, the bank hired banker Samit Ghosh, formerly of Citibank, to run its retail operations. However, he soon quit. In 1999, the bank hired Neeraj Swarup to run its retail operations (Swarup would subsequently go on to become CEO of Standard Chartered Bank in India). The acquisition of Times Bank in February 2000 brought Uma Krishnan into retail banking and also increased the bank's branch count by thirty-five.

The initial thrust of the bank in retail banking was garnering low-cost and less volatile CASA deposits. Unlike Axis Bank, which had branches and ATMs at the heart of its expansion strategy for the retail franchise, HDFC Bank's strategy revolved around superior technology and solutions to clients. What the bank did in cash management and in the capital market business on the corporate side, it replicated in its retail business.

In January 2000, HDFC Bank became the first bank in India to launch mobile banking. Over FY2000–08, the bank expanded its branch network at a CAGR of 27 per cent and its ATM network at a CAGR of 43 per cent. By the end of FY08, HDFC Bank had 761 branches compared to thirty-seven a decade ago (FY98) (see Exhibit 97).

Exhibit 97: Between FY2000–08, HDFC Bank matched its new private sector peers on the network expansion*

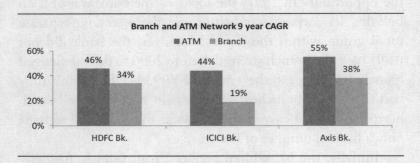

Source: HDFC Bank, Ambit Capital research.

Note: *ICICI Bank's branch numbers are adjusted for acquisition.

Propelled by the expansion in branches and ATMs, the bank's retail deposits have registered a CAGR of 30 per cent over the last fifteen years and were about 80 per cent of its total deposits by FY15. Such strong growth in retail liabilities coupled with strong cash management and clearing business for exchanges, meant that the bank's funding cost remained lower than that of its peers.

Retail lending in India for HDFC Bank in the late 1990s was limited to the bank's parent, HDFC, which dominated the home-loan segment. Foreign banks were present in segments like car loans, credit cards and personal loans. As retail is a scale business, foreign banks were constrained by their limited reach and, hence, were not making much money in this business.

On the retail asset side, HDFC Bank's approach was very cautious in terms of expansion. Loan against Shares (LAS) was the first product launched by the bank in FY98 as it was a natural extension for the bank, given its experience in capital-market-related settlements. In FY99, it launched car loans and in FY2000, personal loans and loans for IPOs. However, the products were still being offered at a limited number of locations. Hence, retail loans were still about 20 per cent of the loan book by March 2000, with LAS and car loans equally contributing to the portfolio.

From 2001, the bank started focusing on increasing the number of products and on geographical expansion. By the end of March 2001, the bank was offering LAS in twenty cities, car loans in sixteen cities, personal loans in ten cities and consumer durable loans in three cities. The number of locations offering consumer loans had doubled by March 2002. By March 2003, the bank started offering credit cards and two-wheeler loans. That year also saw an increase in the number of cities covered.

However, mortgage loans remained the missing piece in the retail business as HDFC was already present in that segment. In FY04, the bank stuck a deal with its parent to become a distributor of HDFC's home loans for a fee of 0.7 per cent of the loan. The bank also had the right to buy back 70 per cent of the loans originated by it. The arrangement was so successful that, by FY15, HDFC Bank originated one-fourth of the total loans disbursed by HDFC. By FY07, the bank had also entered SME lending, agri-financing, rural/microfinance loans, tractor loans and two-wheeler loans.

This focus on retail loans meant that the retail loan book of the bank posted a CAGR of 67 per cent over FY2000–08 and contributed to 57 per cent of the loan book by FY08 (see Exhibit 98).

Exhibit 98: Retail loans as a percentage of total loans for HDFC Bank*

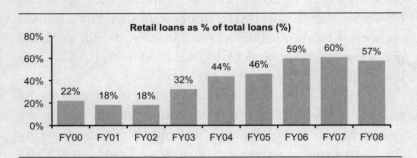

Source: HDFC Bank, Ambit Capital research.

*Note: The retail classification in this chart is as per the RBI norms (based on ticket size). As per internal classification, the share of retail loan is higher than that as per regulatory classification.

Moreover, the retail book was well diversified across products and geographies, which helped HDFC Bank maintain its asset quality, even as the broader asset quality in the banking sector started sliding since FY09.

The two other areas on which the bank focused during this period was selling third-party products and acquiring point-of-sale (POS) terminals. Sale of third-party products helped the bank increase customer stickiness and generate a steady flow of revenue. Third-party distribution has historically contributed 15–20 per cent of the bank's fee income and has grown in line with the overall growth of the bank's balance sheet.

POS terminals at merchants' establishments not only helped the bank earn fee income every time a card was swiped on its machines but also in getting the transaction banking account of the merchant. By December 2015, the bank had installed 2,80,000 POS terminals (the machines where customers swipe their cards to pay for goods purchased) and grabbed 22 per cent market share in this business.

This heady mix of low cost of funds, higher proportion of retail assets in its loan book and higher fee income saw the bank's EPS grow at a rapid pace of 27 per cent over this period with average ROEs of 20 per cent (see Exhibit 99).

Exhibit 99: On EPS growth, HDFC Bank outperformed Axis Bank and ICICI Bank over FY01–08

	Axis Bank	HDFC Bank	ICICI Bank
Loan book CAGR	43%	45%	64%
EPS CAGR	24%	27%	9%
Average ROEs	24%	20%	18%
CASA CAGR	61%	42%	46%
CASA ratio, FY01	15%	41%	27%
CASA ratio, FY08	46%	54%	26%

Source: Company, Ambit Capital research.

Note: Adjusted for acquisitions.

Phase 3: 2009–16

Reaching the Hinterland and Taking on Silicon Valley

'Building a visionary company requires one percent vision and 99 percent alignment.'—Jim Collins and Jerry Porras in *Built to Last* (1994).

At the beginning of this period, HDFC Bank acquired Centurion Bank of Punjab (CBOP) in May 2008 for one share of HDFC Bank for every twenty-nine shares of CBOP. Whilst CBOP was one-fifth of HDFC Bank in terms of balance sheet, it was half in terms of branches. CBOP had most of its branches in Punjab and Kerala where HDFC Bank had a weak presence. CBOP was also a strong rural franchise due to its strong presence in Punjab and was also strong in two-wheeler loan lending. HDFC Bank used this acquisition to build its rural banking franchise and leadership position in two-wheeler loans. Within three years of the acquisition, HDFC Bank was able to get back to its pre-acquisition cost-to-income ratio and NPAs.

This was the time when global financial markets were in deep trouble due to the US sub-prime crisis and retail asset quality had started deteriorating for Indian banks. By the end of FY09, due to the global shock waves generated by Lehman Brothers, growth of retail loans in the Indian banking industry had come down and NPAs had increased in the segment. However, HDFC Bank was less impacted than its peers and its profitability held up nicely.

With rising NPAs in retail loans, most banks and Non-Banking Financial Companies (NBFCs) started scaling down their retail loans. ICICI Bank, which was the leader in retail lending, had seen a huge surge in NPAs in its retail loan book. This resulted in ICICI Bank scaling down operations. HDFC Bank also became cautious in the segment but continued to grow the book. Competition reduced in the segment and yields rose. Thus, the pricing became reasonable enough to offset the risk the bank was taking. Over FY09–15, the bank's retail loan book posted a 20 per cent CAGR compared with industry growth rate of 13 per cent. By FY15, the bank was the top retail lender in the country.

This period is also characterized by HDFC Bank's increased presence in rural India. The bank had started expanding its footprint in non-metro cities right from the early noughties. By 2007, just thirteen years since its launch by a group of foreign bankers, HDFC Bank was offering tractor loans, warehouse receipts and two-wheeler loans. By 2008, more than half the bank's retail loans were already being originated outside the top nine cities.

However, the real thrust in rural expansion came after FY09 after the acquisition of CBOP that year. Regulations require Indian banks to give 40 per cent of their loans to some identified weaker segments of the society, with further specified sub-targets to some of these individual segments. If a bank fails to meet this target or any sub-target, it has to invest the shortfall in low-yield government development bonds. This puts pressure on the bank's profitability as yields on these bonds are often 200–300 bps lower than the cost of raising funds for banks. HDFC Bank was falling short on some sub-targets of this regulatory requirement and this was hurting its profitability. Hence, expansion in rural markets was crucial for maintaining profitability. However, making profits in these markets is not easy due to higher credit losses.

HDFC Bank knew that these smaller towns and cities had potential. After all, rural incomes rose sharply in the late noughties due to schemes like the Mahatma Gandhi National Rural Employment Guarantee Scheme (MGNREGA). The bank sensed an opportunity in rural lending as the market potential was huge and penetration low. 'Around 70 per cent of India lives there and that's the future,' Puri said in one of his media interviews in 2012. 'The semi-urban and rural areas are almost virgin markets.'

Thirty-two per cent of incremental branches opened by the bank over FY09 to the first half of FY16 (or April 2008 to September 2015) were in rural areas. The bank set up dedicated desks at semi-urban and rural branches to cater to agriculture loans. HDFC Bank now has a presence in all major rural loan segments like microfinance loans, gold loans, two-wheeler loans, tractor loans, etc. Whilst specialized rural lenders like Mahindra & Mahindra Financial Services saw NPAs almost tripling between FY13 and FY16 due to a prolonged slowdown in rural India, HDFC Bank's asset quality remains strong in this segment—another testimony to the bank's strong credit-appraisal process.

During the end of this phase, HDFC Bank started a major push towards digital banking as the increase in mobile network speed enabled many services to move online. For example, people now book movie tickets on their BookMyShow app instead of queuing up outside a movie theatre. Financial technology (fintech) companies like Alipay and loan.com had started to encroach on areas which were once the reserve of traditional banks. Moreover, the RBI also granted payments bank licences to ten players in 2015. Puri is aware of the threat posed by the digital world. 'For a banker who has breathed banking for over forty years in ten countries, I was curious to know where the disruptions were happening. I visited Silicon Valley that summer,' Puri said in a media interview. 'When I returned, the question I posed to the team was: We are the market leaders in retail loans, the payments business, and the advisory businesses as well. So why should we allow others to have our lunch? Why don't we disrupt ourselves? We had all the ingredients— the customers, advanced technology in the form of data warehouse and analytics, leading to a better understanding of retail consumer behaviour.'

In FY15, HDFC Bank introduced a slew of products to take on the companies focused on financial technology. It launched mobile wallet, PayZapp, to counter mobile wallets like Paytm and Mobiwik. True to its tradition of using existing technology in novel ways, the bank also launched ten-second pre-approved personal loans for existing customers—the first such product in India.

What is HDFC Bank's secret sauce?

'An organization's ability to learn, and translate that learning into action rapidly, is the ultimate competitive advantage.'— Jack Welch.

Unlike the other companies that we have explored in our Coffee Can analysis, banks are unique in that their core business cannot change, simply because they are heavily regulated by the government and the RBI.

Private sector banks like Axis Bank, HDFC Bank and ICICI Bank are also not owned by any one single promoter or business family. Instead they are led by a chairman and run by a managing director (both are different posts held by different people as per RBI directives). This managing director or chief executive officer—unlike a company promoter—does not hold a controlling stake in the company. This structure is unique and makes banking inherently different from manufacturing companies.

HDFC Bank continued to focus on two key principles in its business—building a stable and low-cost liability base, and winning clients by offering unique solutions. Over the years, the bank has steadily built its competitive advantages across the four criteria of Kay's IBAS framework—innovation, brands and reputation, architecture and strategic assets (see Appendix 1 for more details).

Deepening the competitive moat

Innovation
Other than its conservative, risk-aware culture (described in greater detail further in this section), what distinguishes

HDFC Bank from its competitors is the management's ability to use technology in the broadest sense of the word—hardware/software systems and processes—to create a unique offering. In the late 1990s and for much of the noughties, ICICI Bank was often the bank to come up with the most stylish of technology-driven banking products (e.g. the first to provide Internet banking and the first to introduce mobile ATM). However, HDFC Bank's strength rests not so much on the uniqueness of the technology it uses but in the way that technology is lined up in a clever process flow that is not envisaged by other banks.

In the mid- and late 1990s, when most banks were opting for Infosys's Banks 2000 technology platform, HDFC Bank chose Iflex's Microbanker. This proved to be a master stroke as the bank's management sensed that real-time online banking was the future. Microbanker subsequently allowed HDFC Bank to garner large quantities of low-cost deposits by providing payment solutions to capital market players.

Stocks were traded in physical form before dematerialization started in the early 1990s, a trend that gathered steam by 1995–96. These dematerialized shares were transferred electronically after trade, but the movement of fund transfers was still slow and in physical form. This did not match the speed of movement in stocks as different exchanges used different banks. For example, if a broker in Delhi sold some stock for a customer, the customer would transfer the sold stock from her/his retail Depository Participant (DP) account to the broker immediately and the broker would electronically transfer the shares to the buyer. However, the fund inflow for the seller was manual and it would take two to three days for money to reach the broker and another two to three days to reach the customer as the clearing bank for both the exchanges were different. Stockbrokers had to keep liquid money for their payouts despite having equal pay-ins from other exchanges. This increased the working capital requirements of brokers. For exchanges, the risk was that they were not sure whether stockbrokers had enough money in their accounts to honour payouts. To mitigate this risk, the exchanges had to send data on dues from various brokers to its bank (Canara Bank for the National Stock Exchange [NSE]) at the end of the day to check whether the brokers had enough money to honour their dues.

HDFC Bank pulled in all the players in the supply chain—buyers, sellers, brokers and exchanges—and got them into an automated settlement system. It offered a solution to both brokers and exchanges. If brokers had an account with HDFC Bank, exchanges could see in real time whether brokers had money to settle payouts and, if there was a shortfall, there was enough time before the actual settlement to ask the broker to meet this shortfall. This reduced settlement risk for exchanges drove all major exchanges to sign up with HDFC Bank.

The incentive for brokers to sign up with HDFC Bank was that pay-in money was credited immediately to the broker's account, reducing his working capital requirement. This led all the brokers to open their accounts with HDFC Bank for settlements. Since brokers needed bank guarantees for exchanges, the bank also provided credit lines to these brokers. So the bank not only earned a free float on money kept by brokers for their settlement, it also earned fees by providing credit lines to brokers. Starting with the NSE in 1998, the bank became the clearing member of all major exchanges by FY2000. Eight hundred brokers and a majority of custodians were using HDFC Bank's services by FY2000.

The bank had captured 80 per cent of market share in the settlement business by the mid-noughties. Leveraging its capital market expertise and Depository Participant business, the bank also started LAS as its first retail product in 1998 and its retail broking business in 2001.

'The clearing business also provided asset opportunities for us and we became the largest issuers of bank guarantee for the brokers and also started providing working capital to brokers. Brokers could not move to another bank. So, we actually shifted these broker accounts lock, stock and barrel from all these banks, including their assets, guarantee, etc. Later on, the chain continued because for the retail customers of these brokers too their loans engaged their LAS accounts, their deposit accounts and their family accounts (investor invests in various family names). As each family has two to three accounts, this became viral and we really captured this flow,' says Srikrishnan, who headed transactional banking and operations until 2004.

Buoyed by the success of its capital markets initiative, HDFC Bank implemented similar initiatives in retail banking. This created the foundation of its formidable low-cost deposits platform.

Cash management was another business where the bank used its technological prowess and innovation to gain market share. The bank's centralized real-time system allowed corporates to deposit cheques in any city, which reduced working capital requirement for corporates. This meant that a Delhi-based company could ask all its customers to deposit their cheques at the HDFC Bank branches in their locations. The local bank branches were able to cash out these cheques at the local level and immediately credit money to the customers' accounts. This reduced working capital requirement for customers. In return, the bank was able to keep this cash for free for a day or two. Other banks were not able to offer these services as they did not have a centralized system.

Getting CASA accounts by penetrating the capital market business, acquiring the cash management businesses of corporates, successfully scaling up the retail franchise, establishing leadership in digital banking—the technology that HDFC Bank used in all these initiatives was available to other banks as well. What set it apart was the ability to string the same technology together in a different process flow, which other banks did not envisage.

Another example of innovation was the ten-second personal loan to existing customers, a product which HDFC Bank launched in 2015. The bank used the historical behaviour of its customers and credit bureau data to create algorithms which helped it disburse loans within a minute. The bank's personal loan portfolio grew by 40 per cent following the launch of this product.

Brand

Before he applied for a banking licence, Parekh, the then MD of HDFC, was not comfortable with lending HDFC's brand name to the bank. He was worried that if the bank didn't do well, the HDFC brand would get sullied. His early choice of names included Bank of Bombay and Bombay Bank as it was the only newly licensed bank to have a registered office in Mumbai. However, Puri wanted the bank to be named HDFC Bank. As Miranda told me over lunch in Bandra, 'HDFC was very concerned that foreign bankers would damage the brand. Earlier, the proposed name was Bombay Bank. But Aditya said that he would not support this name;

it had to be HDFC Bank . . . the HDFC brand definitely made a difference at that point of time.' In the end, Puri won.

HDFC did not charge any royalty to the bank for using its brand name, but the agreement between HDFC and the bank did say that if HDFC's shareholding fell below a certain threshold in the bank, it could ask the bank to change its name—a clause which raises all sorts of intriguing possibilities in the years to come.

However, over the years, HDFC Bank has emerged as a strong brand in its own right. In fact, it is now a bigger brand than its original promoter. It was adjudged the most valued brand in India for two consecutive years, 2014 and 2015, by Wire and Plastic Products (WPP), the world's largest communication group.

The most interesting aspect of this brand recognition is that the bank has not spent a lot to create it. In fact, money spent by the bank on advertising is much lower than amounts splurged by other major brands in India. Despite having a higher brand recall, the money spent by HDFC Bank on advertising is similar to ICICI Bank's over the last five years.

Moreover, unlike big brands that have used celebrities to build their brand name (ICICI used Bollywood superstars Amitabh Bachchan and Shah Rukh Khan; Axis Bank used Deepika Padukone), HDFC Bank has never used a celebrity for endorsement. Its high brand recall, despite the relatively low advertising budget and lack of celebrity endorsements, is built on plain, old-fashioned customer service.

Recently, the bank ran a long advertising campaign to position itself as a digital bank with the slogan, *Bank aapki muthi mein*. With changing customer behaviour, the bank wanted to position itself as a complete digital bank and has been largely successful in getting this positioning, which is visible in its 40 per cent market share in mobile banking, compared with just 5 per cent in terms of deposits and advances.

Architecture

HDFC Bank's consistent financial performance (ROE of over 15 per cent in each of the last fifteen years) along with low volatility in earnings and stable asset quality stand testimony to its strong internal architecture. One key feature of this architecture is aversion to both risk and volatility in business.

When the bank started business, it entirely focused on the top-end of the customer segment and never let its portfolio of riskier mid-corporates go beyond 25 per cent (as highlighted in the Axis Bank chapter, mid-corporates had caused asset-quality issues for Axis Bank). When HDFC Bank acquired Times Bank in February 2000, the share of mid-corporates in its loan book increased to 35 per cent. However, in an uncharacteristic move for banks, the bank reduced this portfolio over the next year and brought it down to 25 per cent of the loan book by the end of FY01. Again, when it acquired Centurion Bank of Punjab in May 2008, it reduced a large part of the acquired loan book, given its focus on branch network expansion rather than loans.

This philosophy of not overexposing itself to a single segment helped the bank maintain asset quality. Despite having a very high retail exposure, HDFC Bank remained largely unscathed from asset-quality issues on its retail loan book, something most Indian banks faced in 2009–10. This was not just due to better credit selection than peers but also a function of a well-diversified book.

Indian banks need to invest 22 per cent of their borrowings in government bonds. With movement in interest rates, banks need to mark to market these bonds. This has created significant volatility in earnings for banks. To counter this, HDFC Bank kept the duration of its bonds low (2–2.5 years), compared to the industry average of about four years. Hence, the value of its bonds was less sensitive to interest rate movement. This meant that mark-to-market gains on securities have been much lower for the bank compared to other banks' interest over the last fifteen years. However, it also saved HDFC Bank from incurring losses on its bond portfolio in FY14, while most other banks had to incur large losses in their portfolio due to an unexpected policy rate hike by the RBI.

As mentioned in the previous chapter, HDFC Bank is so well known for its focus on systems and processes that one insider calls it an SOP bank. This focus on systems and processes has helped the bank in terms of business continuity. Many of the senior members of the founding management left the bank in the early noughties. However, this did not affect the bank as its strong focus on systems and procedures meant that the people who succeeded them did not find it difficult to take over responsibilities quickly.

Strategic assets

The branch and ATM network, and the base of deposit holders form the core strategic assets for any bank. On this front, HDFC Bank compares well with Axis Bank and ICICI Bank (all three banks having received their banking licences in 1994). HDFC Bank has 4281 branches, 11,843 ATMs and around twenty-five million retail savings accounts as of December 2015 (see Exhibit 100).

Exhibit 100: Strength of distribution network of new private sector banks

As of December 2015	ATMs	Branches
Axis Bank	12,631	2805
HDFC Bank	11,843	4281
ICICI Bank	13,372	4156
Kotak Mahindra Bank	1987	1298
IndusInd Bank	1621	905
Yes Bank	1480	750

Source: Company, Ambit Capital research.

However, HDFC Bank's key strategic asset has been its low-cost funding franchise, which has helped it effectively compete with other banks without taking higher asset-quality risks. To put this simply, HDFC Bank has excelled at providing steady customer service using clever technology and well-drilled standard operating processes. Such customer service has, in turn, helped the bank maintain a high CASA ratio. The bank has then lent these funds judiciously, ensuring that its NPAs remain low.

With financial technology players trying to disintermediate banks, HDFC Bank's strong technological platform and data-driven insights into the historical behaviour of its large customer base are key strategic assets. A prime example of how the bank leveraged these assets is the ten-second, pre-approved personal loan for existing customers, the first of its kind, launched in 2015.

Sensible capital allocation

A bank's core working model revolves around raising money from deposits and lending this money as loans which generate interest income. The difference between what a bank pays for deposits and what it earns on its loans is the interest spread that a bank generates and this is the foundation of a bank's revenues. The bank then supplements this income with fee income (fees for banking services like demand drafts, issuing chequebooks, etc.), treasury income (income on a bank's investments), commissions, brokerage, etc. However, banks need a certain amount of shareholders' money to run a certain size of lending book. The idea behind putting this shareholder money at work is to stop banks from taking excessive risks with depositors' money. If a bank is not able to recover all the loans it has advanced, it has to dip into shareholders' equity to repay depositors. Whilst as a rule, banks keep Rs 10 equity for Rs 100 of loans, in principle, the riskier the loan, the higher is the shareholders' equity requirement. Hence, equity capital is a big constraint for banks to expand their balance sheets, and growth in shareholder capital should be in line with balance sheet growth. For example, if the bank wants to grow its balance sheet by 20 per cent to Rs 120 the next year, the equity capital for Rs 120 loan book now has to be Rs 12. Hence, the bank has to generate at least Rs 2 of profits this year to grow its balance sheet. This is only possible if the bank constructs its loan portfolio to maximize return on its capital.

HDFC Bank's consistently high ROEs (average of 19 per cent) over the last twenty years suggest it is putting capital to work at the right places. A very good example of the bank's stellar capital allocation is the way it dealt with the loans it originated for HDFC. When the bank was growing rapidly in the high-yield retail loans segment over 2003–13, it used to buy back only a fraction of the loans it originated for HDFC just to meet the priority sector lending requirements imposed on banks by the RBI. The reason behind HDFC Bank's reluctance in the 2003–13 phase to buy more HDFC loans was that the ROE on these loans (after paying a fee to HDFC equal to 0.95 per cent of the value of the loan) was much lower compared to other products that the bank was selling.

However, with growth rates and yields falling in other products in the post-FY13 era and with the RBI reducing the equity capital requirement for home loans from 70 per cent to 30 per cent between FY12 and FY16, HDFC Bank started using its right to buy back 70 per cent of the loans it originates for HDFC. Consequently, the bank's home loan book is its fastest growing book, contributing about 6 per cent of its overall loan book in FY16 compared with just 2 per cent in FY08.

HDFC Bank's high ROE also ensured easy access to fresh equity capital when the bank's growth exceeded its internal capital generation. Investors have been so confident of the bank's ability to use the capital in an efficient way that the bank always raised capital at very high multiples (3.5–4.5 times trailing book value). The bank's ability to raise fresh capital at such higher multiples has helped the bank in maintaining a high dividend payout ratio of 20–25 per cent, while still maintaining a high balance sheet growth.

HDFC Bank's share price outperformance

A rupee invested in HDFC Bank at its IPO in March 1995 is worth Rs 134 now (April 2016), implying a CAGR of 26 per cent. That same would be worth Rs 8 if invested in the Sensex, implying a CAGR of 10 per cent. Thus, HDFC Bank has outperformed the Sensex by over seventeen times in the past twenty-one years.

At the heart of this outstanding performance there have been (a) a risk-aware culture that has focused on generating healthy returns without taking high risks; (b) an internal architecture that has consistently allowed the bank to innovatively rethink the core process flows that characterize the central offerings of the banking sector in areas like cash management and low-cost deposits; and (c) the strength of the iconic HDFC brand.

CHAPTER 8

Astral Poly: To the Brink and Back

'When we own portions of outstanding businesses with outstanding managements, our favourite holding period is forever.'

—Warren Buffet

In its 2015 year-end special issue, *The Economist* carried an article[18] titled 'Going global: Secrets of the world's best businesspeople'. It noted: 'Business, indeed, is the principal business of Gujaratis.' The entrepreneurship of the people of the state of Gujarat is legendary. Count among them, fifty-four-year old Sandeep Engineer, a first-generation entrepreneur and founder of Astral Poly Technik. A chemical engineer from Lalbhai Dalpatbhai College of Engineering, Ahmedabad, Engineer started his career with a job at Cadila Pharma in 1981. Within a year, he quit this job that paid him a monthly salary of Rs 850. After selling

---

[18] http://www.economist.com/news/christmas-specials/21683983-secrets-worlds-best-businesspeople-going-global.

Isabgol (psyllium husks) and manufacturing bulk drugs in the late 1980s, Engineer bet his fortunes on chlorinated polyvinyl chloride (CPVC)—an expensive, but high-quality alternative to galvanized iron (GI) pipes. He failed instantly, and teetered on the brink of bankruptcy. After hitting rock bottom, Engineer gathered his wits and resources and in the next two decades built Astral Poly Technik, now India's largest manufacturer of CPVC.

Phase 1: 1997–2003

To the Brink of Bankruptcy

> 'Fall down seven times, stand up eight times.'
>
> —Chinese Proverb

By all accounts, Engineer enjoyed mixed success in his early entrepreneurial days. He shut down his first pharmaceutical business in 1984 after a major client, Gujarat Drugs and Chemicals, collapsed. He incorporated Shree Chemicals in 1986 to manufacture bulk drugs and closed it in 1993, following stringent pollution norms implemented by the state government. In 1991, he started another company— Kairav Chemicals—named after his son, to manufacture active pharmaceutical ingredients (APIs), the entity in a drug that directly treats the medical condition it is meant for. (An API is mixed with other inert ingredients to form a drug.)

Engineer's fascination with CPVC began in the mid-1990s. During this period, in the construction and plumbing industry, pipes were still made of iron and copper. Engineer saw that corrosion was a major problem with galvanized pipes and India was materially behind the evolution curve in the use of plastics for pipes. In the United States, CPVC was the new anti-corrosion solution for plastic pipes, which was swiftly replacing metal (iron and copper) pipes in industrial applications. CPVC was also a superior product compared to PVC because of higher ductile strength, which gave it the ability to handle hot water up to 200 degrees Fahrenheit (93° Celsius) (PVC can handle hot water only up to 140 degrees Fahrenheit [60° Celsius]).

B.F. Goodrich (now known as Lubrizol) held the patent for CPVC resin technology, and Engineer decided to tie up with them to bring CPVC to India. He travelled to the United States to forge a techno-financial joint venture (JV) deal with Thompson Plastics of USA, which provided Astral with the technical know-how for setting up the CPVC plant. Astral also acquired the licence for CPVC resin procurement from Lubrizol (the first Indian company to do so). With a JV partner on board and a licence in his hand, Engineer set up Astral Poly Technik in March 1996. Thompson put up 20 per cent of equity for the company and Engineer approached his uncle to fund another 20 per cent. For his personal equity contribution, Engineer sold his house in Ahmedabad. I met Engineer at Astral's corporate office located off the bustling Sarkhej–Gandhinagar Highway and behind the prestigious Rajpath Club in Ahmedabad. Recalling those early days, Engineer told me, 'There was a time when everything my father-in-law and I owned was mortgaged to build Astral.'

Astral began its CPVC journey by launching industrial pipes (Corzan) in 1999. In those days, GI pipes were used for fluid transportation and were prone to scale (blockage due to water impurities), pit (pinhole leaks) and corrosion. At a time when the biggest players in steel pipes were giants such as Tata Steel and Jindal Steel, and plastic pipe segment was dominated by Supreme Industries, Astral chose a product that was 20 per cent costlier than metal pipes. Engineer was aware of the scepticism and scorn. He told me, 'When I launched CPVC in India, industry veterans told me that I was stupid and will go bankrupt soon. In 2000, the plant used to be operational only for four days in a month and was shut for the remaining twenty-six days. The market did not have confidence that sulphuric acid and industrial fluids can pass through plastic (CPVC) pipes.'

Despite selling the pipes at a loss, Astral's CPVC products flopped. GI pipes were so well entrenched in India that no one wanted to switch to an expensive product. Engineer had landed up funding a risky business with his established business of APIs at Kairav Chemicals. With CPVC failing, both businesses suffered. As if this wasn't enough, in January 2001, Gujarat was hit by a devastating earthquake jeopardizing Engineer's already struggling pharma business. This was followed by the collapse of Astral's main bankers, Madhavpura Mercantile Cooperative Bank, following misappropriation of its depositors' funds. Astral's funds dried up and as a result it could not fulfil a large order. By the end of 2003, Astral was staring at imminent bankruptcy.

Phase 2: 2003–06

The Building Blocks

> 'We came to a point where our day-to-day business was to just survive.'
>
> —Sandeep Engineer

Engineer stood resolute in the face of bankruptcy. In 2002, he travelled to Huntsville, Alabama, and convinced the Thompson family to convert their loan into preference shares and infuse capital for buying moulds and injection moulding machines (for manufacturing fittings indigenously rather than purchasing expensive imports). Thompson Plastics was acquired by Charlotte Pipes in 2005 and Thompson's relationship with Engineer stood the test of time; Kyle A. Thompson is now a director on Astral's board.

With his immediate liquidity needs resolved, Engineer embarked on his turnaround plan. He switched to Corporation Bank. K.R. Shenoy, former executive director at Corporation Bank, joined Astral's board as chairman in 2006.

With regard to his core business, Engineer realized that it was difficult to replace copper pipes in the industrial segment and that like any small player, Astral's pricing power was weak due to its low bargaining power with industrial manufacturers. He simply could not compete with established industrial pipes players like Tata Steel and Jindal Steel. So, on B.F. Goodrich's recommendation, he shifted his focus to selling CPVC pipes used for plumbing. He had his job cut out for him: first, he had to convince prospective clients to shift from metal pipes to CPVC; second, he had to convince dealers and distributors to stock his products alongside those of his competitors. It wasn't easy, but Engineer had learnt his lessons.

Engineer started by meeting the big consumers of plumbing pipes—real-estate developers and hotels. In his meetings, he highlighted issues such as corrosion and pinholes in copper pipes and explained the benefits of CPVC for hot and cold water applications and for fire sprinkler systems. In 2003, Astral received the first large order from Rohan Lifescapes, a real-estate developer based in south Mumbai, and subsequently built relationships with other real-estate developers and hotels. This established the proof of concept for CPVC in India and thereon Astral Poly received orders from other large Mumbai-based developers such as Hiranandani and Kalpataru. Soon, developers in other Indian cities such as Bengaluru followed.

To convince distributors and dealers to stock his product, Engineer showcased CPVC at trade exhibitions and travelled across India to meet distributors and consultants. He would mentally mark his meeting with a distributor as a success if the distributor offered him a cup of tea during his meetings. Recalling those tough days, he told me, 'In the early years, distributors did not even offer us a seat when we went to meet them. I used to leave their offices thinking that one day they will insist that I share a cup of tea with them before leaving.' To back up Engineer's claims, I visited some of Astral's large distributors in Mumbai. One of the distributors who was impressed by Engineer in his early days told me, 'We never realized that Sandeepbhai was the promoter, he always looked and behaved like an employee of Astral.'

Engineer's efforts paid off when he bagged a few large institutional projects in Mumbai—such as the Renaissance Hotel in Powai (a suburb of Mumbai) and the Hilton Hotel in Bengaluru. As was the case with industrial pipes, Engineer realized that the dealers refused to pay a premium for CPVC despite its benefits over conventional GI or PVC pipes. This premium was thus the main entry barrier in the retail segment. Engineer then priced CPVC pipes on a par with GI pipes. He made a loss in the process but recovered this with the sale of CPVC fittings at a premium, since customers were not aware of the price of fittings. The pricing parity between GI and CPVC pipes was one of the main reasons for acceptance of CPVC in the retail segment. To expand its product portfolio, Astral became the first Indian company to launch lead-free PVC pipes in 2004. Lead-free PVC was a preferred pipe globally for potable water applications.

Engineer also identified the humble plumber to be his first brand ambassador. In reality, the plumber does the actual work of fixing pipes and—as compared to the real-estate developer or property owner—has a better idea of which brand of pipes works better. Unlike other pipe manufacturers who ignored plumbers, Engineer saw that the plumber was the influencer and decision maker and hence the most important person in the value chain.

To get plumbers on his side, he sponsored the annual meeting of the Plumbers' Association in Mumbai in 2002. At this event, he explained the benefits of CPVC pipes to 300 plumbers. The next day he visited a construction site of a large real-estate developer in Mumbai with snacks and Astral-branded T-shirts for plumbers. Engineer struck gold when, in 2001, he met Shabbir Malwawala, the head of the plumbing department of one of the largest real-estate developers in Mumbai (Hiranandani). Malwawala was also Lubrizol's man in India to train plumbers and, in the process, market Lubrizol's FlowGuard pipes. Malwawala conducted these training sessions for Lubrizol's other licensees, namely, Ajay Pipes and Ashirvad. Engineer joined this bandwagon.

Apart from aggressive branding at these training sessions, Astral benefitted from Lubrizol's plumber certification programme which created strong brand equity with the plumbers for Astral's CPVC pipes. Malwawala told me that Lubrizol trained over 10,000 plumbers in India between 2005 and 2008, but everybody thought that Astral had held these training sessions. Despite being employed by Lubrizol, Astral's competitors referred to Malwawala as, *Ye Astral ka aadmi hai* (this man works for Astral). 'We conducted 15–20 trainings in a month in the remotest parts of the country.

There were times when only three plumbers turned up, but we never stopped,' Malwawala told me.

In FY03, Astral reported profits (Rs 1.10 crore) for the first time in five years as CPVC made inroads in Indian plumbing. Interestingly, in FY03 and FY04, Astral spent its entire profit after tax (PAT)—Rs 1.6 crore and Rs 2.7 crore—on advertising and audaciously raised its advertising spend by 125 per cent in FY05. At that time, advertising campaigns for pipes were unheard of, but Engineer spotted an opportunity during India's general elections in 2004. This is a period in India where advertising on news channels shoots up as viewership increases. He chose two of India's leading Hindi news channels—Aaj Tak and Star News— for an aggressive advertising campaign for his pipes. The campaign went on air from April 2004, the month of the elections, to June 2004, when the new government of the United Progressive Alliance assumed office. As a result, Astral's selling and distribution expenditure as a percentage of its sales rose to 17 per cent in FY05 from 12 per cent in FY03 (see Exhibits 101 and 102).

Exhibit 101: Astral became profitable in FY03 . . .

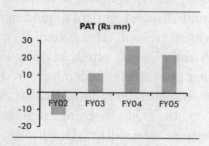

Source: Astral Poly, Ambit Capital research.

Exhibit 102: . . . and invested significant sums on advertisements

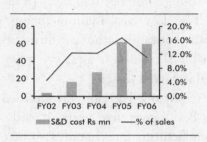

Source: Astral Poly, Ambit Capital research.

Engineer never looked back. Astral had arrived. Astral's operating margin improved over FY04–06. Over these years, it generated cumulative operating cash flow of Rs 7.7 crore and invested nearly thrice as much (Rs 20.3 crore) on capacity expansion, which was partly financed through borrowings (Rs 11 crore).

Despite the small scale of his operations (in those days, Astral's competitors Supreme and Finolex were 10 times its size in revenues) and limited management bandwidth, Engineer took a gutsy decision to set up a CPVC fitting capacity in Baddi, Himachal Pradesh (HP). The HP government offered excise incentives for manufacturing capacities in the state. As manufacturing operations in the north would also provide Engineer with an entry into the large markets of northern India like Delhi, Gurgaon and Jaipur, he made a quick decision to set up a fittings capacity in HP. The excise incentives ensured that fittings made in the HP plant would lower Astral's overall cost of fittings. To limit his capital expenditure, Engineer took a ready-made shed in Baddi on rent, with the right to buy the shed at a fixed valuation within six months.

During this period, Astral's advertising campaigns were in full swing—sales more than doubled between FY04 and FY06. At this time, Engineer had enough capacity to meet this demand. The low-cost manufacturing plants in HP improved overall profitability (net profit margin expanded to 9.4 per cent in FY07, which is a far cry from the pre-FY03 era when Astral incurred losses).

Whilst the company had initially decided to add three fitting lines in Baddi over five years, it ended up installing twenty-two manufacturing lines in only two years due to better-than-expected demand. In fifteen years since he started Astral in 1996, the firm grew rapidly to become two-thirds the size of the largest plastic pipe manufacturer in India—Supreme Industries. To put things into perspective, in FY06, Astral generated net revenues of Rs 51.8 crore from its HP plant, higher than the Rs 45 crore of revenues generated that year from its Gujarat plant.

Finally, from the outset, Engineer placed tremendous faith in his employees. In 2003, he appointed Hiranand Savlani as Astral's CFO. Savlani, thirty-five years old then, was highly educated, and had a multitude of professional qualifications as a chartered accountant (CA), cost accountant (ICWA), company secretary (CS) and also possessed a law (LLB) degree. Savlani was entrusted with the entire responsibility of setting up the Baddi plant, starting from land acquisition.

Engineer followed this up with the recruitment of Sanjay Shah to run the day-to-day operations at Baddi. Savlani and Shah ensured that the HP operations didn't require constant oversight from Engineer so that he could remain focused on Astral's marketing and brand building.

Engineer also gave professional management a shot, but that experiment lasted for six years, before Engineer reverted to leading his company. In 2004, he hired Mayur Vakil, a veteran in plastic pipe industry from Supreme Industries, and appointed him president at Astral. However, as time went by, Vakil and Engineer encountered professional differences and, eventually, Vakil resigned in FY10. Since then, Engineer has retained the top post at Astral. He has two sons, Kairav and Saumya. Kairav joined the firm as manager, business development, in 2012, while Saumya—who joined in 2014—manages the product development/marketing of the adhesives business.

Exhibit 103: Sales quadrupled over FY04–07 . . .

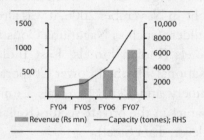

Source: Astral Poly, Ambit Capital research.

Exhibit 104: . . . EBITDA expanded at a 38% CAGR over FY04–07

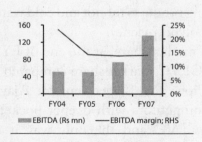

Source: Astral Poly, Ambit Capital research.

Phase 3: 2007–15

Building Scale and Pan-India Brand Recall

> 'We had to build scale. We made the market for CPVC in India and if we didn't increase capacities aggressively, someone else would have borne the fruit of our hard work.'

—Sandeep Engineer

In this final phase, Astral ultimately broke out of the ranks and emerged as India's largest CPVC manufacturer. By the time Astral went public in November 2006, it was already supplying to real-estate builders (such as Nagarjuna Construction, Sobha Developers), hotels (Indian Hotels, East India Hotels), the public sector (National Thermal Power Corporation [NTPC], Mangalore Refinery and Petrochemicals Limited [MRPL]) and large companies in the private sector (Reliance Industries, Hindustan Unilever, Tata Steel).

With marquee clients on his roster, Engineer had established CPVC as a credible product. Obviously, competition latched on to the growth opportunity. Manufacturers such as Supreme Industries and Ashirvad Pipes had either established CPVC manufacturing facilities or had competing products for hot and cold water applications such as PPR (polypropylene).

In terms of market share, at the end of FY07, Astral had 70 per cent of CPVC market share compared to 20 per cent for Ashirvad Pipes and 10 per cent for Ajay Pipes. Astral realized that competitors with deeper pockets could derail its growth in CPVC and the only way it could counter this potential threat was through gaining scale. In March 2007, Astral raised Rs 340 million through a primary public issuance to expand its capacities. Using the funds, Astral tripled capacities from FY07 to FY10, aggressively expanded its distributor network and continued to invest in training plumbers. Engineer didn't stop here. In the next five years (FY10–15), he raised the capacity fivefold. At the end of FY15, Astral's capacities stood at 1,17,164 tonnes, compared to 9074 tonnes at the end of FY07, growing at a rate much faster than the competition.

After establishing scale, Engineer's challenge was to build a pan-India brand. Unlike a Bajaj Auto or a Hindustan Unilever, Astral's target group was not the end-consumer, but the humble plumber who Engineer knew exercised considerable influence in choosing pipes. While the first wave of advertising in 2004 had provided awareness, the next wave would have to entrench Astral as a brand in pipes. He chose Lowe Lintas as their ad agency and in August 2014 announced that Bollywood superstar, Salman Khan, would be its brand ambassador. Khan's superhit movies included *Dabangg* in 2010 and its sequel *Dabangg 2* in 2012. The Hindi word, *dabangg*, means a man who exercises considerable influence and power. As Sagar Kapoor, executive creative director at Lowe Lintas, said at the launch,[19] 'Being a low-involvement category, the homemaker does not take keen interest in deciding the quality and make of the pipes for their homes. With leakage being the most common problem, it is the plumber who decides what to purchase without even consulting the homemaker. Through this television commercial, we want to convey that if you wish to resolve the issue, then it is essential that you tend to the root problem— bad pipes.' The campaign worked and over the past two years, Astral has created a strong brand for its CPVC pipes.

---

[19] http://www.campaignbrief.com/asia/2014/08/actor-salman-khan-appointed-br.html.

Today, it is commonly referred to in the plumber community as the '*Dabangg-wala* pipe'—the pipe from the *Dabangg* movies. Recent entrants in the CPVC pipes industry such as Skipper have also hired celebrities (Skipper hired Navjot Singh Sidhu—a former cricketer) for building their brand.

Astral's growing brand strength allowed it to drive harder bargains with its dealers—which meant lower debtor days as the company tied up with banks to provide working capital financing to its dealers/distributors (after thirty days, the receivables were transferred to the banks from the company). As can be seen in Exhibit 105, this reduced the cash conversion cycle from ninety-nine days in FY07 to forty-three days in FY14, resulting in higher cash flows. Close on the heels of its advertising campaign, Engineer also made two acquisitions in the adhesives business in 2014—Resinova and Seal-It—which I will discuss in the next section.

Exhibit 105: Cash conversion cycle improved leading to acceleration in ROCEs

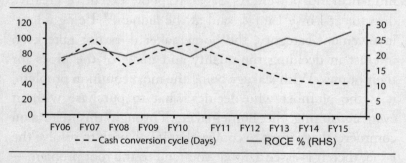

Source: Astral Poly, Ambit Capital research.

Exhibit 106: Astral's EBIT margin has been stable and capital employed turnover has improved consistently*

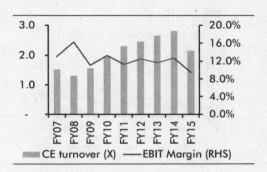

Source: Astral Poly, Ambit Capital research.

Note: *The drop in FY15 is on account of capacity additions.

Exhibit 107: Astral's branding expenditure expanded at a 48% CAGR over FY07–12

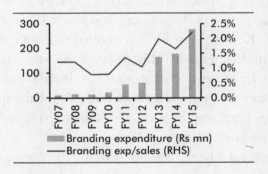

Source: Astral Poly, Ambit Capital research.

Exhibit 108: Astral's growth was significantly higher than Supreme's over FY07–15

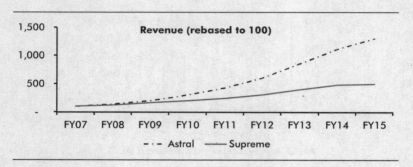

Source: Astral Poly, Ambit Capital research.

However, this last phase was not without mistakes. The first mistake was an ill-thought-of overseas foray. Astral ventured into Kenya in FY08, initially through exports and then by setting up a manufacturing capacity in the country through acquiring a 26 per cent stake in a JV (with Ramco group of Kenya), Astral Technologies Limited. Whilst capital employment in this expansion was insignificant (less than 1 per cent of its capital employed) and no active management was required from Astral, global expansion is a less-than-ideal step by a small-scale company as it reduces management bandwidth.

The second mistake was not hedging its currency exposure on its CPVC resin imports from the United States, leaving the company vulnerable to a sharp depreciation in the Indian rupee, compared to the US dollar. Exporters and importers protect themselves against appreciation and depreciation of the Indian rupee versus other currencies, most commonly the US dollar. This protection is called hedging. Leaving a position (like export or imports) unhedged is risky and can cause forex losses. Astral paid the price in FY09, when a 33 per cent depreciation in the Indian rupee left the firm with a forex loss of Rs 7.7 crore, wiping off 40 per cent of its profit before tax (PBT). Astral's stock price declined by 84 per cent in March 2009 due to these losses, compared to its peak in January 2008. Finally, although investors have broadly responded positively to Astral's acquisitions in 2014 (Resinova and Seal-It), it has only been two years since these acquisitions. How these acquisitions help Astral establish itself in the adhesives market is yet to be seen.

In terms of market capitalization, Astral is the smallest company in this book. Astral's market capitalization stood at Rs 4886 crore as on 30 March 2016, versus a median market capitalization of Rs 58,100 crore for the remaining seven companies in this book. Nevertheless, in a span of fifteen years, Astral has built a formidable business. Along the way, it has met our criteria of (a) achieving 10 per cent revenue growth and 15 per cent ROCE in each year for the past ten years; and (b) featuring at least four times in the past ten iterations of our Coffee Can Portfolio. This achievement puts Astral on par with blue-chips like ITC, Asian Paints and HDFC Bank.

What is Astral's secret sauce?

Focusing on the Core Business

Even though Engineer began his career in the pharma sector, once he was convinced about CPVC, he relentlessly focused on building a large franchise. Like any entrepreneur determined to make a mark with a new product in a market dominated by large players, Engineer faced the problems of (a) strong competitors with large balance sheets (Tata Pipes, Supreme,

Finolex); and (b) convincing dealers and distributors to stock his product. As we saw in Phases 1 and 2, Engineer overcame these hurdles by winning over plumber communities and convincing buyers of the durability and strength of CPVC. To do this, he even travelled to the USA to understand the product. 'He was a man with zero understanding of plumbing. It's a surprise that he learnt the business and built the largest CPVC franchise in India,' Malwawala told me.

Engineer never compromised on quality. In a country where jugaad (low-cost fix) is celebrated, he fostered confidence in his clients with his high standards of service and focus on quality. From the outset, he refrained from the dubious practices used by small-scale players, such as mixing recycled plastic with PVC resin to reduce costs at the expense of quality. He personally took an interest in large projects. Narrating an incident in 2005, Malwawala recalled the time when the Renaissance Hotel (managed by the luxury hotel major, Marriott) in Powai, an eastern suburb in Mumbai, faced a leakage problem. Renaissance was amongst Astral's initial major projects. Pipes started leaking on the terrace due to poor installation. When Engineer was informed about the problem, he just said, 'Give me the list of problems and get it resolved at whatever cost.' Malwawala added, 'Engineer takes criticism very positively. Each and every suggestion of mine was communicated to the quality control team and it was made sure that it was implemented.'

As he did not have a strong understanding of adhesives, Engineer hired Anurag Kothawala (chief operating officer [COO] at Anil Ltd) as a permanent employee in 2015 to learn about adhesive manufacturing. One of the largest individual shareholders in Astral, Miten Mehta, told me in January 2016 that Engineer is never dismissive of new ideas; whenever he learnt of new piping systems or fittings available globally, he would import a few containers in India, test the market, and if successful, start manufacturing them indigenously.

In 2014, nearly two decades since it began operations, Astral forayed outside of CPVC and made two acquisitions in adhesives. In 2014, Astral made two acquisitions—Seal-It in August 2014 for Rs 44 crore and Resinova in November 2014 for Rs 215 crore (and subsequently acquired the balance stake of the promoter for Rs 73 crore). To Engineer, venturing into adhesives was a logical transition to becoming a larger branded home-building materials player since the channel and intermediary of both the products are similar, and both are products wherein there are ample innovation possibilities. Huntsman is India's largest manufacturer of epoxy adhesives and its Araldite brand is ranked number one. Engineer believed that if he could take on established players like Supreme and Finolex, he could give adhesives a try. After all, adhesives and pipes were both based on chemical compounds—a fascination with Engineer since his college days.

Resinova had revenues of Rs 200 crore in FY15 and owned the Bondtite brand in epoxy adhesives. Bondtite was second to industry leader Araldite and a strong brand in north and west India because of its good quality. Resinova's revenues had also grown at a robust 20 per cent CAGR over FY11–15. Astral acquired Resinova at 1.7 times its FY14 revenues, which is inexpensive for an established brand with a top-quality product portfolio. Resinova sells adhesives under three broad categories: (a) maintenance, (b) construction, and (c) wood care, across 4,00,000 retail outlets using 2000 distributors. It sells products under fifty brands (including sub-brands) across 600 stock-keeping units (SKUs). Seal-It had revenues of Rs 135 crore, 100 SKUs and 1600 outlets in the UK.

Deepening the competitive moats

In its fifteen-year journey from a small company with a new product to a leading plastics franchise in India, Astral has steadily built competitive advantages, which are now difficult for competitors to replicate. I analyse these competitive moats using Kay's IBAS (innovation, brands and reputation, architecture and strategic assets) framework (which is explained in detail in Appendix 1). Ambit's building materials analysts believe that (a) Astral's journey began through launching a differentiated product (CPVC pipes) and the firm thus developed a habit of continuously innovating to add new products to its portfolio; (b) Astral has been innovative in branding and has managed to establish its brand in a seemingly commoditized product—plastic pipes; and (c) Astral has well-established relationships with distributors/plumbers.

Innovation

Astral started off with an innovative product, namely CPVC. After the initial failure in the industrial segment, Engineer succeeded in the plumbing segment, as described earlier. Astral has consistently built on this success by launching innovative CPVC products and staying ahead of other plastic pipe manufacturers. Astral continued selling more products, initially by importing them and later by making them at Astral's factories. In most cases, competitors followed suit much later. For example, India's largest pipe manufacturer, Supreme Industries, launched CPVC pipes a decade after Astral's launch despite being a vociferous naysayer initially. Instead of copying foreign technologies, Engineer forged technical partnerships with global majors to launch innovative products in India. Shown below are some of these tie-ups (see Exhibit 109).

Exhibit 109: Astral has consistently launched new products through partnerships with global majors

Year	Product	Strategic Partners
1999	Flowguard CPVC piping and plumbing systems	Lubrizol (then B.F. Goodrich, later Noveon)
2001	CPVC pipes and fittings	Specialty Products LLC (USA)
2004	CPVC and PVC fittings, flanges and valves	Spears (USA)
2004	Solvent chemicals	IPSC (USA)
2005	Underground speciality fittings	Hunter (UK)
2006	Large-diameter PVC pipes	Harvell (USA)
2008	Soundproof piping	Wavin
2013	Bendable pipes	Lubrizol
2014	Blazemaster*	Lubrizol
2015	Acquired Bond It (UK-based adhesives manufacturer)	Seal-It
2015	Acquired Resinova (Bondtite, Resibond, etc.), Indian-based adhesives manufacturer	Resinova

Source: Company, Ambit Capital research.

Note: *In Blazemaster, the company entered into the partnership in 2006, but as is the case in India, the government gave its approval only in 2013.

In its early days, Astral sold pipes at a loss to make CPVC products as attractive as GI pipes. For the real-estate builders, the noise-free, CPVC pipes were sometimes priced lower than the traditional GI pipes that made noise. When I met builders and distributors, they told me that pricing was one of the biggest factors of increasing adoption. One of them said, 'In India, as a manufacturer, you have to not only give a lower price for a new product but you also have to demonstrate more value—Astral did both of these.' Astral's innovation in processes continues with increased adoption of automation; recently, it installed robotic truck-filling machines to reduce loading time by more than half (from two hours to thirty minutes), thereby reducing the probability of work disruption.

Astral was also the first company in India to train plumbers, and that too on a scale which was unheard of— 10,000 plumbers during 2005–08. Malwawala told me that in the plumbing industry, plumbers were regarded as illiterate and unskilled workers, but Astral made them feel important by certifying them. Later, these certificates helped the plumbers get jobs at large construction sites. Astral was also the first Indian company to start barcoding on pipes to prevent counterfeits. The company also innovated in its branding.

Brands and reputation

You never notice pipes until they stop working. Even then, they are concealed or in a place unreachable by hand. Thus, replacing or repairing them, or fixing leakages turns out to be a very costly affair. Astral launched a television commercial on news channels in 2004, highlighting these issues. In an interview[20] to *Business Standard*, Chandan Nath of Mudra, Astral's then advertising agency, said, 'Instead of focusing

---

[20] http://www.business-standard.com/article/economy-policy/astral-eyes-10-fold-increase-in-turnover-104041301031_1.html.

on Astral CPVC plumbing systems, the advertisements communicated the arrival of a "new problem-free solution for life" and the end of an era of "leaking pipes and damp walls".' Timing this advertising campaign with India's 2004 general elections, when the viewership of news channels increased exponentially, worked in Astral's favour.

Astral was also the first Indian pipes company to advertise on public buses and autorickshaws to increase the visibility of its products. Other innovative brand-building exercises included advertisements at Wankhede Stadium, Mumbai, for the India versus West Indies series in November 2013, where India's cricketing superstar Sachin Tendulkar played his last test match before retiring. As mentioned earlier, Astral signed on Bollywood superstar Salman Khan as its brand ambassador in 2014. These campaigns have made an impact. In my discussions at hardware stores, I often hear Gujarati shop owners say 'CPVC *mane* Astral' or CPVC means Astral pipes. Astral has spent 1–2 per cent of sales consistently on advertisements, significantly higher than Supreme Industries, as can be clearly seen from Exhibit 110.

Exhibit 110: Astral's spending on branding is significantly higher than Supreme's

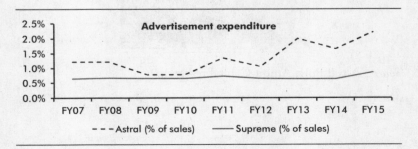

Source: Astral Poly, Ambit Capital research.

Astral's innovative branding campaigns led to the creation of strong brand recall across India and enabled the company to launch other piping systems under the Astral umbrella. Astral booked theatres in several Indian cities for a private screening of *Dabangg* for its distributors, which was another instance of relationship strengthening (see Exhibits 111, 112). I met a large Mumbai-based distributor of pipes including Astral, Supreme and Prince at his office in Nariman Point, Mumbai. He told me, 'Astral's branding is the most aggressive. It knows how to identify the right intermediaries. They have good-quality products and have created a great brand by doing frequent meetings with dealers and plumbers. It has created a lot of buzz in the industry. People look forward to new launches from them.' The company is now leveraging its brand to gain market share in its newly acquired adhesive business, which is sold through the same distributors who sell plastic pipes.

Exhibit 111: Astral was one of the key sponsors of the movie, *Dabangg 2*

Source: Astral Poly, Ambit Capital research.

Exhibit 112: Salman Khan posing as a plumber in an Astral CPVC advertisement

Source: Astral Poly, Ambit Capital research.

While Engineer has established Astral as a brand in the past two decades, the brand also runs on Engineer's own reputation. Like any successful, first-generation entrepreneur, he has given Astral everything he has got. Savlani told me, 'His biggest strength is simplicity and humility. There has been no change in his personality even after the manifold growth of Astral. He still drinks tea from a roadside stall along with his dealers.' Astral's distributors respect Engineer and know him as a trustworthy, honest and intelligent man. Therefore, it comes as no surprise that the distributors support the company in its new ventures such as the adhesive business.

Architecture
Over the years, Astral has steadily built its ties with the plumber community. 'The plumber is also my customer. I give him utmost importance,' Engineer told me. By treating plumbers well and giving them importance, he endeared himself to the community—this makes him stand apart from his competition as none of them attached so much importance to the plumber community.

Malwawala recalls that during training sessions, Engineer would tell plumbers not to see themselves as plumbers, but as doctors who treat the big problem of leaking pipes in homes. Within his company as well, Engineer fostered a culture of loyalty. Savlani told me that each employee associates himself as a part of the Astral family, due to which attrition rates are very low. A majority of the senior employees were hired during the company's struggle in the latter half of the 1990s and have thus grown with the company; this fosters a sense of belonging. From the promoter to the watchman, all employees at Astral wear the company's uniform of a light-blue shirt with the Astral logo on the shirt pocket. Engineer's two sons—twenty-seven-year-old Kairav and twenty-four-year-old Saumya—are now being trained to lead the company. Kairav drove a branding exercise for Astral in 2012 and actively looks after the pipes business. Saumya is involved in business development in the newly acquired adhesives business. Neither of them is on the board of Astral just yet (in contrast to the practice traditionally associated with Indian promoters who like to see their children parachuted into the board as soon as they join their father's company). Instead, Kairav and Saumya regularly visit the plant and work with the distributors/intermediaries during new launches.

Strategic assets

Astral's first strategic asset is its pan-India manufacturing network. It has four manufacturing plants in India—namely, two in Gujarat and one each in Himachal Pradesh and Tamil Nadu. It has the largest capacity in CPVC plumbing pipes in India. Apart from Supreme and Astral, most other pipe manufacturers in India have a presence only in agriculture, and, hence, limited presence in the plumbing pipes business.

Astral's manufacturing facilities, well-entrenched network of distributors, and reputation with plumbers provide a strong entry barrier against any new player who wants to sell CPVC pipes. Exhibit 113 provides the details of the six top pipe manufactures in the country.

Exhibit 113: Comparison of the top-six pipe manufacturers

Company	Capacity (tonnes) FY15	Revenue (Rs cr) FY15	CAGR FY 10–15	Products	Plants (figures in brackets indicate number of plants in the state)
Supreme	340,000	2114	20%	Plumbing and agri	Maharashtra (3), UP (1), WB (1), MP (2)
Astral	102,371	1252	34%	Plumbing, agri and industrials	Gujarat (2), HP (1), TN (1)
Ashirvad	70,000	1360	32%	Plumbing, agri and industrials	Karnataka (2)
Finolex	230,000	1693	15%	Largely agri, now getting into plumbing	Maharashtra (2), Gujarat (1)
Prince	90,000	690	14%	Largely agri, now getting into plumbing	Dadra (2), Uttarakhand (1), Maharashtra (1), Tamil Nadu (1)
Jain Irrigation	100,000	11,62	2%	Agri	Maharashtra (2), Gujarat (1), TN (1)

Source: Company, Ambit Capital research.

Astral's second strategic asset is its relations with global majors. Lubrizol, a company owned by Warren Buffett, is the pioneer of the CPVC compound globally. Astral is one of the two manufacturers (Ashirvad being the second) in India with access to CPVC technology from Lubrizol. The company's tie-up with Lubrizol enables it to produce best-in-class CPVC pipes and also launch new products ahead of competition. Astral was the first company in India to launch silent-piping systems, foam-core pipes and composite pipes, all of which were due to Engineer's inclination towards exploring innovative products launched globally and his experience in partnering with large MNC pipe manufacturers. Astral is also the sole licensee of Lubrizol since 1999 to manufacture and sell all four brands of Lubrizol (Corzan, FlowGuard, Blazemaster and Bendable) in India and the Bendable products across the world. Lubrizol, for its part, is setting up a CPVC resin manufacturing capacity in Gujarat, which will supply CPVC resin only to Astral and Ashirvad.

Besides Astral's relations with Lubrizol, the company has also forged relationships with companies from across the developed world such as Wavin (Netherlands), Spears (US), IPSC (US), Hunter (UK) and Harvell (US) for products like speciality fittings and chemicals like solvent cement. Following these relationships, Astral also commenced manufacturing products under licence from these companies. While Supreme Industries, Astral's biggest competitor, has also ramped up its product portfolio (CPVC, CPVC-based fire sprinkler, noise-free pipes) in fittings over the last few years, it has followed Astral rather than staying ahead of it.

Capital allocation

Astral has shown remarkable restraint in its capital allocation decisions. The company's sales grew at a strong 44 per cent CAGR over FY05–FY15, and this growth was achieved without major strain on the balance sheet. Engineer and Savlani have refrained from breaking the balance sheet on expensive acquisitions and ploughed back profits to build reserves and fund growth.

Astral's prudent capital allocation is evident in the steady ROCE improvement to 28 per cent in FY14 from 19 per cent in FY07. The decline in ROCE in FY15 (to 15 per cent) is due to the two acquisitions that year which are yet to scale up. Through the last decade, Astral made sure that its debt to equity ratio was under 1 and major expansions were funded mainly through two equity issuances (in 2007 via its IPO and in 2014 via its Qualified Institutional Placement) rather than debt.

About 83 per cent of the capital generated by Astral during FY05–15 was invested in capital expenditure (new plants in Himachal Pradesh and Tamil Nadu and expansion of Gujarat plant) and in acquisitions (Resinova and Seal-It). Since its early days, the company had a clear road map for capital allocation (a trait rarely displayed by small-sized Indian corporates). As can be seen in Exhibits 114 and 115, Astral's cash flow from operations accounted for half and fresh equity issuance accounted for one-third of the company's total capital generation over FY05–15. Astral hasn't cut corners in its capital expenditure. Instead, it has installed best-in-class machinery for extrusion (imported from Theysohn Extrusionstechnik GmbH, Austria) and injection moulding (Ferromatik Milacron India Limited).

Exhibit 114: Sources of capital during FY05–15

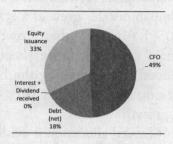

Source: Astral Poly, Ambit Capital research.

Exhibit 115: Application of capital during FY06–15

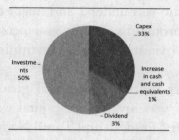

Source: Astral Poly, Ambit Capital research.

With the CPVC business still going strong, Engineer's entry into adhesives holds promise since it will leverage on his distributor network and client relations. Astral is now a popular brand with real-estate developers and plumbers alike. Selling adhesives should not be difficult, if Engineer continues to play his cards right. And he continues to innovate—he recently changed the packaging of Resinova's products to bring it closer to global standards—in the process, he leveraged Astral's brand to make the products more visible in dealers' shops. These innovations on packaging alone have resulted in 10 per cent growth in sales volumes over FY15.

Stellar returns for shareholders

A rupee invested in Astral in March 2007 is worth Rs 36 today (see Exhibit 116), implying a 56 per cent CAGR. The same rupee invested in Sensex and in the NSE mid-cap index would be a meagre Rs 1.9 and Rs 2.6, respectively. Thus, Astral has outperformed the Sensex and NSE mid-cap index by eighteen and thirteen times, respectively, since its listing. The stellar performance was driven by (a) consistent ROCE-focused capital allocation in the pipes business; (b) strengthening competitive advantages through well-thought-through expansion and new product launches; and (c) an intense focus on genuinely helping every stakeholder involved in the company's journey—employees, distributors, plumbers and shareholders.

Exhibit 116: Astral's share price has risen by 36 times in the last eight years

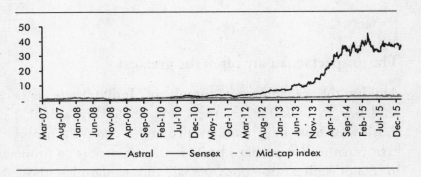

Source: Bloomberg, Ambit Capital research.

CHAPTER 9

Greatness Is Not Everyone's Cup of Tea

'Strategy is about making smart choices and execution is about relentless implementation.'

—Phil Rosenzweig, *The Halo Effect* (2007)

'The business of business is a lot of little decisions every day mixed up with a few big decisions.'

—Tom Murphy, CEO of Capital Cities Broadcasting in William Thorndike's *The Outsiders* (2012)

The unspectacular are often the greatest

Amidst the cacophonous tumult of India, there is a tendency to look for greatness and leadership amongst those who have flair, flamboyance and a certain sense of extroversion. But perhaps because the country is so prone to major upheavals—both social and economic—those who achieve long-lasting success in India are often those who are unflashy, introverted, determined and intelligently tenacious.

As highlighted at the end of Chapter 1, in cricket, no one exemplifies this more than Rahul Dravid. During his sixteen-year international career, he scored more runs than Sachin Tendulkar. His prime coincided with Saurav Ganguly's captaincy and Dravid made an incredible 23 per cent of the runs scored by India in the twenty-one Test victories under Saurav Ganguly (at a 'Bradmanesque' average of 103). Those runs and those victories put India on the road to becoming the number one Test team in the world. And yet underlying these outstanding results was an uncomplicated approach to the game. As the late Peter Roebuck, one of the world's greatest cricket writers puts it, 'Dravid has a simple game founded upon straight lines. Reasoning that runs cannot be scored in the pavilion, he sets out to protect his wicket. Curiously, this thought does not seem to occur to many batsmen, a point many a long-suffering coach could confirm.'[21]

As discussed in Chapter 1, the Coffee Can companies are the Rahul Dravids of the business world—rare, determined and constantly seeking to improve the edge or the advantage they enjoy vis-à-vis their competitors. The in-depth case studies contained in the preceding seven chapters focus on the companies which have featured in our Coffee Can Portfolios most often. In this section, I focus on the underlying common themes among those companies. My case studies and discussions with observers of the Indian business landscape over the past five years have led me to conclude that three factors are central to building a truly great company.

---

[21] http://www.bbc.com/news/world-asia-india-17309801.

Firstly, the management team has to have an obsessive focus on the core franchise instead of being distracted by short-term gambles outside the core segment. Secondly, the company has to relentlessly deepen its competitive moats over the course of time (I'm talking about decades here). And thirdly, the people calling the shots at the company have to be sensible about capital allocation, i.e. refrain from large bets (especially those outside core franchise) and return excess cash to shareholders if the cash cannot be deployed to good effect by the company.

In Chapter 1, I highlighted eight companies—the first among equals—who have delivered on all three fronts over the best part of the last twenty years (see Exhibit 117). The subsequent seven chapters provided in-depth case studies on seven out of these eight companies. In this chapter, I use the material from the case studies to illustrate how delivering on the three points mentioned in the preceding paragraph is central to delivering outstanding financial performance over very long periods of time.

Exhibit 117: The eight companies which are first among equals

Number	Company name	Number of times ROCE> 15% (last 10 years**)	Number of times revenue growth > 10% (last 10 years**)
1	Asian Paints	10	10
2	Astral Poly	10	10
3	Berger Paints	10	10
4	ITC	10	10
5	Marico*	10	10
6	Page Industries	10	10

(*Contd*)

Number	Company name	Number of times ROCE> 15% (last 10 years**)	Number of times revenue growth > 10% (last 10 years**)
7	HDFC Bank	10	10
8	Axis Bank	10	10

Source: Capitaline, Company, Ambit Capital research.

Note: *Marico demerged its Kaya business in 2014. After adjusting for the demerged business, the revenue growth was greater than 10% in FY14. **Last ten years refer to FY06–15.

Common underlying themes . . .

The themes common to the eight companies are as similar as their businesses are diverse. The offices of Asian Paints and Marico are located away from Mumbai's central districts. HDFC Bank consciously chose to set up office in central Mumbai back in 1994 when every bank was located in the more expensive area of south Mumbai. Twenty years later, Axis Bank shifted to the same area.

Some of the promoters maintain a deliberately low profile—the Dhingras of Berger Paints, the Danis of Asian Paints and the Genomals of Page Industries. And yet, all of these promoters—specifically Asian Paints, Berger Paints and Marico—are renowned in their hands-off approach to business and encouraging talent within the company, unlike the typical Indian promoter mentality of centralizing power and wealth in his and his relatives' hands.

The strongest common theme among these first amongst equal companies—that have remained in Ambit's Coffee Can Portfolio longer than anybody else—are their strategies that differentiate them from their competitors. Each of these companies comes from highly competitive sectors where building a brand name and delivering sustained financial performance is, by itself, a considerable achievement. So how did they do it?

. . . separate the first among equals from their competitors

Sustained superior financial performance has driven these companies to be among the leaders in their respective fields. Asian Paints and Berger Paints are the number one and number two brands of paint, whilst HDFC Bank and Axis Bank are two of the largest private banking brands created since India's banking business was opened up to the private sector in the mid-1990s. ITC has almost a vice-like grip on the Indian cigarette market, while Marico has impressively staved off foreign competition to sustain leadership in its home-grown cooking oil and hair oil brands. Over broadly the same time period, Page has created an aspirational brand within an ordinary category like innerwear. Finally, Astral Poly has broken through the ranks of unorganized building material players to create a leading brand in the pipes industry.

The ability to break away from competition and sustain long periods of financial performance has been well documented in Warren Buffett's 1996 letter to shareholders: 'Companies such as Coca-Cola and Gillette might well be labelled "The Inevitables". Forecasters may differ a bit in their predictions of exactly how much soft drink or shaving-equipment business these companies will be doing in ten or twenty years. Nor is our talk of inevitability meant to play down the vital work that these companies must continue to carry out, in such areas as manufacturing, distribution, packaging and product innovation. In the end, however, no sensible observer—not even these companies' most vigorous competitors, assuming they are assessing the matter honestly—questions that Coke and Gillette will dominate their fields worldwide for an investment lifetime. Indeed, their dominance will probably strengthen. Both companies have significantly expanded their already huge shares of market during the past ten years, and all signs point to their repeating that performance in the next decade.'

Only time will tell whether these eight first among equals have what it takes to be part of India's 'Inevitables'. But to decode the DNA of these formidable franchises, I have utilized the perspectives offered not just by Warren Buffett but also by business guru Phil Rosenzweig, the British economist (and my first guru) John Kay, as well as leading Indian strategy consultant, Rama Bijapurkar.

My discussions with these companies, with their former staff members, with their rivals, with their customers, besides my readings, led me to three distinctive themes that, I believe, are common to all of these companies.

These three themes are:

- **Theme A:** Focus on the long term (more than ten years) without being distracted by short-term gambles;
- **Theme B:** Constantly deepen the moat around the core franchise using the IBAS framework (which is explained in detail in Appendix 1); and
- **Theme C:** Sensibly allocate capital whilst studiously avoiding betting the balance sheet on expensive and unrelated forays.

The common thread that ties these three themes, the common factor which differentiates these eight companies from their competitors, is the unusual character of the people running these companies. The Unusual Billionaires—my label for the people running the first among equals companies—have the ability to steadfastly focus on doing the same thing for decades on end whilst gradually strengthening their franchise, generating surplus cash from that endeavour and then giving much of that back to shareholders whilst reinvesting the rest judiciously.

Having sought to simplify the secret sauce of the first among equals companies, let's now look at each of the three themes in detail.

Theme A: Focus on the long term without being distracted by short-term gambles

'Most companies tend to focus on short-term results and hence that makes them frequently do things that deviate away from their articulated strategy . . . these diversions take them away from the path they have to travel to achieve their long-term goals . . . the willingness to resist the temptation of short-term 'off-strategy' profits for long-term sustainable gain is not there in most Indian companies,' writes Rama Bijapurkar, a leading market strategy consultant and independent director (2015).

The typical promoter of the companies profiled in the preceding chapters is patient and persevering, even bordering on the boring. He ignores short-term thrills based on flavour-of-the month ideas. He consciously rejects aggressive forays into unrelated businesses just for the sake of growth. To put it more bluntly, for such a CEO, profitability trumps growth—irrespective of market compulsions and regardless of peer pressure. Such behaviour requires tremendous patience and a willingness to ignore the stock market's proclamations regarding prevailing fads and fashions.

Such behaviour also requires promoters to stay focused on the firm's priorities. In their renowned book, *Execution: The Discipline of Getting Things Done*, authors Larry Bossidy and Ram Charan write, 'A leader who says "I have got ten priorities" doesn't know what he's talking about—he doesn't know himself what the most important things are. You've got to have these few, clearly realistic goals and priorities, which will influence the overall performance of the company.'

In their 2011 book, *Great by Choice*, authors Jim Collins and Morten Hansen describe what it takes to be a '20 Mile March' company: 'To 20 Mile March requires hitting specified performance markers with great consistency over a long period of time. It requires two distinct types of discomfort, delivering high performance in difficult times and holding back in good times.'

In a country like India where the free-market economy is only a generation old and is still changing shape every decade or so, where governmental red tape makes business expansion and contraction a tricky affair, single-mindedly focusing on growing and protecting a franchise is a big task.

Case Study 1: Marico Limited

'We love to be boringly consistent.'—Saugata Gupta, MD and CEO, Marico.

Despite being in the business of selling a simple product such as coconut oil, Marico has been able to retain its market leadership with more than 50 per cent market share over the last two decades—see Exhibits 118 and 119 (note: VAHO stands for Marico's Value-Added Hair Oil). Central to Marico's success has been its focus on oil, its core product—first Parachute hair oil and then Saffola edible oil.

Exhibit 118: VAHO commands ~30% volume share

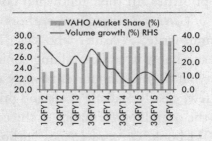

Source: Marico, Ambit Capital research.

Exhibit 119: Saffola commands ~58% value share

Source: Marico, Ambit Capital research.

To appreciate why this focus on a certain product is important, it is worth studying how Marico has taken on Dabur in the *amla* hair oil segment (versus Marico's traditional coconut hair oil segment). With more than 80 per cent market share, Dabur almost had a monopoly in amla hair oils until 2007–08. Marico acquired the brand, Nihar, from HUL in 2005–06. Within a couple of years of that acquisition, Marico relaunched its Shanti Amla hair oil under the Nihar brand name at a price which was around 40 per cent lower than Dabur's amla hair oil. Dabur did not take any action and hence kept losing market share in the amla category to a point where today Marico has about 30 per cent of the market share (by volume) in this category.

From Dabur's perspective, it was not as focused on maintaining market share in amla as Marico was. Hair oils accounted for only about 20 per cent of Dabur's total sales in 2005. Currently, they account for around 17 per cent of domestic revenues and about 12 per cent of consolidated revenues for Dabur.

In my discussion with him, Marico's MD and CEO, Saugata Gupta, explained the company's philosophy behind sticking to long-term goals: 'In today's world, you have to manage contradictions between long-term and short-term plans. I think our philosophy and my personal belief is that you need to strike a balance between the two . . . I have a guideline which is "Never compromise long-term gains for short-term gains."'

Gupta gave us two examples of his guideline. In the FMCG trade, it is routine for salespeople to aggressively push the company's products into the dealers' inventory. Marico does not do this. Instead, it has moved to an auto-replenishment, demand-driven model wherein the company sends fresh supplies to the dealer once the dealer's inventory has been depleted. This helps in matching demand with supply. One could argue that dumping more products with dealers and retailers would mean greater visibility resulting in sales. Indeed, this could be a potential benefit, but if demand for any product is low, retailers remove products from their shelf and carry them as inventory and as inventory rises, a manufacturer's sales will fall because the dealer/retailer already has sufficient inventory. By using an auto-replenishment model, Marico matches demand and supply more accurately.

Secondly, in most B2C sectors, when demand starts flagging, the obvious response from manufacturers is to step up promotional activity. Marico does not do this. Instead, Marico runs promotions for its products for a predefined period each month.

Another example of Marico's ability to focus on the longer term whilst dealing with short-term pressures came following the launch of Fortune rice bran health premium edible oil in 2012. Fortune, a brand owned by Adani Wilmar Limited, spent aggressively on advertising and consumer promotions. However, Marico, instead of increasing consumer promotions to avoid loss of market share for Saffola in the short term, continued to stress on the brand's preventive heart care positioning through higher advertising spends. Once Adani scaled back its advertising and promotion spends, Saffola regained its market share.

These methods, which might seem conservative in the face of achieving targets, helped Marico maintain a balance between its short-term objective of quarterly sales growth and the longer-term objective of maintaining profitability.

Case Study 2: Page Industries

'There is enormous potential in the innerwear space which is yet to be exploited. We are just scratching the surface currently. So there is no point in diluting our focus on the Jockey business until we have fully capitalized on this potential.'—Sunder Genomal, promoter of Page Industries.

Over the past twenty years, Page has focused solely and exclusively on one brand—Jockey. Its single-minded focus has driven the creation of one of the biggest consumer brands in India. The company's strategy was to create an aspirational, premium brand within what was then seen as a low-end, run-of-the-mill segment—innerwear. Whilst Jockey was successful in creating this brand, one of the greatest challenges in entry-level, discretionary consumer-product categories (like premium innerwear, watches, footwear and kitchenware) is the need to maintain the aspirational value of a brand over a long period of time.

This is because the definition of aspirational consumption in every category changes over time and, hence, the brand recall of the market-leading product needs to evolve accordingly in terms of price points, type and mode of branding initiatives, and product characteristics. Examples of brands losing their aspirational value over a period of time include Titan in watches in 2005–12, Bata in footwear in 2000–10, and VIP Frenchie (men's innerwear) from 2005 onwards.

Page constantly undertakes initiatives to maintain the aspirational brand recall of Jockey. These initiatives include not just the consistent use of Caucasian models in its advertisements (arguably the most visible aspect of Jockey's differentiation and a clever play on the world view of many Indians) but also Page's consistent focus on ensuring that it delivers a differentiated product which is upgraded year after year to provide comfort, durability and affordability with fresh designs.

In order to ensure the sustainability of its competitive edge, Page relies on in-house manufacturing and an exclusive distributor-based approach (rather than the outsourced manufacturing and wholesale-driven distribution model followed by peers like Rupa and Maxwell).

As a result, Page has left its rivals far behind (Page's revenues in FY15 were 1.5 times that of Rupa and five times that of Maxwell) and, in the process, created one of the most successful consumer brands in India. Over the period FY09–15, Page's revenues grew at a robust 35 per cent CAGR, far ahead of the median growth for the industry (which includes Rupa, Lux, Maxwell and Lovable).

Case Study 3: HDFC Bank

'(ICICI Bank and HDFC Bank) are as different as chalk and cheese in their approach to banking. ICICI Bank is flamboyant, innovative and quick as a flash when it comes to seizing an opportunity. HDFC Bank is staid and waits for opportunities but emerges a winner at the end of the day.'— Tamal Bandyopadhyay, *A Bank for the Buck* (2013).

The above passage from veteran journalist Bandyopadhyay encapsulates HDFC Bank's consistent focus on profitability over growth (see Exhibit 120). HDFC Bank has differentiated itself from its peers through its strategic focus on building a granular, low-cost franchise along with a market-leading position in most retail products since its early years. Over the last twenty years, the bank has taken a longer-term approach to protecting its margins and asset quality rather than pursuing a near-term aggressive growth (such as infra financing/project finance during the 2004–10 bull run in India).

Exhibit 120: HDFC Bank has demonstrated superior profitability with low risk as compared to peers

	Period	HDFC Bank	ICICI Bank	Axis Bank
Net Interest Margins	FY11-15	4.44%	2.95%	3.27%
Stressed Assets as a % of Loan Book	1QFY16	1.05%	6.86%	4.48%

(*Contd*)

	Period	HDFC Bank	ICICI Bank	Axis Bank
Avg. ROAs	FY11-15	1.77%	1.59%	1.66%
Avg. ROEs	FY11-15	19.28%	12.50%	18.67%
EPS CAGR	FY10-15	27%	22%	20%

Source: Company, Ambit Capital research.

This single-minded focus on maximizing profitability goes back to HDFC Bank's origins. It started its operations as a corporate bank but soon realized that the profit margins to be earned from serving AAA-rated blue-chip corporates were modest at best. Hence, over the years, HDFC Bank started lending to small suppliers of these corporates to enhance its profitability. Eventually, it also entered into retail lending to maximize its profitability. Even within retail lending, HDFC Bank has consciously sought to identify specific niches, such as two-wheelers, where it could lend more profitably than others.

As Bandyopadhyay says in his book: 'In many segments, HDFC Bank learns patiently from the experiences of others before it steps into a new business, whereas ICICI Bank loves playing the pioneer. ICICI Bank is volatile; HDFC shares are range-bound. The same applies to earnings. ICICI Bank is often unpredictable, both surprisingly and shockingly. HDFC Bank is monotonously predictable on most financial parameters.'

For example, during the pre-Lehman days when most lenders were aggressively chasing personal loans and credit cards, HDFC Bank was relatively less active in these segments. After huge losses in these segments in 2009, many lenders withdrew from this segment. However, this was the time when the bank sensed opportunity in the segment and made an aggressive foray into credit cards. Now, it is the market leader in the segment.

In a 2005 interview[22] to rediff.com, Paresh Sukhtankar, then head, credit and market risk, at HDFC Bank (and now deputy managing director) said, 'Although the asset yields may have been lower, we were able to cross-sell products so that the overall returns were better. We may have grown slower than our peers, but the risks were lower.' This approach exemplifies the bank's method of choosing safer bets with lower risks and sticking to its core beliefs instead of expanding in unchartered areas purely to chase growth.

Theme B: Constantly deepen the moat around the core franchise by using IBAS

The second common theme that makes the first-amongst-equals companies stand apart is the use of technology to improve internal efficiencies and an obsession with cost control. By obsessively using technology and talent to improve on internal processes and efficiencies, these companies put considerable distance between themselves and the competition. In particular, this focus on efficiency and cost reduction helps the champion companies sustain high levels of profitability in a way that most of their rivals simply cannot match.

As Kay, the economist and *Financial Times* columnist, writes in his seminal book, *The Foundations of Corporate Success* (1993): 'Often the question, "Why will we be better at doing that than other people?" will have a clear and

---

[22] http://www.rediff.com/money/2005/jun/14spec.html.

affirmative answer, and it is typically those firms that can give that answer and act on it that are successful.'

In *The Halo Effect* (2007), Rosenzweig says: 'The task of strategic leadership is to gather appropriate information and evaluate it thoughtfully, then make choices that, while risky, provide the best chance for success in a competitive industry setting.'

Failure to create and sustain moats using technology will result in loss of market share to industry leaders and, eventually, severe losses in the core business. As an example of this crippling loss, I reproduce a quote from Captain Gopinath, founder of Air Deccan, which was eventually sold to Kingfisher Airlines in spite of being the pioneering low-cost carrier (LCC) in India. In his book, *Simply Fly* (2012), Gopinath laments: 'Given a little more time, Deccan could have weathered the storm and overcome the cash crunch but time was running out. I might have pulled it off had my IT system not collapsed. We had to bear in mind the welfare of four thousand employees; the public insurance funds and retail investors we had to answer to.'

This is not to say that each and every strategy conceived by the seven companies profiled in this book is a guaranteed success. However, these companies—as a matter of routine— learn from their mistakes and build internal environments that foster technological improvement alongside cost control. This attitude, in turn, sustains and strengthens their competitive moats.

Case Study 1: Asian Paints

'It is the task of leadership to create and nurture an environment in which a multitude of talented minds work in harmony so that mutual competence is reinforcing rather than debilitating.'—Champaklal Choksey (2 August 1997).

Asian Paints is India's leading decorative paints company with a dominant market share. Formed by four promoter families, of which one (the Chokseys) sold out in 1997, the company's three other promoter families (Danis, Choksis and Vakils) have kept away from the limelight over the past twenty years.

Discussions with veterans in the paint industry reveal two key features that drive Asian Paint's success and explain how it maintains and strengthens its moat:

a) **Hands-off approach by promoters after recruiting top talent:** As a veteran investor, who has seen Asian Paints grow from the time it went public in 1982, told us, 'Asian Paints is a meritocracy and what many people don't appreciate is that Asian Paints employs some of the best managerial talent in India.' Talent is discovered, rewarded and promoted consistently within the company. Asian Paints has hired only from the top five business schools of the country, especially the IIMs in Ahmedabad and Kolkata. In fact, Asian Paints is a Day-Zero company in both of these business schools, i.e. it gets the chance to pick the best talent in the best business schools in the country. This talent is then assiduously nurtured within the company, a point made by several people who know the company well:

- 'Out of 100 people in Asian Paints, if one person is not a cultural fit, he would be easily visible as a misfit as the remaining ninety-nine would be very similar to each other,' says an ex-employee of Asian Paints who left the firm in 2003.

- 'Their internal reporting standards and processes are the best in class. Accountability levels are very high,' says another ex-employee of Asian Paints who left the firm in 2006.
- 'The promoters treat their employees, as well as their distributors, exceedingly well. In fact, the promoters go over and beyond the call of duty in helping out its employees and distributors in times of need,' opines an ex-employee who worked at Asian Paints from 1982 to 1994.
- 'Asian Paints's ex-employees go on to lead companies. Examples are Abhijit Roy (CEO, Berger Paints), Sanjeev Aga (former CEO, Idea Cellular),' says a veteran investor who has seen Asian Paints grow from the time it went public in 1982.

b) **Focus on technology:** Amongst all the paint companies in India, Asian Paints most effectively capitalized on the concept of colour-tinting machines and thus helped save costs for their dealers. The machines effectively reduced SKUs with a dealer (thus lowering his working capital requirements), whilst increasing the choice of colours for customers. Through the years, the company has intensely focused on using technology to help reduce costs and drive efficiencies. The result of these efforts is evident in the sustained revenue growth and consistent ROCEs delivered by the company (see Exhibit 121).

Exhibit 121: Asian Paints's revenue growth and ROCE over the last 20 years

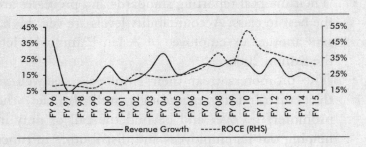

Source: Company, Ambit Capital research.

As market strategy consultant, Rama Bijapurkar, who is a long-standing board member of many of India's leading companies, says, 'I have observed them (Asian Paints) for thirty years and all through this period, they have obsessed about hiring the best people, about having the best IT and the smartest technology-driven process. They started obsessing about talent and technology way before anybody else in India. They would ask the same questions of themselves, of their people and of their consultants year after year, and they relentlessly focused on improving all aspects of their execution.'

Maintaining healthy relationships with employees, dealers and consultants goes a long way in building the 'architecture' aspect of Kay's IBAS framework. Kay defines architecture as a network of relational contracts within or around the firm. Firms may establish these relationships with and among their employees (internal architecture), with their suppliers or customers (external architecture), or among a group of firms engaged in related activities (networks).

Similarly, focusing on technology builds on the 'innovation' aspect of the IBAS framework. Both of these are critical in building and sustaining Asian Paints's brand over the year.

Case Study 2: Astral Poly Technik

'As I planned to enter into plastics, I decided against entering PVC, given the multiple players in the sector. Instead, I chose CPVC for which I travelled to the USA and stayed there for a few months to learn the product and then launched an industrial CPVC product. When we were a small company (Rs 25 crore), we started branding to effectively compete with the stalwarts for building awareness with not only intermediaries but also with end-consumers. Alongside that, we started plumber meets for training them on how to use CPVC product.'—Sandeep Engineer, promoter, Astral Poly.

Astral Poly Technik is one of India's leading plastic pipe companies with leadership in CPVC pipes. Astral was incorporated by Engineer, a chemical engineer, in 1996, when he first entered into a relationship with B.F. Goodrich (which later became Lubrizol, a company owned by Warren Buffett), a leading CPVC player and a patent holder in CPVC resin technology.

My discussions with industry participants suggest that the company's high ROCE-generating rapid growth in the last decade has been driven by innovation in products, in branding and in processes; business architecture built around strong reach; and connect and strategic relationships which have helped in innovation.

a) **Focus on launching novel products:** Since its inception, Astral has continuously launched new products at regular intervals not only in CPVC but also in the otherwise very established market for PVC plumbing systems. Today, Astral is the only licensee of Lubrizol to manufacture and sell all four brands of Lubrizol (Corzan, FlowGuard, Blazemaster and Bendable). In fact, for one Lubrizol brand—Bendable—Astral is the only licensee. Apart from its relationship with Lubrizol, Astral has entered into relationships with multiple players (Wavin, Spears, IPSC, Hunter and Harvell), from across the developed world for various products and then commenced manufacturing of the same. In fact, over the last few years, Astral's key competitor, Supreme Industries, has commenced manufacturing of products once Astral announced its entry (CPVC, CPVC-based fire sprinkler, noise-free pipes).

Pankaj Kajaria, a Mumbai-based pipes dealer for Astral as well as other companies such as Supreme and Prince Pipes, attributes the success of CPVC in India to Astral. Kajaria said, 'Astral's branding is the most aggressive. Astral knows how to catch hold of the right intermediaries. They have good-quality products and have created a great brand by conducting frequent meetings with dealers and plumbers. Astral has created a lot of buzz in the industry. People look forward to new launches from them.'

b) Branding—first pipes company with a big-budget branding campaign: Prompted by a dealer's comment, 'Unless someone asks for your product (CPVC) or your brand (Astral), I will not market or store your product,' Engineer broke away from his peers and started investing in small-scale branding fifteen years ago. Later, in FY05, Astral took its brand nationwide to attract more distributors. It hired Mudra, a leading advertising agency, for an aggressive advertising campaign. Recalling the move, Engineer says,

'That year, we ploughed our profit of Rs 2.5 crore into branding. I was certain there was a huge replacement market in galvanized iron and we needed a pan-India brand if we had to matter.'

In 2013, Astral used aggressive promotional activities such as co-branding with the popular Bollywood movie, *Dabangg-2*, stadium sponsorships for Sachin Tendulkar's last test-match series and heavy outdoor campaigning nationwide to increase visibility with retail customers. In the pipes sector, Astral currently has one of the highest outlays on publicity (2.2 per cent of sales). According to a Mumbai-based retailer, 'Quality and branding have strengthened Astral's recall with builders/plumbers and this leads to relatively higher sales of Astral's pipes compared to Supreme or Ashirvad.'

Exhibit 122: Astral's branding expenditure expanded at a 48% CAGR over FY07–12

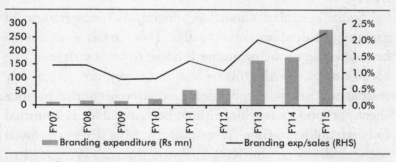

Source: Company, Ambit Capital research.

c) **Process-driven pricing and now automation:** In order to effectively compete against the traditional GI/CI (cast iron) pipes, Astral followed pricing processes to gain customer entry and then demonstrate value before seeking price hikes. For the builders, CPVC or noise-free pipes were sometimes priced lower than the traditional product. Builders and distributors say that pricing was one of the biggest factors of increasing adoption: 'In India, you not only have to give a lower price for a new product but also demonstrate more value, which Astral did,' Kajaria told me.

Astral's innovation in processes continues with increased adoption of automation. The company installed robotic truck-filling machines which not only helped reduce loading time, but more importantly, reduced the likelihood of work getting disrupted.

Theme C: Sensible Capital Allocation

'Good management teams work on proving a concept before investing a lot of capital. They are not likely to put a lot of money in all at once hoping for a big payoff.'— Michael Shearn in *The Investment Checklist* (October 2011).

Sensible capital allocation remains the cornerstone of growing profitably, consistently. This requires a unique bent of mind at the promoter level and this is visible in two specific areas. Firstly, diversifications, if any, are consciously restrained, instead of breaking or stretching the balance sheet. Secondly, surplus cash, when available, is returned to shareholders when it cannot be effectively deployed without dragging the ROCE down sharply. Whilst all of this might sound straightforward, these axioms are rarely implemented by Indian promoters who all too often treat their listed companies as their personal fiefdoms and short-change the minority shareholders. As Rama Bijapurkar told me, 'The standard Indian corporate thinking focuses on the promoter's wealth, not on the shareholders' wealth. The two are not necessarily the same'.

Take, for example, the case of Apollo Tyres, the leader in the domestic truck tyre market. In June 2013, Apollo Tyres decided to buy US-based Cooper Tires, which was nearly twice its size then, at an enterprise value of US$2.5 billion. Moreover, the purchase consideration was to be entirely financed by foreign currency borrowings. As a *Business Standard* article in August 2013 noted,[23] 'The public face of Apollo Tyres for long was Onkar Singh Kanwar, the chairman of the company and Neeraj Kanwar's father. It was Kanwar Senior who battled bankruptcy, labour strife and a series of broken technology pacts with international players to make Apollo Tyres one of India's leading tyre makers. Now, his son wants to take it global. This is where the Cooper acquisition fits in.'

The attempted acquisition was aggressive and over-leveraged, as (a) it would have raised Apollo's consolidated debt-equity to 3.8; and (b) Apollo has had a mixed track record on acquisitions—its 2009 acquisition of Dutch tyre-maker Vredestein was a success but Dunlop South Africa was not measuring up to expectations. No wonder then that Apollo's share price corrected by nearly 31 per cent in the three days after the Cooper announcement. The steep depreciation in the rupee during the months following only added to foreign currency debt concerns. Eventually, Apollo was lucky to find issues (resistance from Cooper's US labour union and its Chinese JV partner) to wriggle out of the deal.

---

[23] http://www.business-standard.com/article/companies/neeraj-kanwar-announces-his-arrival-113082801163_1.html.

Comparing the eight first amongst equal companies with the fifty companies that constitute the benchmark S&P CNX Nifty (or Nifty companies) is instructive as it highlights:

- **Superior cash generation:** The eight companies generate more cash flow from operations (CFO) than the average Nifty company. This superior cash generation is underpinned by high levels of ROCE, and the higher share of this cash flow (in overall sources of cash) also results in stronger balance sheets, reduced reliance on debt and a lower quantum of equity dilution (see Exhibit 123).

Exhibit 123: Nifty companies rely more on debt compared to the first amongst equal (FAE) companies

Sources of cash*	Nifty	FAE
Cash flow from operations	53%	82%
Debt raised	34%	3%
Equity issued	3%	8%
Net cash used	5%	1%
Dividend and interest received	5%	6%
Total	100%	100%

Source: Capitaline, Ambit Capital research.*

Note: For the period FY06-15.

- **Judicious use of funds:** The eight companies are able to plough back funds into their core business and return excess funds to shareholders. As compared to 11 per cent of funds utilized for dividends[24] for Nifty

---

[24] Dividends are, typically, that part of surplus profits that the board of directors pays to its equity shareholders. These are recommended by the board of directors and approved by the shareholders at a company's annual general meeting.

companies, the share of dividend is much higher at 39 per cent for the eight companies. Consequently, hoarding of cash for them is also lower—5 per cent as compared to 9 per cent for Nifty companies (see Exhibit 124).

Exhibit 124: The FAE companies are more shareholder-friendly on dividends than Nifty companies

Application of cash*	Nifty	FAE
Net capex and investments	54%	46%
Debt repayment	18%	3%
Interest paid	7%	2%
Dividend paid	11%	39%
Others	1%	5%
Increase in cash	9%	5%
Total	100%	100%

Source: Capitaline, Ambit Capital research.

Note: *Time period for the above chart is FY06–15.

Here are two case studies demonstrating sensible capital allocations over long periods of time.

Case Study 1: ITC Limited

'Conventional wisdom at that point of time (the 1990s) did not favour diversification as a prudent strategy of growth. However, our confidence in our strategic thrust to create multiple drivers was based on very strong beliefs. For one, we believed that in an emerging economy with huge untapped opportunities, significant growth and success could accrue if diversity were to be managed well through innovative business strategies. Second, we also recognized that diversity could lend unique sources of competitive advantage and growth that we would otherwise not be able to reap if we were present in only one sector.'—Y.C. Deveshwar, ITC chairman, in an interview to Knowledge@ Wharton[25] (2011).

Unlike the companies in this book, ITC has not stuck to its core business of cigarettes. In the past, ITC tried to diversify outside of cigarettes several times into unrelated lines like financial services, IT, hotels, etc. Several other attempts into areas like luxury holidays and golf have been struck down by the board at various times. Despite these attempts, ITC has ensured that its focus on maintaining and growing its leadership in the cigarette industry is never compromised. In fact, its dominance of the organized cigarette industry has actually increased over the past decade, with market share in cigarettes rising to 79 per cent in FY15 from 73 per cent in FY07 (see Exhibit 125).

In comparison to its track record on unrelated diversifications, ITC's track record on acquisitions has been more conservative. It has often resorted to making strategic investments in its competitors though, like in its hotel business where it purchased stakes in East India Hotels and Hotel Leelaventure. Its other acquisitions like Technico (biotech) in FY08 have also been carried out for access to technology for its foods business.

Despite so many diversifications, including its largest and most sustained one into FMCG, how has ITC still delivered ROCEs of more than 15 per cent every year for

25 http://knowledge.wharton.upenn.edu/article/itc-chairman-yogi-deveshwar-creating-a-future-ready-conglomerate/.

Exhibit 125: ITC dominates the cigarette market with nearly 80% market share

Company						Percentage share during			
	FY07	FY08	FY09	FY10	FY11	FY12	FY13	FY14	FY15
ITC	73.1	73.3	79.1	78.0	77.8	77.8	80.1	79.7	79.1
GPI**	12.1	12.7	12.3	13.3	13.1	12.4	11.0	11.0	11.1
VST	8.0	8.2	7.1	7.5	7.9	8.5	7.6	7.9	8.1
PMI (Marlboro)*	0.0	0.0	0.0	0.0	0.2	0.4	0.5	0.6	0.9
Others	6.9	5.8	1.5	1.2	0.9	0.8	0.7	0.7	0.8
Total	100.0	100.0	100.0	100.0	100.0	100.0	100.0	100.0	100.0

Source: Industry sources, Ambit Capital research.

Note: *Since 2009, PMI (Philip Morris International) has licensed GPI to manufacture and distribute Marlboro in India.

**GPI is Godfrey Philip India.

the past decade? There are three reasons for this stellar performance. Firstly, the quantum of unrelated capex has not stressed the balance sheet. Secondly, 50 per cent of cash flow from operations generated over the past decade has been paid out as dividends. And thirdly, about 35 per cent of ITC's cash flow from operations has been deployed towards businesses which have consistently generated very healthy ROCEs (see Exhibit 126).

Exhibit 126: ITC's allocation of cash generated over FY05–15

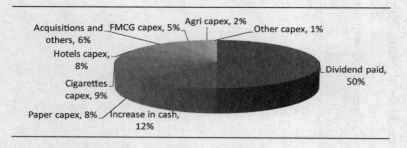

Source: Company, Ambit Capital research.

Case Study 2: Asian Paints

Asian Paints is another example of diversifications without breaking the company's balance sheet. Over the years, the company has forayed into international markets and, within India, in home improvement solutions—both of which are diversifications from the company's large and lucrative domestic paints franchise.

In FY15, Asian Paints's overseas businesses were across the following geographies:

- The Caribbean (Barbados, Jamaica, Trinidad and Tobago),
- The Middle East (Egypt, Oman, Bahrain and the UAE),

- Asia (Bangladesh, Nepal, Sri Lanka, Singapore and Indonesia),
- The South Pacific (Fiji, Solomon Islands, Samoa, Tonga and Vanuatu), and
- Africa (Ethiopia).

Further, Asian Paints also ventured into home improvement solutions with the acquisition of the Sleek Group in 2013 which caters to the organized modern kitchen space. In FY15, Asian Paints acquired the front-end business of Ess Ess, a high-quality player in the bathroom fittings segment. However, the international business foray is far larger than the more recent diversification into the domestic home improvement segment.

Indeed, the international markets were targeted as a major growth driver for the company. Speaking[26] on the acquisition of Berger International (Singapore) and SCIB (Egypt) back in 2002, Jalaj Dani, then head of international operations at Asian Paints and newly appointed chairman of Berger International, said, 'Following the acquisitions this year, we are among the top ten decorative paint companies in the world. The emerging markets have 50 per cent of the world's population and this is where we see the potential upside as we seek to draw more efficiencies out of the acquisitions we have just completed.'

The strategy behind the acquisition was to improve the supply chain management in the subsidiaries by using Asian Paints's well-established domestic track record. As Dani added in the statement above, 'Further, the company will implement cost structures in Berger's operations worldwide for increased

---

[26] http://www.businesswireindia.com/news/news-details/asian-paints-announces-strategy-growth/2314.

plant efficiencies and increased asset productivity. It will focus to improve working capital management through various initiatives and introduce information technology in areas of operations where essential.'

In subsequent years, however, this business has proven to be a drag on Asian Paints's overall balance sheet. The company's capital allocation in overseas business has not borne fruit even after more than a decade of consistent investment. To its credit, Asian Paints has resisted the temptation of pumping in more money and stretching its balance sheet to make the international businesses profitable. Capital employed in international business as a percentage of overall capital employed peaked at 51 per cent in FY06 and has fallen to 26 per cent by FY15. In comparison, the ROCEs of international businesses haven't moved much— from 4.5 per cent in FY06 to 7.6 per cent.

Thus, for the past decade, Asian Paints's track record of capital allocation remains impressive, showing yet again how companies can make unrelated diversifications without breaking their balance sheet or weakening return ratios.

Exhibit 127: Asian Paints—sources of funds over the past decade (FY06–15)

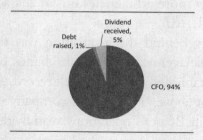

Source: Company, Ambit Capital research.

Exhibit 128: Asian Paints—utilization of funds over the past decade (FY06–15)

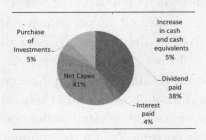

Source: Company, Ambit Capital research.

Summary

The three themes that characterize all eight of our FAE companies are:

- **Theme A:** Focus on the long term (more than ten years) without being distracted by short-term gambles;
- **Theme B:** Constantly deepen the moat around the core franchise using the IBAS (innovation, brands, architecture and strategic assets) framework; and
- **Theme C:** Sensibly allocate capital whilst studiously avoiding betting the balance sheet on expensive and unrelated forays.

Around 99.8 per cent of the listed Indian companies are unable to run their businesses in accordance with these themes not because there is any great mystery associated with the themes but because, as in the highest levels of professional sport, to work hard year after year, in a disciplined manner, with dedication and commitment, is not easy. For that very small minority—0.2 per cent of listed Indian companies—who succeed, the reward is exceptionally strong share price compounding as shown in the next chapter. These companies have, on average, delivered 28 per cent per annum over the last ten years[27] whilst the Sensex has over the same period delivered a mere 14 per cent per annum.

In other words, Rs 100 invested in these companies on 30 June 2005 would have become Rs 1211 by 30 June 2015. In contrast, the same Rs 100 invested in the Sensex on 30 June 2005 would have become Rs 386 by 30 June 2015, implying that the first among equals outperformed the Sensex by a factor of three.

---

[27] I am referring to the period from 30 June 2005 to 30 June 2015.

10

A Checklist for Long-term Investors

'An investment operation is one which, upon thorough analysis, promises safety of principal and an adequate return. Operations not meeting these requirements are speculative.'

—Benjamin Graham, *The Intelligent Investor* (1949)

'The volume and complexity of what we know has exceeded our individual ability to deliver its benefits correctly, safely, or reliably.'

—Atul Gawande, *The Checklist Manifesto: How to Get Things Right* (2009)

As analysts, my community is trained to comprehensively and objectively analyse a company and provide a recommendation to investors to buy or sell that company's stock at its current market price. I routinely study annual reports, read interviews of company promoters, and follow news that affects the

Indian economy and industries. I also have access to some of India's topmost business leaders, and these interactions provide me with a perspective on industries on the Indian economy. These resources—financial accounts, meetings and primary data collection—help me in my work and have also helped me write this book. The distillation of this research and study has thus far focused on the companies that have most often featured in the Coffee Can Portfolios. However, I appreciate that as readers you might not have the same time and resources at your disposal. Hence, to make this book more useful for you (beyond the value of the Coffee Can construct), I have prepared a checklist which is inspired by Atul Gawande, the famous American surgeon, writer and public health researcher.

Writing about checklists in his 2007 column[28] for the *New Yorker*, Gawande spoke of how line infections during surgery were so common that they were considered routine. He went on to give an example of a critical-care specialist who made a simple checklist to address just this one problem of line infections. 'On a sheet of plain paper, he plotted out the steps to take in order to avoid infections when putting a line in. Doctors are supposed to: (1) wash their hands with soap, (2) clean the patient's skin with chlorhexidine antiseptic, (3) put sterile drapes over the entire patient, (4) wear a sterile mask, hat, gown, and gloves, and (5) put a sterile dressing over the catheter site once the line is in. Check, check, check, check, check.' The results were dramatic: in the following years, when results were tracked, the checklist had prevented forty-three infections and eight deaths, and saved US$2 million in costs.

---

[28] http://www.newyorker.com/magazine/2007/12/10/the-checklist.

Investment in stocks is a tough, rigorous and complex process. The checklist that follows is by no means a comprehensive one. Instead, it distils the key lessons from the journeys of the seven companies that you have just read about in the preceding chapters. Before you read this checklist, I must point out that no checklist can be a magic wand that transforms the process of finding valuable stocks into a quick, leisurely exercise. I have met many students, friends and retail investors who are on the lookout for the next ten-bagger, but have no patience to sift through and rigorously analyse companies. For them, this checklist will be of little use! As the great Fidelity fund manager, Peter Lynch, said, 'What distinguishes investment winners, as you'll see in this book, is the willingness to dig deeper, search more widely and keep an open mind to all ideas—including the idea that you might have made a bad call. He or she who turns over the most rocks, looks over the most investment ideas, and is unsentimental about past choices is most likely to succeed.'[29]

Instead, the checklist is designed to help those readers who are genuinely committed to understanding and researching companies. Think of it as a route map that you can use to focus your research efforts better as you go through the journey of understanding and researching a company.

More generally, in the investment management industry and elsewhere, a checklist helps us to stay focused and enforce an effective, objective and thorough decision-making process. Taking another leaf out of Gawande's book, in order to remain simple and practical, my checklist

---

[29] Peter Lynch, in the foreword to Anthony Bolton's book, *Investing Against the Tide* (2009).

focuses only on critical elements. As Gawande writes in *The Checklist Manifesto*, 'Good checklists, on the other hand are precise. They are efficient, to the point, and easy to use even in the most difficult situations. They do not try to spell out everything—a checklist cannot fly a plane. Instead, they provide reminders of only the most critical and important steps—the ones that even the highly skilled professional using them could miss. Good checklists are, above all, practical.'

My checklist is limited to three major heads: industry attractiveness, management quality and competitive advantages. While each of these broad categories, in turn, has numerous subheads within them, I have restricted the checklist to simple questions for the sake of making the material easier to follow.

One last thing to keep in mind is that this is a checklist for evaluating businesses and not stocks. In other words, the aim of this book and this chapter is to help you identify outstanding businesses which have a high probability of producing outstanding results in the long turn. The book is not intended to help you construct speculative trading strategies that will successfully generate short-term returns. Why, you might ask, am I biased towards long-term focused investment strategies?

Whilst there are other successful modes of investing in the equity market—for example, some speculators use share price charts to trade in and out of the stocks over the course of a single day—their ability to deliver sustained market outperformance over long periods of time, (say, three years or more) is unproven in the Indian context.

In more mature markets, such as those found in some developed economies, which have much greater liquidity and greater transparency, short-term trading has been successfully practised over long periods of time by legendary American investors such as George Soros, Julian Robertson and Michael Steinhardt.

However, given that India is the least liquid[30] amongst the world's fifteen largest equity markets, the only viable option open to those who want to deploy large sums of capital successfully is long-term investing. Hence, this book has focused on how a handful of companies have consistently delivered good results over very long periods of time. In doing so, they have created astonishing amounts of wealth for their shareholders.

As Exhibit 129 shows, Rs 100 invested at the end of June 1995 in these companies would have become Rs 7850 by the end of June 2015, implying a compounded rate of return of 24 per cent per annum (in contrast, over the same period the Sensex compounded at 11 per cent per annum). Similarly, Rs 100 invested at the end of June 2005 in these companies would have become Rs 1211 by the end of June 2015, implying a compounded rate of return of 28 per cent per annum (over the same period the Sensex compounded at 14 per cent per annum).

---

[30] Liquidity for a stock is usually measured by how much trading (measured in million US$) takes place in that counter on a daily basis. This is called the Average Daily Value or ADV. ADV: Market Cap is therefore a simple measure of how liquid a stock market is. Most large stock markets have a ratio of around 0.30 per cent, i.e. 0.30 per cent of the market cap is being traded in that market on a daily basis. For India, the corresponding figure, in June 2015, was 0.18 per cent even if we sum up the liquidity on the NSE and the BSE.

Exhibit 129: The first amongst equal (FAE) companies have produced outstanding shareholder returns

Company	Rs 100 invested on 30 June 1995 has become by 30 June 2015 Rs	Annualized return over the 20-year period	Rs 100 invested on 30 June 2005 has become by 30 June 2015 Rs	Annualized return over the 10-year period
Asian Paints	5629	22%	1838	34%
Berger Paints	9086	25%	1046	26%
Marico	NA (since IPO was on 2 May '96)	NA	1841	34%
ITC	3905	20%	569	19%
Astral Poly	NA (since IPO was on 19 Mar '07)	NA	NA (since IPO was on 19 Mar '07)	NA
Page Industries	NA (since IPO was on 15 Mar '07)	NA	NA (since IPO was on 15 Mar '07)	NA
HDFC Bank	12,780	27%	839	24%
Axis Bank	NA (since IPO was on 30 Nov '98)	NA	1133	27%
Equally weighted average	7850	24%	1211	28%

The checklist

Industry attractiveness

Every company operates within an industry in India and, in some cases—like Tata Motors, Tata Steel, Bharti, Infosys—in other countries as well. Each industry has strong and weak points compared to other industries. Thus, the relative attractiveness of the industry that a company belongs to has an important bearing on the company's own fortunes. The first part of my checklist measures the difficulty level of each industry along several dimensions:

- **Is the company's business heavily dependent on government regulation?**
  Many industries in India are heavily regulated. In most cases, this regulation protects the consumer and the government's interests over the company's interests and, in the process, takes away from the producer and redistributes profits in favour of the consumer or the government. In some cases, this regulation provides a monopoly; for example, until recently, mining coal in India was controlled by Coal India, thus providing it with a natural monopoly. Similarly, the return on equity for government-owned power utility companies is regulated by the government—which means that these companies cannot earn any excess returns above stipulated limits.

  In general, public resources are owned and controlled by the government. Unfortunately in India, the allocation of these public resources has also been the subject of intense public debate. Well-known examples include the Comptroller and Auditor General's (CAG's) reports on the mispricing of telecom spectrum in the infamous 2G scam (2009), on Reliance Industries and the dispute over the Krishna–Godavari D6 (KGD6) gas block (2011), and on the grants of coal blocks in the Coalgate scam (2012). Since companies in all of these sectors have suffered from regulatory uncertainty, finding good investments in such heavily regulated sectors is an arduous task compared with sectors which are more lightly regulated such as FMCG or IT.

More generally, consumer goods, automobiles, paints and electrical items can be easily produced and sold in India without any significant government regulation regarding how these goods are priced or distributed to consumers. In contrast, companies in industries with extensive government intervention have less control both on the process of production and on the profits arising from productive activity. Industries with moderate government regulation and minimal intervention are preferable since they are predictable and allow the forces of free markets to play out. In comparison, industries that involve government intervention aren't as predictable, and involve regulatory risk. Examples include industries that deal with public resources such as telecom, energy resources (oil, gas and coal), public utilities (electricity), etc.

- **How many competitors are present in the industry and how strong is the competitive intensity?**
  Other than sectors that require licensing (like banks, media, telecom, etc.), most other industries in India are open to competition, with relatively low barriers to entry. Hence, it is much easier for new entrants to come

in. As new entrants come in, prices drop, competition rises, leading to lower profitability for the companies in that industry. Textiles in India, especially spinning—an activity politicians love to subsidize—is one example of a highly competitive industry.

However, just looking at the number of players may not be the best way to measure competitive intensity. If the industry size itself has a high growth potential, a larger number of players can profitably coexist. For example, companies in the field of pharma and information technology saw rapid growth in the early noughties on the back of rising exports. On the other hand, in a mature, low-growth industry, even a small number of players can dent each other's profitability. For example, in FMCG, price wars have broken out in the past between the top two players in detergents (Hindustan Unilever and Procter & Gamble) and the top two players in hair oil (Hindustan Unilever and Marico). In telecom, new players like Reliance entered the market in 2002 with aggressive mobile tariffs. Companies in intensely competitive industries will experience greater pressure on their profit margins. Hence, the more preferable option is to look for those companies that rise up the ranks to become one of the top two players in that sector. These companies usually are able to build sustainable competitive advantages vis-à-vis the smaller players in the sector. This is demonstrated in the way Asian Paints and Berger Paints have withstood competition from Kansai Nerolac, Akzo Nobel, Shalimar Paints and a host of other companies who have fallen by the wayside.

- **What is the overall size of the industry and its growth potential?**
  Companies in high-growth industries tend to have better prospects than those in mature industries. Sixty-five per cent of India's population of 1.25 billion is below the age of thirty-five. This represents a large market for almost all industries, especially given that economic liberalization in India is less than thirty years old, and thus, ownership of many services and products is still low compared to other emerging markets. For example, car ownership in India is at around sixteen per thousand compared to Brazil which is at around 120 per thousand. In contrast, mobile telephones, for example, have reached near-full penetration in India. In comparison, penetration of consumer durables like air conditioners, cars and washing machines is still low compared to more matured categories like hair oils, soaps, toothpaste, etc (see Exhibits 130 and 131).

Exhibit 130: Personal care products such as soaps, hairoils are amongst sectors with high penetration . . .

Sectors with high penetration	
Sector	Penetration level
Soaps/Detergents	99%
Hair-oils	90%
Toothpaste	85%
Mobile phones*	79%

Source: Ambit Capital research.

Note: *Denotes this is penetration level on a per capita basis, everything else is on a per household basis.

Exhibit 131: . . . ACs, cigarettes and cars on the other hand have low penetration

Sectors with low penetration	
Sector	Penetration level
Two wheelers	9%
Cars	8%
Cigarettes	5%
Air-conditioners	5%

Source: Ambit Capital research.

Note: The penetration levels above are on a per capita basis.

Even in mature industries, growth potential exists in the form of moving up the value chain—for example, from voice to data in telecoms, from standard definition to high definition in Direct-to-Home broadcasting, from hatchbacks to sedans in cars, etc. Thus, identifying the growth potential within the industry is important. An example of how one can use back-of-the-envelope calculations to get a broad sense of growth potential is given in the example below which focuses on the two-wheeler sector:

The cumulative sales for motorcycles, scooters and mopeds in India over the last ten years have been around 109 million units. Dividing this by India's total population of around 1.3 billion in 2015 suggests the two-wheeler penetration in India is somewhere close to 9 per cent.

As you can see in Exhibit 132, developed countries have a much lower two-wheeler penetration level as compared to developing countries. In developed markets such as the USA, Japan and Germany, two-wheeler penetration levels are lower at 3–9 per cent. On the other hand, in developing countries, the two-wheeler penetration levels are higher, particularly in China and the East Asian countries like Indonesia (26 per cent), Vietnam (32 per cent) and Thailand (29 per cent).

Plotting this on a chart shows that as a Third World country gets richer, two-wheeler penetration steadily increases. That, in turn, suggests that India's two-wheeler penetration should continue to rise for some time to come.

Exhibit 132: Significant divergence in two-wheeler penetration levels across different countries

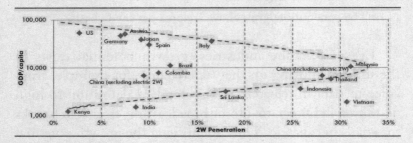

Source: Industry, Ambit Capital research (first published in December 2015).

Yet, at the same time, one must consider that an industry with large opportunity is also likely to attract more competition. The balance between these two contrasting factors, industry potential and competitive intensity must be weighed to determine the opportunity available to the firm in question.

- **Is the company in an industry where the proportion of value addition is high?**
  In simple words, value addition is the difference between the value of raw materials and the value of finished

goods; it is the value of the manufacturing and marketing processes that a company uses to convert raw materials into a finished product that it sells under its brand name to the final consumer. Using the previous example of the textile industry, initial processes that involve converting cotton into a fabric including spinning, weaving and knitting are low value-addition processes, while the eventual step of branding and retailing a ready-made garment like a shirt is a higher value-addition process. In general, a company's profitability increases as it moves up the value-addition chain. As pointed out in the preceding subsection, such a company is also able to deal with competitive intensity more effectively. So, why then are only a small minority of firms in any given sector able to generate more value addition than their competitors? I will delve further into this in the third subsection under the checklist.

- **What is the capital intensity and capital efficiency of the industry?**
  Every industry has different requirements of capital. For example, an FMCG company outsources manufacturing of its products to contract manufacturers and adds value via branding, distribution and reach. An FMCG company thus invests more in its brand than in its plants and machinery. This is different compared to, say, a steel company that needs to buy land, mines, invest in machinery, etc. to manufacture and sell its products. Thus, some industries have significantly higher capital requirements than others. These requirements can be either for working capital or for capital expenditure (buildings, equipment, machinery, etc.). In general, given

India's high cost of capital, higher capital requirements translate into lower return on capital, implying lower capital efficiency. No wonder then that lower-capital-intensive companies like those in the consumer staples sector enjoy much better return ratios than, say, companies in the capital goods space. As I have highlighted in Chapter 1, research shows that companies with higher ROCEs have generated better stock price returns.

- **Is the industry's business dependent on India's broader economic cycle?**
  A company or an industry is called cyclical when its main business is closely linked with the overall economic growth of the country where it operates. As GDP growth rises, so does production, employment and incomes. This increases demand for products. Conversely, when GDP growth stalls, it drags down production, employment and incomes. Sectors like airlines, cement, metals, infrastructure, housing, banking and finance are examples of cyclical industries. On the other hand, industries like consumer staples, information technology and pharmaceuticals are comparatively immune to economic cycles. Given that these companies are more immune, they carry the promise of relatively stable financial performance year after year and investors are usually willing to ascribe premium valuations to these firms. Measured in terms of Price-to-Earnings[31] (more

---

[31] The P/E ratio is a very popular valuation method to measure and compare stocks versus their earnings. The ratio is a number arrived at by dividing a company's current stock price (P) and its earnings per share (E—which could be trailing or forecasted earnings). A high P/E indicates, among other things, higher earnings growth

popularly known as P/E), the pharmaceuticals, consumer staples and IT sectors traded at an average P/E of twenty-seven times FY16 earnings, compared to eighteen times, which is the average of the remaining sectors (namely, telecom, industrials, financials, utilities, energy and consumer discretionary).

- **Does the business generate excess returns for shareholders?**
  The first section of my checklist wraps up with a quick quantitative check: measure the average ROCE for the companies in an industry and compare it with the cost of capital (see Exhibit 133). In India, a safe estimate for cost of capital—as explained in Chapter 1—is 15 per cent. This is derived from the sum of (a) the long-term risk-free rate, which is about 8 per cent (derived from the ten-year government bond yield which is considered as the safest investment since the sovereign rarely defaults); and (b) the country risk premium for India, which is around 7 per cent. If, after averaging across the companies in an industry and averaging over the past ten years, you find that the industry's ROCE is above 15 per cent, that should be viewed as a relatively positive indicator of the industry's health, even if there are doubts on all the questions raised above.[32]

---

potential. Industry P/E ratios are calculated by dividing the total market capitalization of all the companies in an industry with the total of their earnings.

[32] The reason for calculating the industry ROCE using data from the previous ten years is that it will help you adjust the ups and downs of a typical economic cycle which lasts for around ten years.

Exhibit 133: FY15 ROCEs for each of the BSE Sensex sectors*

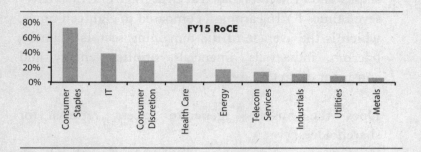

Source: Bloomberg, Capitaline, Ambit Capital research.

Note: *Sector classification is based on GICS Sector Classification. The above exhibit does not include the 'Financials' sector, given that it is not directly comparable to the other sectors. According to GICS Sector Classification, Tata Steel and Asian Paints are clubbed under the 'Materials' sector. Given their distinct nature of businesses, for the purpose of this exhibit, I have classified Asian Paints as belonging to the 'Consumer discretionary' sector and Tata Steel as belonging to the 'Metals' sector. Sector ROCEs have been calculated based on free-float mcap (or the market capitalization of each company based on its readily available shares in the market) weights for each of the sector constituents as on 8 February 2016.

Management quality

While industry attractiveness is an important starting point in evaluating your investment in a company, the single most important factor in evaluating a business is the quality of its management. Good management teams will not only see through the various challenges facing an industry and navigate through them, they also transform their business models towards more attractive industries. There is more to management quality than good articulation and impressive educational degrees. In this second part of my checklist, I describe the key factors which I reckon make or break the quality of a management team.

- **Does the management have a track record of good governance and clean accounting?**

  For a listed company, there are two types of shareholders: the promoters who own control of the company and the remaining non-promoter shareholders termed as minority shareholders, which include retail and institutional investors. The board of directors of any listed company must include promoters as well as independent (i.e. unrelated to the promoters) directors who are responsible for major decisions like approving dividends, large capital expenditure, mergers, compensation for the senior executives, etc. While such decisions tend to be rubber-stamped in the annual general meetings, the day-to-day operations are run by promoters along with managers hired by them. Thus, the process of running a company involves balancing relationships and interests between the board, the promoters, the management, minority shareholders, auditors as well as other stakeholders like employees and the government. This intricate balancing act is called corporate governance.

  For a listed company to be viewed positively by the broader stock market, it should adhere to the highest standards of corporate governance. For example, since minority shareholders have no say in how a company is run, the board should protect their interests. Often this isn't the case as promoters can coerce the board to take decisions that benefit them at the cost of minority shareholders—for example, indulging in transactions with unlisted companies owned by the promoters. One of the most high-profile examples of these transactions was in January 2014 when the board of Maruti Suzuki approved the expansion of its Gujarat plant through a 100 per cent Suzuki subsidiary. Doing this would short-change the minority shareholders of Maruti, since the benefits of the plant would flow directly to Suzuki. Maruti's stock price declined by over 8 per cent on the day of the announcement of the project (28 January 2014) and in the months that followed, institutional investors opposed the proposal.

By now, I am sure you are wondering, 'How do I know that a company is following high standards of corporate governance?' The answer is simple: Start from the annual report. It includes the director's report, the auditor's report, the profit and loss, balance sheet and cash flow statements, and also a section on corporate governance.

At Ambit, my colleagues have spent a considerable amount of time and resources in establishing the link between accounting quality and shareholder returns. In companies where minority shareholders are being short-changed, the financial statements will be rosier than the underlying performance of the business. Therefore, taking reported financials at face value is the most common and perhaps the most damaging mistake investors make. To put this simply: companies which have high-quality accounts also tend to be companies which have high-quality management. These stocks tend to do significantly better than those with inferior management, whose accounts often tend to be dodgy. My colleagues' analysis proves this thesis.[33] Deciles constructed on the basis of accounting scores (which are in turn based on Ambit's forensic accounting model—summarized in Exhibit 134) show a tight link with share price performance. Stocks in the top decile (i.e. the top 10 per cent of BSE500 stocks on accounting quality) outperformed stocks in the bottom decile (i.e. the bottom 10 per cent) by a whopping 39 per cent CAGR over the six-year period (FY10–15) covered in this study.

Exhibit 134: Decile-level analysis points to a strong link between accounting scores and stock price performance

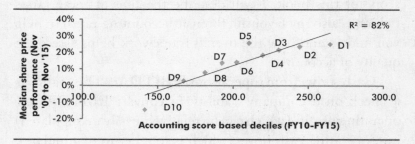

Source: Bloomberg, Ace Equity, Capitaline, Ambit Capital research.

Note: Accounting score is based on annual financials over FY10–15; stock price performance is from November 2009 to November 2015 on a CAGR basis. Universe for this exhibit is BSE500 (ex-financials).

Whilst a solid set of financial statements cannot act as a guarantee against a board hell-bent on taking decisions

---

[33] http://reports.ambitcapital.com/reports/Ambit_Strategy_AccountingThematic_AreyouintheZoneofDarkness_17Dec2015.pdf.

against minority shareholders, these audited financial statements, however, remain the strongest check. Over time, the behaviour of promoters and the board and their efforts in shoring up corporate governance show up in how they run the firm and how the promoter writes his chairman's report. You can read the chapters on Marico and Asian Paints to find out how the promoters have ceded management control to top-notch professional talent; together these teams have taken decisions such as increasing dividend payouts to favour all shareholders and not just the promoters. While each sector would have its own set of metrics to assess accounting quality, I present a generic framework below that my colleagues at Ambit use to assess accounting quality for corporate India (see Exhibits 135).

While a full description of this framework is beyond the scope of this book, I will describe the first of these ratios (which is also my favourite forensic accounting ratio) to help you understand how the overall framework helps assess the quality of accounts.

Cash flow from operations/EBITDA: This ratio is a check on a company's ability to convert EBITDA, i.e. operating profits (which can be relatively easily manipulated) into operating cash flows (which is tougher to manipulate). For example, a firm might be inclined to meet its annual targets by pushing inventory in the channel, i.e. with distributors, dealers, etc., without the quantity actually being sold to the end-consumer. While this inventory will reflect in revenues, operating profit and net profit numbers, to the extent that the quantity hasn't actually been sold to the customer there will not be commensurate cash flow. Such a firm will have lower cash flow from operations EBITDA ratio compared to a firm where the sales have actually materialized to the end consumer. A lower number on this ratio therefore is a red flag and warrants deeper scrutiny. Using eleven such parameters, Ambit's analysts grade-listed companies on the basis of accounting quality relative to each other.

- **Do the owners of the company have connections to political parties?**
  The politician–corporate nexus model isn't new in India. However, this model went into overdrive during 2004–10. During these years, connectivity to politicians formed the basis of success for several companies. Such firms also did well in terms of stock-market performance. However, the Comptroller and Auditor General's report on spectrum allocation in October 2010 marked an inflection point; after that landmark report, share prices of such politically connected corporates began underperforming. At Ambit, my colleagues have maintained a Connected Companies Index consisting of seventy-five companies drawn from the BSE500. This index highlights the underperformance of politically connected companies (see Exhibit 136).

  The old, crony capitalist model of politicians and businessmen doing each other favours has become unsustainable in India. Investors, therefore, need to carefully evaluate firms, especially in highly regulated sectors, so that they can steer clear of companies where the promoter's proximity to politicians is the core driver of success.

Exhibit 135: Key categories of accounting checks

Category	Ratios	Rationale
P&L misstatement checks	Cash flow from operations/ EBITDA	Check on a firm's revenue recognition (or the accounting rule used to record revenues in financial statements) policy; a low ratio may be indicative of aggressive revenue recognition practices
	Unusual fluctuation in depreciation rate from year to year	Penalize firms where volatility in depreciation rate is unusually high
	Volatility in Non-operating Income (or NOI, such as income from investments, rent, etc.) (as a percentage of net revenues)	Penalize firms where volatility in NOI is unusually high, as this could imply intent to inflate profitability in years of low profits by resorting to such means as sale of assets, investments, and so on
	Provisioning for doubtful debts as a proportion of debtors more than six months	Check on a firm's debtor provisioning policy; a low ratio raises concerns regarding earnings being boosted through aggressive provisioning practices

(Contd)

Category	Ratios	Rationale
Balance sheet misstatement checks	Cash yield	A low cash yield may either imply balance sheet misstatement or that the cash is not being used in the best interests of the firm
	Change in reserves (excluding share premium) to net income excluding dividends	A ratio of less than 1 may denote direct knock-offs from equity
	Contingent liability as a proportion of net worth	Indicative of the extent of off-balance-sheet risk
Pilferage checks	Miscellaneous expenses as a proportion of total revenues	Check on a firm's expenditure policy; a high ratio raises concerns regarding the authenticity of such expenses
	Capital work in progress (CWIP) to gross block	A high CWIP to gross block ratio could either indicate unsubstantiated capex or delay in commissioning
	Cumulative cash flow from operations plus cash flow from investments to median revenues	Check on whether the firm has historically been able to generate positive cash flows after investing activities
Audit quality checks	CAGR in auditors' remuneration to CAGR in consolidated revenues	Check on the audit quality; ideally growth in auditors' remuneration should be consistent with growth in consolidated revenues

Source: Ambit Capital research.

Exhibit 136: Ambit's Connected Companies Index has underperformed the BSE500 Index since the publication of the CAG report

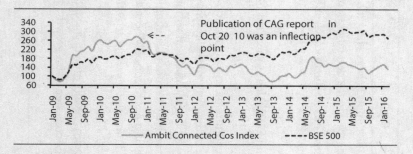

Source: Bloomberg, Ambit Capital research. Note: Both Ambit's Connected Companies Index and BSE500 have been rebased to 100 at the beginning of 2009. This chart has been updated until 1 February 2016.

- **Does the company have a strong track record of efficient capital allocation?**

    Capital allocation is perhaps the single most important decision through which a management adds value to a company's shareholders. Several promoters realize this and hire top-quality executives to run the business on a day-to-day basis, thus freeing themselves to focus solely on identifying the next best opportunity to allocate the firm's capital. However, effective capital allocation is not just about growing but growing profitably. While management teams have a natural desire for growth and scale, growth creates shareholder value only when the returns on capital exceed the cost of capital. ROCE, therefore, is of utmost importance in assessing a firm's performance. All five companies and the two banks mentioned in this book have stellar records of capital allocation as can be seen in their consistently high ROCEs and ROEs (for banks). No wonder then that these stocks have provided stellar returns.

In fact, my colleagues have shown that ROCE is the single biggest driver for stock prices. When ranked on three categories—superior revenue growth, superior ROCE and both (i.e. superior revenue growth and superior ROCEs)—companies with superior ROCEs beat those with superior revenue growth. Those with both, obviously, provide the highest outperformance as can be seen in Exhibit 137.

Exhibit 137: A combination of superior ROCE and revenue growth is a winner in the Indian context

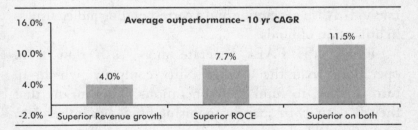

Source: Bloomberg, Ambit Capital research.

Note: The universe is 2005's BSE200 firms (ex-financials); the outperformance is relative to the BSE200 Index. The chart is based on price data from 31 March 2005 to 31 March 2015. Superior ROCE is defined as the top quartile stocks from the BSE200 universe basis their median ROCE over FY05–15. Superior revenue growth is defined as top quartile stocks from the BSE200 universe basis their revenue growth over FY05–15.

Efficient capital allocation requires a unique bent of mind at the promoter level and this is visible in two specific areas: (a) diversifications—if any—are consciously restrained instead of breaking or stretching the balance sheet; and (b) surplus cash, when available, is returned to shareholders in case it cannot be effectively deployed without dragging the ROCE down sharply. In fact, the seven firms highlighted in this book are stellar examples of judicious capital allocation when compared to the broader market.

To explain this further, I'm using data from Chapter 9, wherein my colleagues aggregated the sources of cash generated by Nifty companies and the utilization of this cash by the same companies over the past decade (i.e. FY06–FY15). They also collected the same data for the eight FAE companies. I then compared the two data sets. The results were startling. The FAE companies showed a superior method of cash generation and a corresponding judiciousness in utilization of funds.

Firstly, the FAEs generate more cash flow from operations than the average Nifty company, which, in turn, is used to fund their operations. This means that they do not rely frequently on raising funds (via either debt or equity). This superior cash generation is a key factor for sustaining high levels of ROCEs and also results in stronger balance sheets. For example, while the average Nifty company depends heavily on debt (34 per cent of sources of cash), the average FAE company barely needs debt (3 per cent of sources of cash) largely because the cash generated from its operations is sufficient to fund operations (see Exhibit 138).

Exhibit 138: Nifty companies rely more on debt compared to the FAE companies

Sources of cash*	Nifty	FAE
Cash flow from operations	53%	82%
Debt raised	34%	3%
Equity issued	3%	8%
Net cash used	5%	1%
Dividend and interest received	5%	6%
Total	**100%**	**100%**

Source: Capitaline, Ambit Capital research.*
Note: *For the period FY06–15.

Secondly, the average FAE company is far more judicious when it comes to deploying the cash that's generated. After ploughing back sufficient funds for their core business, the seven companies believe in paying out dividends instead of hoarding cash. Thus during FY06–15, the average FAE company paid back 39 per cent of cash generated to shareholders as compared to 11 per cent for the average Nifty company (see Exhibit 139).

Therefore, while analysing financial statements, you should delve into a company's cash flow statement and pay particular attention to analysing how, over long periods of time, the company is raising and spending cash and the impact this has on ROCE.

As a thumb rule, a company that uses cash from operations to fund its growth is superior to a company that frequently raises funds via debt or equity. Similarly, a company with a track record of returning excess cash to shareholders is superior to a company that believes in hoarding cash and depressing ROCEs.

Exhibit 139: The FAE companies are more shareholder-friendly on dividends than Nifty companies

Application of cash*	Nifty	FAE
Net capex and investments	54%	46%
Debt repayment	18%	3%
Interest paid	7%	2%
Dividend paid	11%	39%
Others	1%	5%
Increase in cash	9%	5%
Total	100%	100%

Source: Capitaline, Ambit Capital research.

Note: *Time period for the above chart is FY06–15.

- **Do the promoters have a track record of remaining focused on their core operations?**
  In his 1996 annual letter to shareholders, Warren Buffett wrote, 'Loss of focus is what most worries Charlie (Munger) and me when we contemplate investing in businesses that in general look outstanding. All too often, we have seen value stagnate in the presence of hubris or of boredom that caused the attention of managers to wander.' In their 2011 book, *Great by Choice*, authors Jim Collins and Morten Hansen gave the example of two people walking from San Diego, California, to the tip of Maine, a journey of 3000 miles.

  The first person walks assiduously at a steady pace of twenty miles per day with focus and discipline, irrespective of good or bad terrain or weather conditions; the second person walks large distances on good days and waits in his tent on days with bad weather—figuring that he would make up for the slack on good days. Eventually, the second walker tires himself out by the time he reaches Kansas City, while the first walker, maintaining his strict discipline, has already reached Maine by then. Collins and Hansen use this example to describe John Brown, the CEO of Stryker Corporation, a Fortune 500 medical technologies firm.

Brown had understood that consistent performance required both parts of a twenty-mile march: 'a lower bound and an upper bound, a hurdle that you jump over and a ceiling that you will not rise above—the ambition to achieve and the self-control to hold back'. Describing what it takes to be a 20 Mile March company, the authors wrote 'To 20 Mile March requires hitting specified performance markers with great consistency over a long period of time. It requires two distinct types of discomfort, delivering high performance in difficult times and holding back in good times.' This steady pace comes only with tremendous focus on your core business and refraining from betting massive amounts of time and resource on unrelated diversification.

I see this discipline in each of the companies mentioned in this book. Even ITC, renowned for its seemingly unrelated forays, has never broken its balance sheet or compromised its near-monopoly in cigarettes to consistently hit 10 per cent revenue growth and 15 per cent ROCE every year for the past decade. Focusing on the core business is directly linked to efficient capital allocation because as soon as the management's focus diverts from its core, it inevitably leads to faulty capital allocation in unrelated diversifications. This seemingly maniacal focus also helps investors to assess whether the promoter group has other listed/unlisted business entities outside the company in question because the existence of many such interests may lead to a dilution in focus. Similarly, within the listed entity, the business interests should be focused; several businesses within the company that are unrelated to the core activity, either product-wise or geography-wise, may act to both dilute management bandwidth and lead to suboptimal capital allocation.

Competitive Advantage

If value added is the difference between the cost of a company's inputs and that of its output, then competitive advantage allows a company to add more value than its rivals. Furthermore, a sustainable competitive advantage enables a company to continue sustaining this extra value addition over long periods of time. Warren Buffett has captured the concept of sustainable competitive advantages more memorably than anyone else by using the metaphor of competitive moats: 'I don't want an easy business for competitors. I want a business with a moat around it. I want a very valuable castle in the middle and I want the duke who is in charge of that castle to be very honest and hard-working and able. Then I want a moat around that castle. The moat can be various things. The moat around our auto insurance business, GEICO, is low cost.'[34]

By their very nature, competitive advantages are difficult to sustain. For example, location is often seen as a key competitive advantage in the retail sector. However, if a particular McDonald's outlet is popular because of its

---

[34] Lecture by Warren Buffett at the University of Florida's School of Business (15 October 1998).

location, there is nothing to stop Burger King from opening a similar outlet in the vicinity. Hence, location is often not a source of sustainable competitive advantage. In fact, companies which possess genuine sustainable competitive advantages are relatively few in number.

John Kay has been my guru when it comes to understanding sustainable competitive advantages. In his 1993 classic, *Foundations of Corporate Success*, Kay uses the IBAS—or innovation, brands and reputation, architecture, strategic assets—framework to analyse a company's competitive advantages. This framework forms the final section of our checklist and can be found in more detail in Appendix 1.

- **What is the company's track record on innovation?**
  Apple's legendary founder, Steve Jobs, said, 'Innovation distinguishes between a leader and a follower.' Apple is renowned for its path-breaking innovative products starting from the Macintosh computers in the 1980s to today's favourites like the iPhones and iPads. The world's most famous prize for manufacturing excellence—the Deming Prize—is named after the American statistician, professor and author, W. Edwards Deming who said, 'Learning is not compulsory . . . neither is survival.'

  While the benefits of innovation are well known and extensively trumpeted in the business press, innovation on its own is the weakest source of sustainable competitive advantage. By its very nature, innovation is expensive, uncertain and hard to manage given the inherent randomness in the nature of the process. Even when the expensive innovation process yields a commercially useful result, the benefits can easily be replicated by competition.

For example, Jenson and Nicholson first introduced colour tinting machines in India, but this was imitated eventually by Asian Paints and Berger Paints. Similarly, tag-less labels in garments—which make the cloth more comfortable to wear, as compared to having tags that tend to itch and scratch the skin—were first introduced by Hanes in the Western world but eventually copied by Jockey. In fact, it was the latter that first brought the concept to India—Page Industries is the exclusive licensee of Jockey in India.

Moreover, employees and innovators who drive the innovation process will either be poached or extract higher compensation. Thus, innovation has to be supported by a very strong architecture (discussed in a subsequent subsection) that encourages the process of innovation over a period of time. Unless innovation becomes a process which a firm lives day in and day out, the firm will appear impressive initially (by having one of two innovative products) and then ultimately disappoint.

- **What is the company's investment in brands and reputation?**
Stephen King, the famous American novelist, author and TV producer, once said, 'A product can be quickly outdated, but a successful brand is timeless.' Brands and reputation are extremely expensive to build, maintain and sustain. However, once built, they are a very powerful source for competitive advantage. Customers use the strength of the company's reputation as a proxy for the quality of the product or the service. Brands and reputations are often built by consumers using the product over a long period. Asian Paints, for example, commands

a premium over its competition. Page Industries' Jockey brand of innerwear sells at a higher price point and is seen as an aspirational brand in India. When analysing a company, look at (a) trends in expenditure on advertising and promotion; (b) trends in the company's market share; and (c) the premium a company's products command relative to similar offerings from competitors.

- **How strong is the company's architecture?**
Kay defines architecture as the network of contracts and relationships that a company has with its employees, suppliers and customers. Within the company, this is more commonly known as work culture. Strong architecture is found in companies with a distinctive organizational style or ethos, because such firms tend to have a well-organized and long-established set of processes or routines for doing business. For example, Asian Paints and Berger Paints are well known for the freedom that the promoters have given to their top management. In turn, their respective CEOs have built a culture of attracting and retaining talent. Similarly, both firms are known for looking after their paint dealers.

How can you assess the strength of architecture? If you have access to management, check the extent to which the employees of the firm cooperate with each other across various departments and locations; also track the extent to which the staff in different parts of the firm give the same message when asked the same question. Secondly, check the rate of staff attrition. This is sometimes given in the annual report and, if it is not, it can be procured from the company. Thirdly, assess the extent to which the firm is able to generate innovations in its products or services or production processes on an ongoing basis. At the core of successful architecture is cooperation (within teams, across various teams in a firm and between a firm and its suppliers) and sharing (of ideas, information, customer insights and, ultimately, rewards). Built properly, architecture allows a firm with ordinary people to produce extraordinary results.

- **Does the company own any strategic assets?**
In contrast to the three distinctive capabilities discussed above, strategic assets are easier to identify as sources of competitive advantages. Examples include intellectual property, licences and regulatory permissions, access to natural resources and natural monopolies. Whilst strategic assets can come in different forms, all of them result in a lower cost per unit of production for the firm owning the asset relative to its competitors. For example, Tata Steel's decades-old access to coal and iron ore from its captive mines allows it to make more money per tonne of steel produced than any other steel manufacturer in India. According to Ambit Capital's analysts, even at the currently subdued domestic steel prices, on a tonne of steel produced, Tata Steel earns EBITDA of Rs 6400 compared to Rs 3450 for JSW Steel and an EBITDA loss for SAIL.

- **Does the company have ROCEs that are higher than the industry average?**
A company's ROCE (measured over a long period of time, say, ten years) can be used as a broad measure of its sustainable competitive advantages. Generally speaking, a firm with ROCEs which are more than 15 per cent (that being our rough guide to the cost of capital) and significantly better than the industry average, is likely to

have sustainable competitive advantages. For example, Asian Paints's ROCE, at an average of 36 per cent over the past decade, is much higher than that of the paints industry (of listed companies), whose average is 21 per cent.

The Final Checklist

Industry Attractiveness

- Is the company's business heavily dependent on government regulation?
- How many competitors are present in the industry and how strong is the competitive intensity?
- What is the overall size of the industry and its growth potential?
- Is the company in an industry where the proportion of value addition is high?
- What is the capital intensity and capital efficiency of the industry?
- Is the industry's business dependent on India's overall economic cycle?
- Does the business generate excess returns for shareholders?

I look for industries which are relatively free of regulation, low on competitive intensity and growing at double-digit rates (examples include heavy trucks, cars, speciality chemicals). Such industries usually tend to have a small number of relatively large companies and in such situations, the top two players in that industry are usually able to generate ROCEs in excess of the cost of capital.

Management Quality

- Does the management have a track record of good governance and clean accounting?

- Do the owners of the company have connections to political parties?
- Does the company have a strong track record of efficient capital allocation?
- Do the promoters have a track record of remaining focused on their core operations?

I look for management teams which maintain a clean set of accounts and allow genuinely independent directors (who can look after the interest of minority shareholders) to sit on the board. I look for promoters who are humble, hard-working, self-aware of their limitations and are focused on the well-being of their business. I am keen to avoid promoters who build business relationships with politicians.

Competitive Advantage

- What is the company's track record on innovation?
- What is the company's investment in brands and reputation?
- How strong is the company's architecture?
- Does the company own any strategic assets?
- Does the company have ROCEs that are higher than the industry average?

I look for companies which can sustainably drive ROCEs in excess of 15 per cent and in excess of the industry average by deriving sustainable competitive advantages from: (a) a culture of innovation; (b) strong brands; (c) architecture, i.e. unique relationships between people within the firm and/or between the firm and its suppliers or customers; and (d) strategic assets such as intellectual property, physical property or licences.

APPENDIX 1

John Kay's IBAS Framework[35]

'No formula in finance tells you that the moat is twenty-eight feet wide and sixteen feet deep. That's what drives the academics crazy. They can compute standard deviations and betas, but they can't understand moats. Maybe I'm being too hard on the academics.'

—Warren Buffett[36]

Sustainable competitive advantages allow firms to add more value than their rivals and to continue doing so over long

---

[35] Some of this material originally appeared in Ambit Capital Research's thematic report, 'On the Cusp of GREATNESS', dated 14 July 2014. I have also written about John's work in some of my columns which appear in the media e.g. http://www. moneycontrol.com/news/features/3-bookschanged- ambit-ceo-saurabh-mukherjeas- life_1157700.html.

[36] http://www.thebuffett.com/quotes/How-to-Think-About-Businesses.html#i92.

periods of time. But where do these competitive advantages come from? And why is it that certain firms seem to have more of these advantages than others? Although I started thinking about these questions when I was studying undergraduate economics at the London School of Economics (LSE), I simply did not have the necessary experience or perspective at that stage to be able to answer these questions. It was my great fortune that, thanks to a recommendation from my professors at the LSE, on a crisp, spring day in 1998, I went for a day of interviews with a consultancy firm called London Economics.

London Economics was founded by John Kay to advise companies on how to use the basic principles of microeconomics to enhance profitability in a sustainable manner. I worked in John's firm for two years and then, a few years later, co-founded an equity research firm in the UK, Clear Capital, where John became the chairman and a shareholder. His mode of thinking about the world in general and about sustainable competitive advantage in particular helped me make sense of the world. So what exactly does Kay say and why is it so useful?

In his 1993 book, *Foundations of Corporate Success*, Kay states that 'sustainable competitive advantage is what helps a firm ensure that the value that it adds cannot be competed away by its rivals'. He goes on to state that sustainable competitive advantages can come from two sources: distinctive capabilities or strategic assets. Whilst strategic assets can be in the form of intellectual property (patents and proprietary know-how), legal rights (licences and concessions) or a natural monopoly, the distinctive capabilities are more intangible in nature.

Distinctive capabilities, says Kay, are those relationships that a firm has with its customers, suppliers or employees, which cannot be replicated by other competing firms and which allow the firm to generate more value additions than its competitors. He further divides distinctive capabilities into three categories:

- Brands and reputation
- Architecture
- Innovation.

Let us delve into these in more detail, as understanding them is at the core of understanding the strength of a company's franchise.

Brands and reputation

> 'A product can be quickly outdated, but a successful brand is timeless.'
>
> —Stephen King, American novelist, author and TV producer

> 'Reputations are created in specific markets. A reputation necessarily relates to a product or a group of products. It is bounded geographically, too. Many reputations are very local in nature. The good plumber or doctor neither has nor needs a reputation outside a tightly defined area. Retailing reputations are mostly national. But an increasing number of producers of manufactured goods, from Coca-Cola to Sony, have established reputations worldwide, and branding has

> enabled international reputations to be created
> and exploited for locally delivered services in
> industries as diverse as accountancy and car hire.'

—John Kay[37]

In many markets, product quality, in spite of being an important driver of the purchase decision, can only be ascertained by a long-term experience of using that product. Examples of such products are insurance policies and healthcare. In many other markets, the ticket price of the product is high; hence, consumers are only able to assess the quality of the product after they have parted with their cash. A few examples of such products would be cars and high-end TVs.

In both these markets, customers use the strength of the company's reputation as a proxy for the quality of the product or the service. For example, people gravitate towards the best hospital in town for critical surgery and tend to prefer world-class brands whilst buying expensive home entertainment equipment. Since the reputation for such high-end services or expensive equipment takes many years to build, reputation tends to be difficult and costly to create. This, in turn, makes it a very powerful source for a competitive advantage.

For products that are used daily, investors tend to be generally aware of the strength of a firm's brand. In more niche products or B2B products (e.g. industrial cables, mining equipment, municipal water purification and semiconductors), investors often do not have first-hand knowledge of the key brands in the relevant market. In such instances, to assess the strength of the brand, they turn to:

---

[37] http://www.johnkay.com/1993/06/01/the-structure-of-strategy-business-strategy-review-1993.

- Brand recognition surveys conducted by the trade press.
- The length of the warranties offered by the firm (the longer the warranties, the more unequivocal the statement it makes about the firm's brand).
- The amount of time the firm has been in that market (e.g. 'Established 1915' is a fairly credible way of telling the world that since you have been in business for over a century, your product must have something distinctive about it).
- How much the firm spends on its marketing and publicity (a large marketing spend figure, relative to the firm's revenues, is usually a reassuring sign).
- How much of a price premium the firm is able to charge vis-à-vis its peers.

One way to appreciate the power of brands and reputation to generate sustained profits and, hence, shareholder returns, is to look at how India's most trusted brands, according to an annual *Economic Times* survey, have fared over the last decade. As can be seen from Exhibit 140, over the past decade, the listed companies with the most powerful brands have comfortably beaten the most widely acknowledged front-line stock market index by a comfortable margin on revenues, earnings and share price movement.

In Exhibit 140, I have compared large FMCG companies, their popular brands (with their ranking in a brand survey) with the revenue growth, EPS growth and share price growth associated with them for the past decade. Therefore, HUL, which has six highly ranked brands (Clinic Plus, Lifebuoy, Rin, Surf, Lux, Ponds) has strong revenue growth (12 per cent), EPS growth (14 per cent) and therefore, a stock price growth (21 per cent) that has outperformed the Nifty (15 per cent). To reiterate, companies with huge and successful brands have delivered strong financial returns and also beaten the Nifty over the past decade.

Exhibit 140: Performance of listed companies with the most trusted brands

Sr. No.	Company	Trusted Brands*	Ten-Year Growth (FY05–15) (% CAGR)		
			Revenues	EPS	Share price**
1	Colgate-Palmolive	Colgate (1)	15	17	27
2	Hindustan Unilever	Clinic Plus (4), Lifebuoy (10), Rin (12), Surf (13), Lux (14), Ponds, etc.	12	14	21
3	Nestle	Maggi (9), Nestle Milk Chocolate (62), etc.	16	17	27
4	GSK Consumer	Horlicks (16)	17	24	34
5	Bharti Airtel	Airtel (18)	28	15	14
	Average for the listed companies with the top five brands		**18**	**17**	**25**
	For the index, Nifty		**13**	**11**	**15**

Source: Economic Times and Ambit Capital analysis using Bloomberg data.

Note: *Figures in brackets indicate the rank in the 2012 *Economic Times*'s brand equity survey to find the 100 most trusted brands in India.

**Share price performance has been measured from March 2005 to March 2015.

Architecture

'Architecture is a system of relationships within the firm, or between the firm and its suppliers and customers, or both. Generally, the system is a complex one and the content of the relationships implicit rather than explicit. The structure relies on continued mutual commitment to monitor and enforce its terms. A firm with distinctive architecture gains strength from the ability to transfer firm product and market specific information within the organization and to its customers and suppliers. It can also respond quickly and flexibly to changing circumstances. It has often been through their greater ability to develop such architecture that Japanese firms have established competitive advantages over their American rivals.'

—John Kay[38]

'A dream you dream alone is only a dream. A dream you dream together is reality.'

—John Lennon

Architecture refers to the network of contracts, formal and informal, that a firm has with its employees, suppliers and customers. Thus, architecture would include the formal employment contracts that a firm has with its employees and it would also include the more informal obligation it has to provide ongoing training to its employees. Similarly, architecture would include the firm's legal obligation to pay its suppliers on time

---

[38] http://www.johnkay.com/1993/06/01/the-structure-of-strategy-business-strategy-review-1993.

and its more informal obligation to warn its suppliers in advance if it were planning to cut production in three months.

Such architecture is most often found in firms with a distinctive organizational style or ethos, because such firms tend to have a well-organized and long-established set of processes or routines for doing business. So, for example, if you have ever taken a home loan in India, you will find a marked difference in the speed and professionalism with which HDFC processes a home loan application as compared to other lenders. The HDFC branch manager asks the applicant more specific questions than other lenders and this home loan provider's due diligence on the applicant and the property appears to be done more swiftly and thoroughly than most other lenders in India.

So, how can an investor assess whether the firm they are scrutinizing has architecture or not? In fact, whilst investors will often not know the exact processes or procedures of the firm in question, they can assess whether a firm has such processes and procedures by gauging the:

- extent to which the employees of the firm cooperate with each other across various departments and locations;
- rate of staff attrition (sometimes given in the annual report);
- extent to which the staff in different parts of the firm give the same message when asked the same question; and
- extent to which the firm is able to generate innovations in its products or services or production processes on an ongoing basis.

At the core of successful architecture there cooperation (within teams, across various teams in a firm, and between a firm and its suppliers) and sharing (of ideas, information, customer insights and, ultimately, rewards). Built properly, architecture allows a firm with ordinary people to produce extraordinary results.

Perhaps the most striking demonstration of architecture in India is the unlisted non-profit agricultural cooperative, the Gujarat Cooperative Milk Marketing Federation Ltd (GCMMF), better known to millions of Indians as Amul.

With its roots stretching back to India's freedom movement, GCMMF was founded by the legendary Verghese Kurien in 1973. This farmers' cooperative generated revenues[39] of Rs 20,700 crore (around US$3.1 billion) in FY15, thus making it significantly larger than its main private sector competitor, Nestle (CY15 revenues of Rs 8175 crore or around US$1.2 billion). Furthermore, GCMMF's revenues have grown over the past five years by 16 per cent as opposed to Nestle's[40] 5 per cent over the same period. In fact, GCMMF's revenue growth is markedly superior to the vast majority of the top Indian brands shown in Exhibit 140.

GCMMF's daily milk procurement of thirteen million litres from over 16,000 village milk cooperative societies (which include 3.2 million milk producer members) has become legendary. The way GCMMF aggregates the milk produced by over three million families into the village cooperative dairy, further aggregates that into the district cooperative and then feeds the milk federation has been studied by numerous management experts.

---

[39] Nestle reporting is calendar year (CY) and GCMMF is financial year.
[40] Nestle's revenue was impacted in CY15 due to a ban on Maggi noodles.

Not only does the GCMMF possess impressive logistical skills, its marketing acumen is also comparable to that of the multinational giants cited in Exhibit 140 earlier. In key FMCG product categories such as butter, cheese and packaged milk, Amul has been the long-standing market leader in the face of sustained efforts by the multinationals to break its dominance. GCMMF is also India's largest exporter of dairy products.

So how does GCMMF do it? How does it give a fair deal to farmers, its management team (which includes the alumni of India's best business schools), its 5000 dealers, its one million retailers and its hundreds of millions of customers? Although numerous case studies have been written on GCMMF, the following appear to be the dominant factors at the core of this cooperative's success:

(a) its fifty-year-old brand with its distinctive imagery of the little girl in the red polka-dotted dress;
(b) the idea of a fair deal for the small farmer and the linked idea of the disintermediation of the unfair middleman; and
(c) the spirit of Indian nationalism in an industry dominated by globe-girdling for-profit corporates.

A more prosaic but equally effective example of architecture would be the way India's largest car manufacturer, Maruti Suzuki, is tied up in a common architecture with its suppliers. This company has around 250 local suppliers based in the vicinity of its plants on the outskirts of Delhi and another twenty global suppliers.[41] Each of these 270-odd suppliers

---

[41] http://indiatransportportal.com/a-peek-into-maruti%E2%80%99s-supply-chain-management-3024.

understands Maruti's design specifications for specific components and has its own Enterprise Resource Planning (ERP) software hooked into Maruti's. These suppliers have long-term contracts with the company and, as a result, they are able to work in sync over the course of several decades.

Even more interestingly, several of these suppliers, in turn, will have smaller suppliers in the Gurgaon–Manesar region who will supply them components which, when put together, will make a larger subsystem which would go into a Maruti car. In spite of this complex web of interlinkages, Maruti's supply chain functions seamlessly. In the 1980s, Maruti used to give its suppliers thirty days of notice for the components it needed. Now, it instructs the supplier the previous night about the specific two-hour slot the next day when the components have to reach Maruti's assembly line. It takes a new entrant into the Indian auto market many years, sometimes decades, to create a supply chain as efficient as this. That's the power of architecture—it brings different companies together into a common network with a common goal in mind.

Innovation

'Some leaders push innovations by being good at the big picture. Others do so by mastering details. (Steve) Jobs did both, relentlessly.'—Walter Isaacson in *Steve Jobs* (2011).

'Innovation is an obvious source of distinctive capability, but it is less often a sustainable or appropriable source because successful innovation quickly attracts imitation. Maintaining an advantage is most easily possible for those few innovations for which patent production is effective. There are others where process secrecy or other characteristics make it difficult for other firms to follow. More often, turning an innovation into a competitive advantage requires the development of a powerful range of supporting strategies. What appears to be competitive advantage derived from innovation is frequently, in fact, the return to a system of organization capable of producing a series of innovations.'—John Kay.[42]

Whilst innovation is often talked about as a source of competitive advantage, especially in the technology and pharmaceutical sectors, it is actually the most tenuous source of sustainable competitive advantage as:

- innovation is expensive;
- innovation is uncertain—it tends to be a hit-or-miss process; and
- innovation is hard to manage due to the random nature of the process.

Furthermore, even when the expensive innovation process yields a commercially useful result, the benefits can be competed away, as other firms replicate the innovator and/ or the employees who have driven the innovation, process tend to extract the benefits of innovation through higher compensation.

In fact, innovation is more powerful when it is twinned with the two other distinctive capabilities I have described above—reputation and architecture. Apple is the most celebrated example of a contemporary firm which has clearly built a reputation for innovation (think of the slew of

---

[42] http://www.johnkay.com/1993/06/01/the-structure-of-strategy-business-strategy-review-1993.

products from Apple over the past decade—first changing how people access music, then how they perceive phones and, finally, how they use personal computers).

Strategic assets

In contrast to the three distinctive capabilities discussed above, strategic assets are easier to identify as sources of competitive advantages. Such assets can come in different guises:

- Intellectual property, i.e. patents or proprietary know-how (e.g. the recipe for Coke's famous syrup which is a closely held secret and kept in the company's museum in Atlanta, Georgia);
- Licences and regulatory permissions to provide a certain service to the public, e.g. telecom, power, gas or public transport;
- Access to natural resources such as coal or iron-ore mines;
- Political contacts at the national, state or city level;
- Sunk costs incurred by the first mover which result in other potential competitors deciding to stay away from that market, e.g. given that there already is a Mumbai–Pune highway operated by IRB, it does not make sense for anyone else to set up a competing road; and
- Natural monopolies, i.e. sectors or markets which accommodate only one or two firms. For example, the market for supplying power in Mumbai is restricted to one firm, Tata Power.

Whilst strategic assets can come in different forms, all of them result in a lower cost per unit of production for the firm owning the asset relative to its competitors. For example, Tata Steel's decades-old access to coal and iron ore from its captive mines allows it to make more money per tonne of steel produced than any other steel manufacturer in India. According to Ambit Capital's analysts, even at the subdued domestic steel prices (prevalent in April 2016), on a tonne of steel produced, Tata Steel earns EBITDA of Rs 6400 as against Rs 3450 for JSW Steel and an EBITDA loss for Steel Authority of India Limited (SAIL).

Unsurprisingly therefore, among the top fifty companies by market cap in India since the Nifty was launched in 1995, there is only one conglomerate—Tata Sons—which has had three companies which have been in the index more or less throughout this period, i.e. Tata Power, Tata Steel and Tata Motors.

In fact, the Tatas are almost a textbook case of how to build businesses which, without being the most innovative players in town, combine architecture and brands to great effect, thereby creating robust sources of sustainable competitive advantages. The group seems to have created at least three specific mechanisms to ensure that these sources of competitive advantage endure.

Firstly, Tata Sons, an unlisted company (owned by several philanthropic trusts endowed by members of the Tata family), is the promoter of the major operating Tata companies and holds significant shareholdings in these companies. Tata Sons' patient, long-term orientation in terms of building large and robust businesses gradually has played a major role in the stability of the listed Tata businesses.

Secondly, Tata Quality Management Services (TQMS), a division of Tata Sons, assists Tata companies in their business excellence initiatives through the Tata Business Excellence Model, Management of Business Ethics and the Tata Code of Conduct. TQMS, quite literally, provides the architecture to harmonize practices in various parts of the Tata empire.

Thirdly, Tata Sons is also the owner of the Tata name and several Tata trademarks, which are registered in India and around the world. These are used by various Tata companies under a licence from Tata Sons as part of their corporate name and/or in relation to their products and services. The terms of use of the group mark and logo by Tata companies are governed by the Brand Equity and Business Promotion (BEBP) agreement entered into between Tata Sons and the other Tata companies.

To sum up, to get ahead—and remain consistently ahead—of competition, companies should continuously invest in innovation, brands and building strong architecture around its stakeholders. These sustainable competitive advantages are essentially the moats that companies build to remain ahead of the game. As ever, nobody explains the practical application of the sustainable competitive advantage construct better than Kay:

> BMW cars are not the most powerful, or the most reliable, or the most luxurious on the market, although they score well against all these criteria. No one has ever suggested that they are cheap, even for the high level of specification that most models offer. Although BMW rightly emphasises the quality and advanced nature of its technology, its products are not exceptionally innovative . . . . The achievements of BMW are built on two closely associated factors. The company achieves a higher quality of engineering than

is usual in production cars. While most car assembly has now been taken over by robots or workers from low-wage economies, BMW maintains a skilled German labour force. The company benefits, as many German firms do, from an educational system which gives basic technical skills to an unusually high proportion of the population. Its reputation has followed from these substantial achievements . . . .

Yet BMW's success was neither easy nor certain . . . The turning point came when the firm identified a market which most effectively exploited its capabilities—the market for high-performance saloon cars, which has since become almost synonymous with BMW. The BMW 1500, launched in 1961, established a reputation for engineering quality in the BMW automobile brand. The brand in turn acquired a distinctive identity as a symbol for young, affluent European professionals. That combination—a system of production which gives the company a particular advantage in its chosen market segment, a worldwide reputation for product quality, and a brand which immediately identifies the aims and aspirations of its customers—continues to make BMW one of the most profitable automobile manufacturers in the world.

Today, the BMW business is structured to maximise these advantages. Retail margins on BMW cars are relatively high. The company maintains tight control over its distribution network. This control supports the brand image and also aids market segmentation. BMW cars are positioned differently and priced very differently in the various national markets. The same tight control is reflected in BMW's relationships with suppliers, who mostly have continuing long associations with the company. BMW's activities are focused almost exclusively on two product ranges—high-performance saloon cars and motorbikes which reflect its competitive strengths.

BMW is a company with a well-executed strategy. It is a company which came—after several false starts—to recognise its distinctive capabilities and chose the market, and subsequent markets, which realised its full potential. Its dealings with its suppliers and distributors, its pricing approach, its branding and advertising strategies, are all built around that recognition and these choices. There was no master plan, no single vision which took BMW from where it was in 1959 to where it is today.[43]

---

[43] http://www.johnkay.com/1993/06/01/the-structure-of-strategy-business-strategy-review-1993._

The Detailed Coffee Can Portfolios

In Chapter 1, I explained how we build Coffee Can Portfolios with the simple philosophy of filtering listed companies across specific parameters and then—for the portfolio of companies that pass those filters—holding their stocks for the next ten years. Let me give you an example. My first screening is for financial years FY1991 to FY2000. I looked at the universe of listed stocks with a market capitalization of more than Rs 100 crore and looked for companies that meet the parameters of:

(a) revenue growth of 10 per cent and ROCE of 15 per cent every year for non-financial services companies; or
(b) for financial services companies, ROE of 15 per cent and loan book growth of 15 per cent every year.

In the ten-year period of FY1991 to FY2000, I found that there are five companies that meet these requirements. These are NIIT, Cipla, Hero Moto, Swaraj Engines and

HDFC Limited. This set of five companies is my Coffee Can Portfolio 2000 (CCP 2000). I then tracked the stock price performance of CCP 2000 for the next ten years (i.e. from 30 June 2000 to 30 June 2010). Similarly, running the screen from FY92 to FY01 gives me the Coffee Can Portfolio 2001 (CCP 2001), and I then track the stock price performance of this portfolio for the subsequent ten-year period from 30 June 2001 to 30 June 2011.

In this appendix, I have listed the details of all of the Coffee Can Portfolios from 2000 through to 2015 and also provided the detailed stock-by-stock share price performance of these portfolios. Given that each time bucket is ten years, I have six fully completed Coffee Can Portfolios: FY1991–2000 (CCP 2000), FY1992–2001 (CCP 2001), FY1993–2002 (CCP 2002), FY1994–2003 (CCP 2003), FY1995–2004 (CCP 2004), and FY1996–2005 (CCP 2005).

However, the CCPs of companies that were constructed on the basis of financial data from FY97 to FY06 will complete ten years of price performance on 30 June 2016. Similarly, CCP 2007, which uses financial data from FY98 to FY07, will end its ten-year stock price performance on 30 June 2017 and so on. Thus I have ten CCPs which are incomplete in the sense that they have not yet run for the full duration of ten years. For these uncompleted CCPs, I have used a cut-off date of 5 April 2016 for measuring price performance.

The results can be summarized in one sentence: Each of the sixteen CCPs (six with complete price performance back-testing and ten partially complete back-testing) has outperformed the benchmark large-cap index in India, the Sensex. In fact, as can be seen in Exhibit 141, the outperformance of the CCP to the Sensex is almost always in excess of 4 percentage points per annum. (Note: in financial markets, this outperformance relative to the benchmark is called alpha.)

To further assess the robustness of these findings, I also stress-tested these results for maximum drawdown to evaluate the strength of the portfolio during periods of market volatility:

- First, I calculate CAGR returns for each of the sixteen portfolios and the Sensex;
- Next, I compute the maximum drawdown for each portfolio (defined as the maximum drop in cumulative returns from the highest peak to the lowest subsequent trough); and
- Finally, I calculate the risk-adjusted returns, i.e. returns in excess of the risk-free rate (assumed to be 8 per cent) divided by the maximum drawdown.

The results can be summarized as follows:

- Each of the sixteen CCPs has outperformed the benchmark Sensex.
- Even a subset of the CCP, i.e. the large-cap version of the CCP has been successful in beating the Sensex on all sixteen occasions. (The large-cap version of the CCP consists only of those CCP stocks which were in the top 100 stocks in India based on the market capitalization on the day the portfolio was created.)
- On a risk-adjusted basis (where we define risk as maximum drawdown) as well, all sixteen iterations

of the all-cap CCP as well as the large-cap CCP have outperformed the Sensex.

I have summarized the results of each of these sixteen iterations in Exhibits 141 and 142 with a detailed description of each portfolio following these.

If you plan to use the Coffee Can method to invest money, you should read the following paragraph carefully. While each of the sixteen iterations has generated strong performance relative to the Sensex on an overall portfolio basis, a few of the companies within a portfolio might not be able to perform as expected. To put things in perspective, over the sixteen iterations, an average CCP consists of twelve companies. Out of these twelve companies, there are usually two to three companies that will give stellar returns over a ten-year period (we highlight such stocks when we discuss each portfolio in detail later) and there are two to three companies that will give low to negative returns over the ten-year period. The rest of the portfolios will give broadly market returns. This is the nature of the construct of a CCP. However, in spite of this, every single CCP outperforms the overall market due to four reasons:

- As the time period increases, the probability of generating positive returns goes up. Using annualized Sensex returns of 16 per cent and standard deviation of 29 per cent over the past thirty years, the probability of generating positive returns goes up from around 70 per cent in a one-year horizon to almost 100 per cent if the time horizon is increased to ten years.

- ‐ Over the longer term, the portfolio comes to be dominated by the winning stocks whilst losing stocks keep declining to eventually become inconsequential. Thus, the positive contribution of the winners disproportionately outweighs the negative contribution of losers to eventually help the portfolio compound handsomely.
- Investing and holding for the long term is the most effective way of killing the noise that interferes with the investment process. As soon as you try to time that entry/exit, you run the risk of noise rather than fundamentals driving our investment decisions.
- With no churn, transaction costs are reduced which adds to the overall portfolio performance over the long term. A hypothetical portfolio started on 30 June 2005, with 50 per cent churn per annum for instance loses almost 1.2 per cent CAGR return when run for a ten-year period.

Each of these four reasons is explained in more detail in Appendix 3.

Completed portfolio (Period 1): 2000–10 (5.3 per cent alpha relative to the Sensex; 19.3 per cent per annum absolute returns)

All-cap portfolio stocks: NIIT, Cipla, Hero MotoCorp, Swaraj Engines, HDFC.

Large-cap portfolio stocks: NIIT, Cipla, Hero MotoCorp, HDFC.

In the first iteration, both versions of the CCP outperformed the benchmark. Whilst the all-cap CCP delivered a 19.3 per cent return (5.3 per cent alpha relative

Exhibit 141: Back-testing results of completed six iterations of the Coffee Can Portfolio (i.e these iterations have run their complete course of ten years of price-performance check)

Kick-off year*	All-cap CCP (start)	All-cap CCP (end)	CAGR return	Outperformance relative to Sensex	Large-cap CCP (start)	Large-cap CCP (end)	CAGR return	Outperformance relative to Sensex
2000	500	2923	19.3%	5.3%	400	2602	20.6%	6.5%
2001	600	7362	28.5%	10.0%	300	2685	24.5%	6.0%
2002	800	6057	22.4%	4.1%	500	3348	20.9%	2.6%
2003	900	8668	25.4%	7.1%	600	6754	27.4%	9.1%
2004	1000	14618	30.8%	12.6%	500	3097	20.0%	1.9%
2005	900	5795	20.5%	6.0%	500	2517	17.5%	3.1%

Source: Bloomberg, Capitaline, Ambit Capital research.

Note: *Portfolio at start denotes an equal allocation of Rs 100 for the stocks qualifying to be in the CCP for that year.

Exhibit 142: Back-testing results of incomplete ten iterations of the Coffee Can Portfolio (i.e., these iterations have not run their complete course of ten years of price–performance check)

Kick-off year*	All-cap CCP (start)	All-cap CCP (end)	CAGR return	Outperformance relative to Sensex	Large-cap CCP (start)	Large-cap CCP (end)	CAGR return	Outperformance relative to Sensex
2006	1000	4708	17.2%	8.1%	600	2333	14.9%	5.8%
2007	1500	5322	15.5%	9.3%	1000	3282	14.5%	8.3%
2008	1100	4346	19.3%	11.1%	800	2689	16.9%	8.7%
2009	1100	3806	20.1%	11.8%	900	2430	15.8%	7.5%
2010	700	1438	13.4%	7.3%	300	693	15.6%	9.5%
2011	1400	1864	6.3%	0.3%	400	682	11.8%	5.8%
2012	2200	4143	18.3%	8.4%	500	802	13.3%	3.4%
2013	1800	3784	30.7%	21.3%	600	1068	23.1%	13.7%
2014	1600	2114	17.1%	18.3%	700	966	20.0%	21.1%
2015	2000	1957	-2.7%	10.6%	1,200	1139	-6.6%	6.8%

Source: Bloomberg, Capitaline, Ambit Capital research.

Note: *Portfolio at start denotes an equal allocation of Rs 100 for the stocks qualifying to be in the CCP for that year. The portfolio kicks off on 30 June of the kick off year. #CAGR returns for portfolios since 2006 have been calculated until 5 April 2016.

to the Sensex), the large-cap portfolio delivered a 20.6 per cent return (6.5 per cent alpha relative to the Sensex). The maximum drawdown, which is the largest single drop from the peak to the bottom in the value of a stock, for both the portfolios in this period was also less than the maximum drawdown for the Sensex.

Exhibit 143: First iteration summary

2000-2010*	All-cap CCP	Large-cap CCP	Sensex
CAGR returns	19.3%	20.6%	14.1%
Maximum drawdown**	-35.2%	-30.1%	-52.4%
Excess returns	0.32	0.42	0.12

Source: Bloomberg, Ambit Capital research.

Note: *Portfolio kicks off on 30 June 2000. Excess returns have been calculated as returns in excess of risk-free rate (assumed to be 8%) divided by absolute maximum drawdown. Maximum drawdown is defined as the maximum drop in cumulative returns from the highest peak to the lowest subsequent trough.

**Maximum drawdown took place from December 2007 to December 2008 for the all-cap CCP, large-cap CCP and for the Sensex.

The five stocks that constituted the first iteration of the Coffee Can Portfolio consisted of one IT, one pharma company, one BFSI company and two companies from the automobile/auto-ancillary sector. These were NIIT, Cipla, Hero MotoCorp, HDFC Ltd and Swaraj Engines. The star performer during this period was Hero MotoCorp which proved to be a ten-bagger (i.e. its stock price rose ten times in ten years) whilst NIIT's stock price collapsed 78 per cent (or, an annual rate of decline of 14 per cent) in this period (see Exhibits 144 and 145).

Exhibit 144: Portfolio performance during the first iteration

Company	Price at Start (Rs)	Price at End (Rs)	Share price CAGR	FY2000–10 PAT CAGR
Date from/to	30/06/2000	30/06/2010		
NIIT	295	65	-14.1%	-11%
Cipla	69	339	17.2%	23%
Hero MotoCorp	198	2049	26.4%	27%
Swaraj Engines	118	378	12.4%	7%
HDFC Ltd	56	589	26.5%	23%
Portfolio*	**500**	**2923**	**19.3%**	
Sensex	4749	17,701	14.1%	

Source: Bloomberg, Ambit Capital research.

Note: *Portfolio price at start of Rs 500 denotes an equal allocation of Rs 100 in each stock at the start of the period. Portfolio price at end is the value of the portfolio at the end of the period. Thus, for this period, the value of the portfolio rose from Rs 400 at the start to Rs 2923 at the end.

Exhibit 145: Hero and HDFC rose exponentially whilst NIIT collapsed in 2000–2010

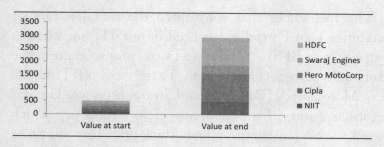

Source: Bloomberg, Ambit Capital research.

Note: Value at start denotes an equal allocation of Rs100 in each stock at the start of the period. Value at end is the value of each stock at the end of the period. Thus, for this period, the value of the portfolio rose from Rs 500 at the start to Rs 2923 at the end.

Completed portfolio (Period 2): 2001–11 (10.0 per cent alpha relative to the Sensex; 28.5 per cent per annum absolute returns)

All-cap portfolio stocks: Cipla, Hero MotoCorp, Apollo Hospitals, Roofit Inds, HDFC Ltd and LIC Housing Finance.

Large-cap portfolio stocks: Cipla, Hero MotoCorp and HDFC Ltd.

Both versions of the CCP performed well during the second iteration as well, beating the Sensex. The all-cap and large-cap CCP gave an impressive alpha of 10 per cent and 6.0 per cent, respectively, for this iteration. The portfolio was remarkably steady as compared to the maximum drawdown, delivering an excess return of 0.76–0.53 times (Exhibit 146).

Exhibit 146: Second iteration summary

2001–2011*	All-cap CCP	Large-cap CCP	Sensex
CAGR returns	28.5%	24.5%	18.5%
Maximum drawdown**	-26.8%	-31.0%	-52.4%
Excess returns	0.76	0.53	0.20

Source: Bloomberg, Ambit Capital research.

Note: *Portfolio kicks off on 29 June 2001. Excess returns have been calculated as returns in excess of risk-free rate (assumed to be 8%) divided by absolute maximum drawdown. Maximum drawdown is defined as the maximum drop in cumulative returns from the highest peak to the lowest subsequent trough.

**Maximum drawdown took place from December 2007 to December 2008 for the all-cap CCP, large-cap CCP and for the Sensex.

During the second iteration, the Coffee Can Portfolio consisted of six stocks with three repeats (Cipla, Hero and HDFC from Period 1) and three new entries (Apollo Hospitals, Roofit Industries and LIC Housing Finance). During this period, note that one of the stocks in the portfolio, Roofit Industries, was delisted during 2001–11. Despite this, the portfolio performed admirably. The star performer was LIC Housing Finance whose stock price rose 35 times whilst Cipla was a laggard at 3.6 times (Exhibits 147 and 148).

Exhibit 147: Portfolio performance during the second iteration

Company	Price at Start (Rs)	Price at End (Rs)	Share price CAGR	FY01–11 PAT CAGR
Date from/to	29/06/2001	29/06/2011		
Cipla	91	331	13.7%	19%
Hero MotoCorp	145	1877	29.2%	22%
Apollo Hospitals	40	478	28.1%	19%
Roofit Industries	106	NA	NA	NA
HDFC Ltd	69	706	26.2%	25%
LIC Housing Finance	7	243	42.6%	23%
Portfolio*	**600**	**7362**	**28.5%**	
Sensex	3457	18,846	18.5%	

Source: Bloomberg, Ambit Capital research.

Note: Data for Roofit is not available because the company was delisted during this period.

*Portfolio price at start of Rs 600 denotes an equal allocation of Rs 100 in each stock at the start of the period. Portfolio price at end

is the value of the portfolio at the end of the period. Thus, for this period, the value of the portfolio rose from Rs 600 at the start to Rs 7362 at the end.

Exhibit 148: LIC Housing Finance became the stellar performer during 2001–11

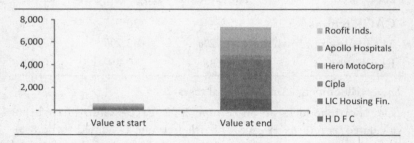

Source: Bloomberg, Ambit Capital research.

Note: Data for Roofit Ind is not available from FY03 onwards. Value at start denotes an equal allocation of Rs 100 in each stock at the start of the period. Value at end is the value of each stock at the end of the period. Thus, for this period, the value of the portfolio rose from Rs 600 at the start to Rs 7362 at the end.

Completed portfolio (Period 3): 2002–12 (4.1 per cent alpha to the Sensex; 22.4 per cent per annum absolute returns)

All-cap portfolio stocks: Infosys, Hero MotoCorp, Cipla, Container Corporation of India, Gujarat Gas, Aurobindo Pharma, HDFC Ltd and LIC Housing Finance.

Large-cap portfolio stocks: Infosys, Hero MotoCorp, Cipla, Container Corporation of India, HDFC Ltd.

During the third iteration, the Coffee Can delivered an alpha of 4.1 per cent alpha whilst the large-cap Coffee Can delivered an alpha of 2.6 per cent. Both versions of the Coffee Can performed well during maximum drawdown as well, delivering excess returns of 0.38–0.39 times (Exhibit 149).

Exhibit 149: Third iteration summary

2002–2012*	All-cap CCP	Large-cap CCP	Sensex
CAGR returns	22.4%	20.9%	18.3%
Maximum drawdown**	-38.2%	-33.2%	-52.4%
Excess returns	0.38	0.39	0.20

Source: Bloomberg, Ambit Capital research.

Note: *Portfolio kicks off on 28 June 2002. Excess returns have been calculated as returns in excess of risk-free rate (assumed to be 8%) divided by absolute maximum drawdown. Maximum drawdown is defined as the maximum drop in cumulative returns from the highest peak to the lowest subsequent trough.

**Maximum drawdown took place from December 2007 to December 2008 for the all-cap CCP, large-cap CCP and for the Sensex.

The Coffee Can Portfolio expanded in size during the third iteration. A total of eight stocks qualified to be part of the Coffee Can Portfolio in the third iteration. Cipla, Hero MotoCorp, HDFC Ltd and LIC Housing were repeated yet again whilst the other four stocks were Infosys, Container Corporation, Gujarat Gas and Aurobindo Pharma. LIC Housing Finance was the winner yet again, while Aurobindo Pharma lagged (Exhibits 150 and 151).

Exhibit 150: Portfolio performance during the third iteration

Company	Price at Start (Rs)	Price at End (Rs)	Share price CAGR	FY02–12 PAT CAGR
Date from/to	28/06/2002	29/06/2012		
Infosys	411	2509	19.8%	26%
Hero MotoCorp	308	2149	21.4%	17%
Cipla	75	317	15.4%	18%
Container Corporation	99	613	20.0%	13%
Gujarat Gas Company	50	310	20.0%	17%
Aurobindo Pharma	24	110	16.6%	11%
HDFC	65	653	25.9%	26%
LIC Housing Finance	17	270	32.2%	20%
Portfolio*	**800**	**6057**	**22.4%**	
Sensex	3245	17,430	18.3%	

Source: Bloomberg, Ambit Capital research.

Note: *Portfolio price at start of Rs 800 denotes an equal allocation of Rs 100 in each stock at the start of the period. Portfolio price at end is the value of the portfolio at the end of the period. Thus, for this period, the value of the portfolio rose from Rs 800 at the start to Rs 6057 at the end.

Exhibit 151: Portfolio's outperformance was led by LIC Housing Finance once again

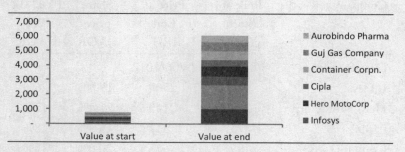

Source: Bloomberg, Ambit Capital research.

Note: Value at start denotes an equal allocation of Rs 100 in each stock at the start of the period. Value at end is the value of each stock at the end of the period. Thus, for this period, the value of the portfolio rose from Rs 800 at the start to Rs 6057 at the end.

Completed portfolio (Period 4): 2003–13 (7.1 per cent alpha to the Sensex; 25.4 per cent per annum absolute returns)

All-cap portfolio stocks: Infosys, Hero MotoCorp, Cipla, Sun Pharma, Container Corporation of India, Gujarat Gas, Aurobindo Pharma, HDFC Ltd, LIC Housing Finance.

Large-cap portfolio stocks: Infosys, Hero MotoCorp, Cipla, Container Corporation of India, Sun Pharma and HDFC Ltd.

Whilst the all-cap version of the Portfolio delivered a 7.1 per cent alpha, the large-cap version gave a higher 9.1 per cent alpha in the fourth iteration. In a maximum drawdown situation, both versions remained steady and beat the Sensex, thereby delivering excess returns of 0.57–0.75 times (Exhibit 152).

Exhibit 152: Fourth iteration summary

2003–2013*	All-cap CCP	Large-cap CCP	Sensex
CAGR returns	25.4%	27.4%	18.3%
Maximum drawdown**	-30.4%	-25.7%	-52.4%
Excess returns	0.57	0.75	0.20

Source: Bloomberg, Ambit Capital research.

Note: *Portfolio kicks off on 30 June 2003. Excess returns have been calculated as returns in excess of risk-free rate (assumed to be 8%) divided by absolute maximum drawdown. Maximum drawdown is defined as the maximum drop in cumulative returns from the highest peak to the lowest subsequent trough.

**Maximum drawdown took place from December 2007 to December 2008 for the all-cap CCP, large-cap CCP and for the Sensex.

Barring one addition (Sun Pharma), the Coffee Can Portfolio in its fourth iteration was the same as that in the third iteration. Performance was driven by Sun Pharma's stellar performance, while Gujarat Gas lagged. However, the performance of the large-cap version was better than the all-cap version of the Coffee Can Portfolio (Exhibits 153 and 154).

Exhibit 153: Portfolio performance during the fourth iteration

Company	Price at Start (Rs)	Price at End (Rs)	Share price CAGR	FY03–13 PAT CAGR
Date from/to	30/06/2003	30/06/2013		
Infosys	408	2499	19.9%	26%
Cipla	60	392	20.6%	20%
Hero Motocorp	253	1663	20.7%	13%
Sun Pharma	16	506	41.1%	30%

(*Contd*)

Company	Price at Start (Rs)	Price at End (Rs)	Share price CAGR	FY03–13 PAT CAGR
Date from/to	30/06/2003	30/06/2013		
Container Corporation	115	719	20.1%	13%
Aurobindo Pharma	37	181	17.1%	14%
Gujarat Gas Company	45	191	15.4%	18%
HDFC	82	879	26.8%	26%
LIC Housing Finance	25	255	26.0%	19%
Portfolio*	**900**	**8668**	**25.4%**	
Sensex	3607	19,396	18.3%	

Source: Bloomberg, Ambit Capital research.

Note: *Portfolio price at start of Rs 900 denotes an equal allocation of Rs 100 in each stock at the start of the period. Portfolio price at end is the value of the portfolio at the end of the period. Thus, for this period, the value of the portfolio rose from Rs 900 at the start to Rs 8668 at the end.

Exhibit 154: Sun Pharma delivered outstanding performance in Period 4

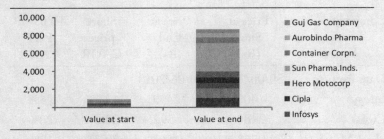

Source: Bloomberg, Ambit Capital research.

Note: Value at start denotes an equal allocation of Rs 100 in each stock at the start of the period. Value at end is the value of each

stock at the end of the period. Thus, for this period, the value of the portfolio rose from Rs 900 at the start to Rs 8668 at the end.

Completed portfolio (Period 5): 2004–14 (12.6 per cent alpha relative to the Sensex; 30.8 per cent per annum absolute returns)

All-cap portfolio stocks: Infosys, Hero MotoCorp, Cipla, Container Corporation of India, Gujarat Gas, Alok Industries, Munjal Showa, and Havells India, HDFC Ltd and LIC Housing Finance.

Large-cap portfolio stocks: Infosys, Hero MotoCorp, Cipla, Container Corporation of India and HDFC Ltd.

The fifth iteration of our Coffee Can Portfolio yielded a whopping 12.6 per cent alpha over the Sensex. The portfolio was equally divided between large-caps and mid-caps/small-caps. The higher share of the mid-caps/small-caps compared to earlier iterations was instrumental in delivering higher alpha during this period (Exhibit 155).

Exhibit 155: Fifth iteration summary

2004–2014*	All-cap CCP	Large-cap CCP	Sensex
CAGR returns	30.8%	20.0%	18.1%
Maximum drawdown**	-61.1%	-32.2%	-52.4%
Excess returns	0.37	0.37	0.19

Source: Bloomberg, Ambit Capital research.

Note: *Portfolio kicks off on 30 June 2004. Excess returns have been calculated as returns in excess of risk-free rate (assumed to be 8%) divided by absolute maximum drawdown. Maximum drawdown is defined as the maximum drop in cumulative returns from the highest peak to the lowest subsequent trough.

**Maximum drawdown took place from December 2007 to December 2008 for the all-cap CCP, large-cap CCP and for the Sensex.

The price performance among mid-cap/small-cap stocks was extreme: Havells' stock price rose by 89 times whilst the stock price of Alok Industries fell 70 per cent by the end of the iteration. As a result, the price performance of the large-cap portfolio (20 per cent CAGR) lagged behind the all-cap portfolio (30.8 per cent CAGR) (Exhibits 156 and 157).

Exhibit 156: Portfolio performance during the fifth iteration

Company	Price at Start (Rs)	Price at End (Rs)	Share price CAGR	FY04–14 PAT CAGR
Date from/to	30/06/2004	30/06/2014		
Infosys	690	3256	16.8%	24%
Hero Motocorp	508	2635	17.9%	11%
Cipla	85	438	17.8%	16%
Container Corporation	188	1189	20.2%	10%
Gujarat Gas Company	43	415	25.4%	17%
Alok Industries	45	14	-10.9%	19%
Munjal Showa	34	142	15.4%	12%
Havells India	3	235	56.7%	37%
HDFC	103	993	25.4%	25%
LIC Housing Finance	28	327	28.1%	23%
Portfolio*	**1000**	**14,618**	**30.8%**	
Sensex	4795	25,414	18.1%	

Source: Bloomberg, Ambit Capital research.

Note: *Portfolio price at start of Rs 1000 denotes an equal allocation of Rs 100 in each stock at the start of the period. Portfolio price at end is the value of the portfolio at the end of the period. Thus, for this period, the value of the portfolio rose from Rs 1000 at the start to Rs 14,618 at the end.

Exhibit 157: Havells India was the star performer in Period 5

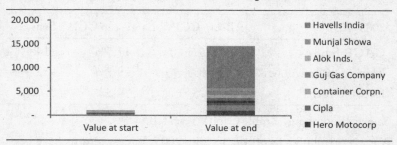

Source: Bloomberg, Ambit Capital research.

Note: Value at start denotes an equal allocation of Rs 100 in each stock at the start of the period. Value at end is the value of each stock at the end of the period. Thus, for this period, the value of the portfolio rose from Rs 1000 at the start to Rs 14,618 at the end.

Completed portfolio (Period 6): 2005–15 (6.0 per cent alpha relative to the Sensex; 20.5 per cent per annum absolute returns)

All-cap portfolio stocks: Infosys, Hero MotoCorp, Cipla, Container Corporation of India, Geometric, Havells India, Ind-Swift, Munjal Showa and HDFC Ltd.

Large-cap portfolio stocks: Infosys, Hero MotoCorp, Cipla, Container Corporation of India and HDFC Ltd.

In the sixth iteration, our Coffee Can Portfolio again outperformed the Sensex with an alpha of 6.0 per cent. The large-cap version also outperformed the Sensex with an alpha of 3.1%. In this period, while the all-cap version generated a higher alpha than the large-cap version on an absolute basis, on a risk-adjusted basis, large-cap version beat the all-cap version mainly on account of lower maximum drawdown (excess return of 0.32 times for large-cap versus 0.23 times for all-cap). Both versions, however, continued to perform better than Sensex on risk-adjusted basis as well (Exhibit 158).

Exhibit 158: Sixth iteration summary

2005–2015*	All-cap CCP	Large-cap CCP	Sensex
CAGR returns	20.5%	17.5%	14.5%
Maximum drawdown**	-54.8%	-29.7%	-52.4%
Excess returns	0.23	0.32	0.12

Source: Bloomberg, Ambit Capital research.

Note: *Portfolio kicks off on 30 June 2005. Excess returns have been calculated as returns in excess of risk-free rate (assumed to be 8%) divided by absolute maximum drawdown. Maximum drawdown is defined as the maximum drop in cumulative returns from the highest peak to the lowest subsequent trough.

**Maximum drawdown took place from December 2007 to December 2008 for the all-cap CCP, large-cap CCP and for the Sensex.

The extreme price performance among mid-cap/small-cap stocks continued during this iteration as well: Havells' stock price rose by 28 times whilst Ind-Swift's stock price fell 94 per cent by the end of the iteration (Exhibits 159 and 160).

Exhibit 159: Portfolio performance during the sixth iteration

Company	Price at Start (Rs)	Price at End (Rs)	Share price CAGR	FY05–15 PAT CAGR
Date from/to	30/06/2005	30/06/2015		
Infosys*	295	984	12.8%	21%
Hero Motocorp	583	2524	15.8%	12%
Cipla	125	615	17.2%	12%
Container Corporation	315	1678	18.2%	9%
Geometric	104	110	0.6%	7%
Havells India	10	283	40.0%	29%

(Contd)

Company	Price at Start (Rs)	Price at End (Rs)	Share price CAGR	FY05–15 PAT CAGR
Date from/to	30/06/2005	30/06/2015		
Ind-Swift	65	4	-24.0%	NA
Munjal Showa	63	168	10.3%	17%
HDFC	178	1296	22.0%	26%
Portfolio*	**900**	**5795**	**20.5%**	
Sensex	7,194	27,781	14.5%	

Source: Bloomberg, Ambit Capital research.

Note: *Portfolio price at start of Rs 900 denotes an equal allocation of Rs 100 in each stock at the start of the period. Portfolio price at end is the value of the portfolio at the end of the period. Thus, for this period, the value of the portfolio rose from Rs 900 at the start to Rs 5795 at the end. Exhibits for Periods 1–5 have not been adjusted for bonus issuance of Infosys shares in December 2014 and June 2015. This exhibit, however, reflects the prices adjusted for the bonus.

Exhibit 160: Havells India continued being the star performer in the sixth iteration as well

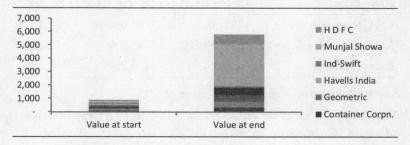

Source: Bloomberg, Ambit Capital research.

Note: Value at start denotes an equal allocation of Rs 100 in each stock at the start of the period. Value at end is the value of each stock at the end of the period. Thus, for this period, the value of the portfolio rose from Rs 900 at the start to Rs 5795 at the end.

Incomplete portfolio (Period 7): 2006–Present (8.1 per cent alpha relative to the Sensex; 17.2 per cent per annum absolute returns)

All-cap portfolio stocks: Infosys, Cipla, Hero MotoCorp, Container Corporation of India, Geometric, Havells India, Suprajit Engineering, Munjal Showa, HDFC Ltd and HDFC Bank.

Large-cap portfolio stocks: Infosys, Hero MotoCorp, Cipla, Container Corporation of India, HDFC Ltd and HDFC Bank.

In the seventh iteration, which also denotes our first incomplete portfolio (incomplete in the sense that the ten-year run of the portfolio has not yet ended), our Coffee Can Portfolio has again outperformed the Sensex till date with an alpha of 8.1 per cent. The large-cap version has also outperformed the Sensex with an alpha of 5.8 per cent. On a risk-adjusted basis as well, both versions beat the Sensex with excess return of 0.19–0.21 times as against 0.02 times for the Sensex (Exhibit 161).

Exhibit 161: Seventh iteration summary

2006–Present*	All-cap CCP	Large-cap CCP	Sensex
CAGR returns	17.2%	14.9%	9.1%
Maximum drawdown**	-49.0%	-33.5%	-52.4%
Excess returns	0.19	0.21	0.02

Source: Bloomberg, Ambit Capital research.

Note: *Portfolio kicks off on 30 June 2006. Excess returns have been calculated as returns in excess of risk-free rate (assumed to be 8%) divided by absolute maximum drawdown. Maximum drawdown is defined as the maximum drop in cumulative returns from the highest peak to the lowest subsequent trough.

**Maximum drawdown took place from December 2007 to December 2008 for the all-cap CCP, large-cap CCP and for the Sensex.

Mid-cap/small-cap stocks again outperformed in this period with Havells and Suprajit Engineering's stock price rising by 11 times and 7 times, respectively (Exhibits 162 and 163).

Exhibit 162: Portfolio performance during the seventh iteration

Company	Price at Start (Rs)	Price at End (Rs)	Share price CAGR	FY06–15 PAT CAGR
Date from/to	30/06/2006	05/04/2016		
Infosys*	384.87	1219.8	13%	20%
Cipla	216	503	9%	7%
Hero Motocorp	793.65	2963.3	14%	11%
Container Corporation	479.97	1254.9	10%	8%
Havells India	27.56	315.5	28%	22%
Geometric	88.2	232.6	10%	9%
Munjal Showa	64.97	170	10%	15%
Suprajit Engineering	19.16	135.1	22%	17%
HDFC	227.96	1103.45	18%	24%
HDFC Bank	159.19	1057.45	21%	32%
Portfolio*	**1000**	**4,708**	**17.2%**	
Sensex	10,609	24,884	9.1%	

Source: Bloomberg, Ambit Capital research.

Note: *Portfolio price at start of Rs 1000 denotes an equal allocation of Rs 100 in each stock at the start of the period. Portfolio price at end is the value of the portfolio at the end of the period. Thus, for this period, the value of the portfolio rose from Rs 1000 at the start to Rs 4708 at the end. Exhibits for Periods 1–5 have not been adjusted for bonus issuance of Infosys shares in December 2014 and June 2015. This exhibit, however, reflects the prices adjusted for the bonus.

Exhibit 163: Mid-caps continued their outperformance in the seventh iteration

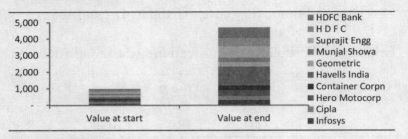

Source: Bloomberg, Ambit Capital research.

Note: Value at start denotes an equal allocation of Rs 100 in each stock at the start of the period. Value at end is the value of each stock at the end of the period. Thus, for this period, the value of the portfolio rose from Rs 1000 at the start to Rs 4708 at the end.

Incomplete portfolio (Period 8): 2007–Present (9.3 per cent alpha relative to the Sensex; 15.5 per cent per annum absolute returns)

All-cap portfolio stocks: Infosys, Wipro, Cipla, Tech Mahindra, Hindalco, Hero MotoCorp, Container Corporation of India, Asian Paints, Havells India, Geometric, Aftek, Munjal Showa, Suprajit Engineering, HDFC Ltd and HDFC Bank.

Large-cap portfolio stocks: Infosys, Wipro, Cipla, Tech Mahindra, Hindalco, Hero MotoCorp, Container Corporation of India, Asian Paints, HDFC Ltd and HDFC Bank.

In the eighth iteration, our Coffee Can Portfolio continued its outperformance versus the Sensex both on an absolute and risk-adjusted basis. The large-cap CCP beat the all-cap CCP on a risk-adjusted basis (0.17 times for large-cap CCP as against 0.15 times for all-cap CCP) (Exhibit 164).

Exhibit 164: Eighth iteration summary

2007–Present*	All-cap CCP	Large-cap CCP	Sensex
CAGR returns	15.5%	14.5%	6.2%
Maximum drawdown**	-51.4%	-38.9%	-52.4%
Excess returns	0.15	0.17	-0.03

Source: Bloomberg, Ambit Capital research.

Note: *Portfolio kicks off on 30 June 2007. Excess returns have been calculated as returns in excess of risk-free rate (assumed to be 8%) divided by absolute maximum drawdown. Maximum drawdown is defined as the maximum drop in cumulative returns from the highest peak to the lowest subsequent trough.

**Maximum drawdown took place from December 2007 to December 2008 for the all-cap CCP, large-cap CCP and for the Sensex.

In this iteration, large-caps lead the charge with Asian Paints being the star performer with a jump in stock price of almost 11 times. Extreme movements were seen in mid-cap stocks again with stocks like Suprajit Engineering rising almost 8.5 times whereas Aftek lost 97 per cent of its value before its suspension (Exhibits 165 and 166).

Exhibit 165: Portfolio performance during the eighth iteration

Company	Price at Start (Rs)	Price at End (Rs)	Share price CAGR	FY07–15 PAT CAGR
Date from/to	30/06/2007	05/04/2016		
Infosys	482	1219.8	11.2%	16%
Wipro	277	559	8.3%	14%
Cipla	208	503	10.6%	7%

(Contd)

Company	Price at Start (Rs)	Price at End (Rs)	Share price CAGR	FY07–15 PAT CAGR
Date from/to	30/06/2007	05/04/2016		
Tech Mahindra	349	462.25	3.3%	22%
Hindalco	145	84.9	-5.9%	NA
Hero Motocorp	693	2963.3	18.0%	14%
Container Corporation	778	1254.9	5.6%	5%
Asian Paints	81	869.85	31.1%	22%
Havells India	48	315.5	23.9%	18%
Geometric	125	232.6	7.4%	5%
Aftek	71	NA	NA	NA
Munjal Showa	50	170	15.1%	14%
Suprajit Engineering	16	135.1	27.7%	17%
HDFC	407	1103.45	12.0%	22%
HDFC Bank	229	1057.45	19.0%	32%
Portfolio*	**1500**	**5322**	**15.5%**	
Sensex	14,651	24,884	6.2%	

Source: Bloomberg, Ambit Capital research.

Note: *Portfolio price at start of Rs 1500 denotes an equal allocation of Rs 100 in each stock at the start of the period. Data for Aftek is not available because the company was suspended during this period. Portfolio price at end is the value of the portfolio at the end of the period. Thus, for this period, the value of the portfolio rose from Rs 1500 at the start to Rs 5322 at the end. Exhibits for Periods 1–5 have not been adjusted for bonus issuance of Infosys shares in December 2014 and June 2015. This exhibit, however, reflects the prices adjusted for the bonus.

Exhibit 166: Asian Paints was the star performer in the eighth iteration

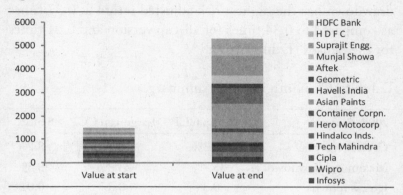

Source: Bloomberg, Ambit Capital research.

Note: Value at start denotes an equal allocation of Rs 100 in each stock at the start of the period. Value at end is the value of each stock at the end of the period. Thus, for this period, the value of the portfolio rose from Rs 1500 at the start to Rs 5322 at the end.

Incomplete portfolio (Period 9): 2008–Present (11.1 per cent alpha relative to the Sensex; 19.3 per cent per annum absolute returns)

All-cap portfolio stocks: Infosys, Wipro, Cipla, Asian Paints, Tech Mahindra, Havells India, Automotive Axles, Geometric, HDFC Ltd, HDFC Bank and Punjab National Bank.

Large-cap portfolio stocks: Infosys, Wipro, Cipla, Asian Paints, Tech Mahindra, HDFC Ltd, HDFC Bank and Punjab National Bank.

Our ninth iteration that begins in June 2008 is also outperforming the Sensex with an alpha of 11.1 per cent.

The large-cap version also beats the Sensex with an alpha of 8.7 per cent. The large-cap version on account of lower drawdown has the highest risk adjusted return at 0.37 times as compared to 0.34 times for all-cap version and 0.01 times for the Sensex (Exhibit 167).

Exhibit 167: Ninth iteration summary

2008–Present*	All-cap CCP	Large-cap CCP	Sensex
CAGR returns	19.3%	16.9%	8.2%
Maximum drawdown**	-33.7%	-23.8%	-28.3%
Excess returns	0.34	0.37	0.01

Source: Bloomberg, Ambit Capital research.

Note: *Portfolio kicks off on 30 June 2008. Excess returns have been calculated as returns in excess of risk-free rate (assumed to be 8%) divided by absolute maximum drawdown. Maximum drawdown is defined as the maximum drop in cumulative returns from the highest peak to the lowest subsequent trough.

**Maximum drawdown took place from December 2007 to December 2008 for the all-cap CCP, large-cap CCP and for the Sensex.

Both large-caps and mid-caps shared the outperformance during this iteration with Asian Paints's and HDFC Bank's stock prices rising by 30 per cent and 24 per cent, respectively, on an annualized basis whilst Havells India continuing its dream run with a 33 per cent annualized return (Exhibits 168 and 169).

Exhibit 168: Portfolio performance during the ninth iteration

Company	Price at Start (Rs)	Price at End (Rs)	Share price CAGR	FY08–15 PAT CAGR
Date from/to	30/06/2008	05/04/2016		
Infosys	434	1219.8	14.2%	15%
Wipro	235	559	11.8%	15%
Cipla	211	503	11.8%	7%
Asian Paints	115	869.85	29.8%	19%
Tech Mahindra	179	462.25	13.0%	21%
Havells India	34	315.5	33.2%	13%
Automotive Axles	242	571.9	11.7%	-13%
Geometric	47	232.6	22.9%	8%
HDFC	393	1103.45	14.2%	18%
HDFC Bank	201	1057.45	23.8%	31%
Punjab National Bank	75	82.8	1.3%	6%
Portfolio*	**1100**	**4346**	**19.3%**	
Sensex	13,462	24,884	8.2%	

Source: Bloomberg, Ambit Capital research.

Note: *Portfolio price at start of Rs 1100 denotes an equal allocation of Rs 100 in each stock at the start of the period. Portfolio price at end is the value of the portfolio at the end of the period. Thus, for this period, the value of the portfolio rose from Rs 1100 at the start to Rs 4346 at the end. Exhibits for Periods 1–5 have not been adjusted for bonus issuance of Infosys shares in December 2014 and June 2015. This exhibit, however, reflects the prices adjusted for the bonus.

Exhibit 169: Large-caps and mid-caps shared outperformance in this iteration

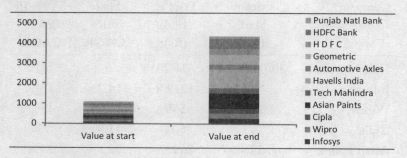

Source: Bloomberg, Ambit Capital research.

Note: Value at start denotes an equal allocation of Rs 100 in each stock at the start of the period. Value at end is the value of each stock at the end of the period. Thus, for this period, the value of the portfolio rose from Rs 1100 at the start to Rs 4346 at the end.

Incomplete portfolio (Period 10): 2009–Present (11.8 per cent alpha relative to the Sensex; 20.1 per cent per annum absolute returns)

All-cap portfolio stocks: Infosys, Wipro, Jindal Steel, Cipla, Asian Paints, Oracle Financial Services, Tech Mahindra, Motherson Sumi, HDFC Ltd, HDFC Bank and Punjab National Bank.

Large-cap portfolio stocks: Infosys, Wipro, Jindal Steel, Cipla, Asian Paints, Oracle Financial Services, HDFC Ltd, HDFC Bank and Punjab National Bank.

In the iteration beginning in 2009, both all-cap and large-cap CCP beat Sensex comprehensively again with alpha of 11.8 per cent and 7.5 per cent, respectively. On a risk-adjusted basis, they gave a stable performance as well with excess returns of 0.40–0.61 times (Exhibit 170).

Exhibit 170: Tenth iteration summary

2009–Present*	All-cap CCP	Large-cap CCP	Sensex
CAGR returns	20.1%	15.8%	8.3%
Maximum drawdown**	-20.0%	-19.3%	-24.6%
Excess returns	0.61	0.40	0.01

Source: Bloomberg, Ambit Capital research.

Note: *Portfolio kicks off on 30 June 2009. Excess returns have been calculated as returns in excess of risk-free rate (assumed to be 8%) divided by absolute maximum drawdown. Maximum drawdown is defined as the maximum drop in cumulative returns from the highest peak to the lowest subsequent trough.

**Maximum drawdown took place from December 2010 to December 2011 for the all-cap CCP, large-cap CCP and for the Sensex.

Motherson Sumi was the star performer in this iteration with the stock price rising 11 times during this period (Exhibits 171 and 172).

Exhibit 171: Portfolio performance during the tenth iteration

Company	Price at Start (Rs)	Price at End (Rs)	Share price CAGR	FY09–15 PAT CAGR
Date from/to	30/06/2009	05/04/2016		
Infosys	444	1219.8	16%	13%
Wipro	202	559	16%	14%
Jindal Steel	415	60.1	-25%	NA
Cipla	253	503	11%	7%
Asian Paints	119	869.85	34%	23%
Oracle Financial Services	1249	3538.15	17%	7%
Tech Mahindra	183	462.25	15%	17%
Motherson Sumi	22	251.3	43%	33%

(Contd)

Company	Price at Start (Rs)	Price at End (Rs)	Share price CAGR	FY09–15 PAT CAGR
Date from/to	30/06/2009	05/04/2016		
HDFC Bank	299	1057.45	21%	30%
HDFC	469	1103.45	13%	25%
Punjab National Bank	136	82.8	-7%	1%
Portfolio*	**1100**	**3,806**	**20.1%**	
Sensex	14,494	24,884	8.3%	

Source: Bloomberg, Ambit Capital research.

Note: *Portfolio price at start of Rs 1100 denotes an equal allocation of Rs 100 in each stock at the start of the period. Portfolio price at end is the value of the portfolio at the end of the period. Thus, for this period, the value of the portfolio rose from Rs 1100 at the start to Rs 3806 at the end. Exhibits for Periods 1–5 have not been adjusted for bonus issuance of Infosys shares in December 2014 and June 2015. This exhibit, however, reflects the prices adjusted for the bonus.

Exhibit 172: Motherson Sumi was the star performer in this iteration

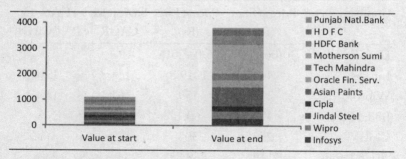

Source: Bloomberg, Ambit Capital research.

Note: Value at start denotes an equal allocation of Rs 100 in each stock at the start of the period. Value at end is the value of each stock at the end of the period. Thus, for this period, the value of the portfolio rose from Rs 1100 at the start to Rs 3806 at the end.

Incomplete portfolio (Period 11): 2010–Present (7.3 per cent alpha relative to the Sensex; 13.4 per cent per annum absolute returns)

All-cap portfolio stocks: Asian Paints, Amar Remedies, Motherson Sumi, Tulip Telecom, HDFC Bank, Punjab National Bank and Dewan Housing Finance.

Large-cap portfolio stocks: Asian Paints, HDFC Bank and Punjab National Bank.

In this iteration, our Coffee Can Portfolio outperformed the Sensex with an alpha of 7.3 per cent. The large-cap version beat both the Sensex and the all-cap version in this iteration with an outperformance of 9.5 per cent and 2.2 per cent, respectively.

Exhibit 173: Eleventh iteration summary

2010–2015*	All-cap CCP	Large-cap CCP	Sensex
CAGR returns	13.4%	15.6%	6.1%
Maximum drawdown**	-20.4%	-20.1%	-24.6%
Excess returns	0.26	0.38	0.08

Source: Bloomberg, Ambit Capital research.

Note: *Portfolio kicks off on 30 June 2010. Excess returns have been calculated as returns in excess of risk-free rate (assumed to be 8%) divided by absolute maximum drawdown. Maximum drawdown is defined as the maximum drop in cumulative returns from the highest peak to the lowest subsequent trough.

**Maximum drawdown took place from December 2010 to December 2011 for the all-cap CCP, large-cap CCP and for the Sensex.

The performance of the portfolio in this iteration was led by Motherson Sumi and Asian Paints in this iteration. In spite of suspension of trading in two of the constituent stocks through the period (Amar Remedies and Tulip Telecom), the portfolio gave a stellar performance with a 13.4 per cent CAGR (Exhibits 174 and 175).

Exhibit 174: Portfolio performance during the eleventh iteration

Company	Price at Start (Rs)	Price at End (Rs)	Share price CAGR	FY10–15 PAT CAGR
Date from/to	30/06/2010	05/04/2016		
Asian Paints	230	870	26%	12%
Amar Remedies	77	NA	NA	NA
Motherson Sumi	43	251	36%	31%
Tulip Telecom	175	NA	NA	NA
HDFC Bank	384	1057	19%	29%
Punjab National Bank	210	83	-15%	-3%
Dewan Housing Finance	117	190	9%	32%
Portfolio*	**700**	**1438**	**13.4%**	
Sensex	17,701	24,884	6.1%	

Source: Bloomberg, Ambit Capital research.

Note: *Portfolio price at start of Rs 700 denotes an equal allocation of Rs 100 in each stock at the start of the period. Data for Amar Remedies and Tulip Telecom is not available because the companies were suspended during this period. Portfolio price at end is the value of the portfolio at the end of the period. Thus, for this period, the value of the portfolio rose from Rs 700 at the start to Rs 1438 at the end. Exhibits for Periods 1–5 have not been adjusted for bonus issuance of Infosys shares in December 2014 and June 2015. This exhibit, however, reflects the prices adjusted for the bonus.

Exhibit 175: Motherson Sumi was the star performer in this iteration

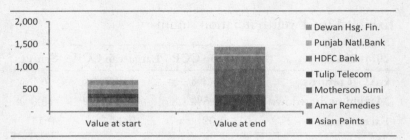

Source: Bloomberg, Ambit Capital research.

Note: Value at start denotes an equal allocation of Rs 100 in each stock at the start of the period. Value at end is the value of each stock at the end of the period. Thus, for this period, the value of the portfolio rose from Rs 700 at the start to Rs 1438 at the end. Data for Amar Remedies and Tulip Telecom is not available because the companies were delisted during this period.

Incomplete portfolio (Period 12): 2011–Present (0.3 per cent alpha relative to the Sensex; 6.3 per cent per annum absolute returns)

All-cap portfolio stocks: ITC, Asian Paints, Motherson Sumi, Ipca, Tulip Telecom, Zylog Systems, Pratibha Industries, Unity Infra, Amar Remedies, Setco Automotive, HDFC Bank, Punjab National Bank, Dewan Housing and City Union Bank.

Large-cap portfolio stocks: ITC, Asian Paints, HDFC Bank and Punjab National Bank.

This iteration gave the weakest result in terms of both the absolute performance of our Coffee Can Portfolio and the alpha generated versus the Sensex. The large-cap version continued its outperformance in this iteration as well beating both the all-cap version and the Sensex on both absolute and risk-adjusted return measures (Exhibit 176).

Exhibit 176: Twelfth iteration summary

2011–2015*	All-cap CCP	Large-cap CCP	Sensex
CAGR returns	6.3%	11.8%	6.0%
Maximum drawdown**	-21.5%	-15.7%	-18.0%
Excess returns	-0.08	0.24	-0.11

Source: Bloomberg, Ambit Capital research.

Note: *Portfolio kicks off on 30 June 2011. Excess returns have been calculated as returns in excess of risk-free rate (assumed to be 8%) divided by absolute maximum drawdown. Maximum drawdown is defined as the maximum drop in cumulative returns from the highest peak to the lowest subsequent trough.

**Maximum drawdown took place from June 2011 to December 2011 for the all-cap CCP, large-cap CCP and for the Sensex.

Extreme price performance among mid-cap/small-cap stocks was seen during this iteration. Motherson Sumi's stock price rose by 3.7 times during this period whilst Zylog Systems lost 98 per cent of its value (Exhibits 177 and 178).

Exhibit 177: Portfolio performance during the twelfth iteration

Company	Price at Start (Rs)	Price at End (Rs)	Share price CAGR	FY11–15 PAT CAGR
Date from/to	30/06/2011	05/04/2016		
ITC	203	326	10%	18%
Asian Paints	319	870	23%	13%
Motherson Sumi	67	251	32%	26%

(*Contd*)

Company	Price at Start (Rs)	Price at End (Rs)	Share price CAGR	FY11– 15 PAT CAGR
Date from/to	30/06/2011	05/04/2016		
Ipca Labs	344	555	11%	-1%
Tulip Telecom	162	NA	NA	NA
Zylog Systems	200	4	-56%	NA
Pratibha Industries	54	33	-10%	-7%
Unity Infra.	64	11	-31%	NA
Amar Remedies	101	NA	NA	NA
Setco Automotive	21	30	8%	-12%
HDFC Bank	503	1057	17%	28%
Punjab National Bank	218	83	-18%	-7%
Dewan Housing Finance	111	190	12%	20%
City Union Bank	39	96	21%	16%
Portfolio*	**1400**	**1864**	**6.3%**	
Sensex	18,846	24,884	6.0%	

Source: Bloomberg, Ambit Capital research.

Note: *Portfolio price at start of Rs 1400 denotes an equal allocation of Rs 100 in each stock at the start of the period. Data for Amar Remedies and Tulip Telecom is not available because the companies were suspended during this period. Portfolio price at end is the value of the portfolio at the end of the period. Thus, for this period, the value of the portfolio rose from Rs 1400 at the start to Rs 1864 at the end. Exhibits for Periods 1–5 have not been adjusted for bonus issuance of Infosys shares in December 2014 and June 2015. This exhibit, however, reflects the prices adjusted for the bonus.

Exhibit 178: Extreme price performance was seen in mid/ small-caps in this iteration

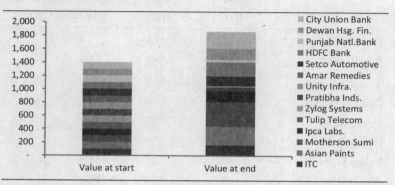

Source: Bloomberg, Ambit Capital research.

Note: Value at start denotes an equal allocation of Rs 100 in each stock at the start of the period. Value at end is the value of each stock at the end of the period. Thus, for this period, the value of the portfolio rose from Rs 1400 at the start to Rs 1864 at the end. Data for Amar Remedies and Tulip Telecom is not available because the companies were suspended during this period.

Incomplete portfolio (Period 13): 2012–Present (8.4 per cent alpha relative to the Sensex; 18.3 per cent per annum absolute returns)

All-cap portfolio stocks: ITC, Asian Paints, Marico, Opto Circuits, Ipca Labs, Berger paints, Page Industries, Balkrishna Industries, Grindwell Norton, Zylog Systems, Tecpro Systems, Pratibha Industries, Astral Poly Technik, Amar Remedies, Unity Infra, Setco Automotive, HDFC Bank, Axis Bank, Punjab National Bank, Allahabad Bank, Dewan Housing and City Union Bank.

Large-cap portfolio stocks: ITC, Asian Paints, HDFC Bank, Axis Bank and Punjab National Bank.

In the iteration beginning June 2012, the all-cap version again came to the fore beating both the Sensex and the large-cap CCP on both absolute basis and risk-adjusted basis (Exhibit 179).

Exhibit 179: Thirteenth iteration summary

2012–Present*	All-cap CCP	Large-cap CCP	Sensex
CAGR returns	18.3%	13.3%	9.9%
Maximum drawdown**	-16.2%	-12.9%	-11.0%
Excess returns	0.64	0.42	0.17

Source: Bloomberg, Ambit Capital research.

Note: *Portfolio kicks off on 30 June 2012. Excess returns have been calculated as returns in excess of risk-free rate (assumed to be 8%) divided by absolute maximum drawdown. Maximum drawdown is defined as the maximum drop in cumulative returns from the highest peak to the lowest subsequent trough.

**Maximum drawdown took place from December 2012 to September 2013 for the all-cap CCP, and large-cap CCP and from September 2015 to 05 April 2016 for the Sensex.

With twenty-two companies making the cut in this iteration, this was the biggest Coffee Can Portfolio in terms of number of constituent companies. Astral Poly Technik was the star performer in this iteration with almost 9 times increase in the stock price. Zylog Systems and Tecpro Systems, on the other hand, lost almost their entire value with a drop of 99 per cent and 98 per cent in their stock price, respectively (Exhibits 180 and 181).

Exhibit 180: Portfolio performance during the thirteenth iteration

Company	Price at Start (Rs)	Price at End (Rs)	Share price CAGR	FY12–15 PAT CAGR
Date from/to	30/06/2012	05/04/2016		
ITC	259	326	6%	13%
Asian Paints	389	870	24%	21%
Marico	90	245	31%	-46%
Opto Circuits	154	10	-52%	-3%
Ipca Labs.	359	555	12%	13%
Berger Paints	69	246	40%	30%
Page Industries	2885	12,143	46%	21%
Balkrishna Inds	253	627	27%	-1%
Grindwell Norton	245	650	30%	NA
Zylog Systems	310	4	-68%	NA
Tecpro Systems	158	3	-65%	-12%
Pratibha Inds.	46	33	-9%	25%
Astral Poly	45	416	81%	NA
Amar Remedies	135	NA	NA	NA
Unity Infra.	46	11	-31%	-25%
Setco Automotive	29	30	2%	27%
HDFC Bank	564	1057	18%	21%
Axis Bank	203	433	22%	-12%
Punjab National Bank	162	83	-16%	-30%
Allahabad Bank	150	55	-24%	24%
Dewan Housing Finance	83	190	25%	11%
City Union Bank	45	96	22%	16%

(*Contd*)

Company	Price at Start (Rs)	Price at End (Rs)	Share price CAGR	FY12–15 PAT CAGR
Date from/to	30/06/2012	05/04/2016		
Portfolio*	**2200**	**4143**	**18.3%**	
Sensex	17430	24,884	9.9%	

Source: Bloomberg, Ambit Capital research.

Note: *Portfolio price at start of Rs 2200 denotes an equal allocation of Rs 100 in each stock at the start of the period. Data for Amar Remedies is not available because the company was suspended during this period. Portfolio price at end is the value of the portfolio at the end of the period. Thus, for this period, the value of the portfolio rose from Rs 2200 at the start to Rs 4143 at the end. Exhibits for Periods 1–5 have not been adjusted for bonus issuance of Infosys shares in December 2014 and June 2015. This exhibit, however, reflects the prices adjusted for the bonus.

Exhibit 181: Astral Poly Technik outperformed other stocks in this iteration

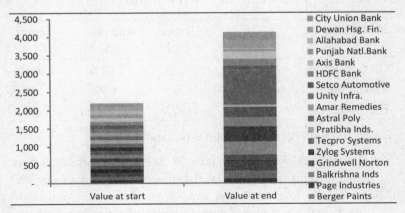

Source: Bloomberg, Ambit Capital research.

Note: Value at start denotes an equal allocation of Rs 100 in each stock at the start of the period. Value at end is the value of each stock at the end of the period. Thus, for this period, the value of the portfolio rose from Rs 2200 at the start to Rs 4143 at the end.

Incomplete portfolio (Period 14): 2013–Present (21.3 per cent alpha relative to the Sensex; 30.7 per cent per annum absolute returns)

All-cap portfolio stocks: ITC, HCL Technologies, Asian Paints, Marico, Berger Paints, Ipca, Page Industries, Balkrishna Industries, Solar Industries, Astral Poly Technik, Pratibha Industries, Unity Infra, Sarla Performance Fibers, HDFC Bank, Axis Bank, Indian Bank, City Union Bank and Dewan Housing.

Large-cap portfolio stocks: ITC, HCL Tech, Asian Paints, Marico, HDFC Bank, Axis Bank.

This iteration has given the best results thus far with a whopping return of 30.7 per cent on a CAGR basis. Sensex over the same period has generated a CAGR return of 9.4 per cent whereas the large-cap portfolio has generated a CAGR return of 23.1 per cent (Exhibit 182).

Exhibit 182: Fourteenth iteration summary

2013–Present*	All-cap CCP	Large-cap CCP	Sensex
CAGR returns	30.7%	23.1%	9.4%
Maximum drawdown**	-6.0%	-1.9%	-11.0%
Excess returns	3.77	7.94	0.13

Source: Bloomberg, Ambit Capital research.

Note: *Portfolio kicks off on 30 June 2013. Excess returns have been calculated as returns in excess of risk-free rate (assumed to be 8%) divided by absolute maximum drawdown. Maximum drawdown is defined as the maximum drop in cumulative returns from the highest peak to the lowest subsequent trough.

**Maximum drawdown took place from June 2013 to September 2013 for the all-cap CCP, from September 2015 and April 2016 for the large cap CCP and Sensex.

Mid-cap stocks led the performance of the profile in this iteration with some of the stock prices increasing three to four times since the beginning of this portfolio in June 2013. These stocks included names like Astral Poly Technik, Solar Industries, Balkrishna Industries and Page Industries (Exhibits 183 and 184).

Exhibit 183: Portfolio performance during the fourteenth iteration

Company	Price at Start (Rs)	Price at End (Rs)	Share price CAGR	FY13–15 PAT CAGR
Date from/to	30/06/2013	05/04/2016		
ITC	324	326	0%	13%
HCL				35%
Technologies	388	843	32%	
Asian Paints	464	870	25%	13%
Marico	101	245	37%	23%
Berger Paints	115	246	32%	9%
Ipca Labs.	655	555	-6%	-12%
Page Industries	4097	12,143	48%	32%
Balkrishna				16%
Industries	205	627	50%	
Solar Industries				12%
	928	3,439	60%	
Astral Poly	111	416	61%	13%
Pratibha				-19%
Industries	27	33	7%	
Unity Infra.	26	11	-26%	NA
Sarla Performance	16	65	65%	0%
HDFC Bank	670	1,057	18%	25%

(*Contd*)

Company	Price at Start (Rs)	Price at End (Rs)	Share price CAGR	FY13–15 PAT CAGR
Axis Bank	265	433	19%	19%
Indian Bank	115	102	-4%	-19%
City Union Bank	55	96	22%	10%
Dewan Housing Finance	80	190	37%	18%
Portfolio*	**1800**	**3784**	**30.7%**	
Sensex	19396	24,884	9.4%	

Source: Bloomberg, Ambit Capital research.

Note: *Portfolio price at start of Rs 1800 denotes an equal allocation of Rs 100 in each stock at the start of the period. Portfolio price at end is the value of the portfolio at the end of the period. Thus, for this period, the value of the portfolio rose from Rs 1800 at the start to Rs 3784 at the end. Exhibits for Periods 1–5 have not been adjusted for bonus issuance of Infosys shares in December 2014 and June 2015. This exhibit, however, reflects the prices adjusted for the bonus.

Exhibit 184: Mid-caps led the charge in this iteration generating most of the portfolio's value

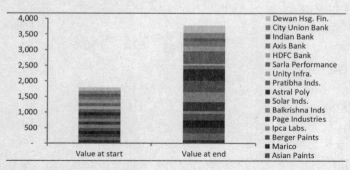

Source: Bloomberg, Ambit Capital research.

Note: Value at start denotes an equal allocation of Rs 100 in each stock at the start of the period. Value at end is the value of each

stock at the end of the period. Thus, for this period, the value of the portfolio rose from Rs 1800 at the start to Rs 3784 at the end.

Incomplete portfolio (Period 15): 2014–Present (18.3 per cent alpha relative to the Sensex; 17.1 per cent absolute returns till date)

All-cap portfolio stocks: ITC, Asian Paints, Godrej Consumer, Marico, Ipca, Berger Paints, Page Industries, Balkrishna Industries, eClerx Services, Mayur Uniquoters, V-Guard Industries, HCL Tech, HDFC Bank, Axis Bank, City Union Bank, Gruh Finance.

Large-cap portfolio stocks: ITC, Asian Paints, Godrej Consumer, Marico, HCL Tech, HDFC Bank and Axis Bank.

The returns shown in the tables below denote the performance of the portfolio since 30 June 2014. As can be seen, the portfolio has outperformed the Sensex by a handsome margin of 18.3 per cent over this period.

Exhibit 185: Fifteenth iteration summary

2014–Present*	All-cap CCP	Large-cap CCP	Sensex
CAGR returns	17.1%	20.0%	-1.2%
Maximum drawdown**	-0.9%	-1.0%	-11.0%
Excess returns	10.10	11.47	-0.84

Source: Bloomberg, Ambit Capital research.

Note: *Portfolio kicks off on 30 June 2014. Excess returns have been calculated as returns in excess of risk-free rate (assumed to be 8%) divided by absolute maximum drawdown. Maximum drawdown is defined as the maximum drop in cumulative returns from the highest peak to the lowest subsequent trough.

**Maximum drawdown took place from November 2014 to September 2015 for the all-cap CCP and large-cap CCP and from March 2015 to April 2016 for the Sensex.

The performance was mainly driven by Marico during this period by generating a CAGR return of 48 per cent.

Exhibit 186: Portfolio performance during the fifteenth iteration

Company	Price at Start (Rs)	Price at End (Rs)	Share price CAGR	FY14–15 PAT CAGR
Date from/to	30/6/2014	05/04/2016		
ITC	325	326	0%	9%
Asian Paints	594	870	24%	15%
Godrej Consumer	824	1352	32%	21%
Marico	122	245	48%	18%
Ipca Labs	878	555	-23%	-48%
Berger Paints	145	246	35%	5%
Page Industries	7162	12,143	35%	28%
Balkrishna Industries	754	627	-10%	0%
eClerx Services	870	1325	27%	-10%
Mayur Uniquoters	376	400	4%	14%
V-Guard Industries	590	893	26%	1%
HCL Technologies	750	843	7%	14%
HDFC Bank	822	1057	15%	22%
Axis Bank	384	433	7%	18%

(*Contd*)

Company	Price at Start (Rs)	Price at End (Rs)	Share price CAGR	FY14–15 PAT CAGR
City Union Bank	75	96	15%	12%
Gruh Finance	201	250	13%	15%
Portfolio*	**1600**	**2114**	**17.1%**	
Sensex	25,414	24,884	-1.2%	

Source: Bloomberg, Ambit Capital research.

Note: *Portfolio price at start of Rs 1600 denotes an equal allocation of Rs 100 in each stock at the start of the period. Portfolio price at end is the value of the portfolio at the end of the period. Thus, for this period, the value of the portfolio rose from Rs 1600 at the start to Rs 2114 at the end. Exhibits for Periods 1–5 have not been adjusted for bonus issuance of Infosys shares in December 2014 and June 2015. This exhibit, however, reflects the prices adjusted for the bonus.

Exhibit 187: Marico was the best performer in the fifteenth iteration of the CCP

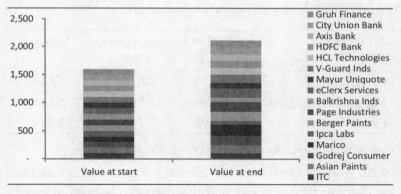

Source: Bloomberg, Ambit Capital research.

Note: Value at start denotes an equal allocation of Rs 100 in each stock at the start of the period. Value at end is the value of each

stock at the end of the period. Thus, for this period, the value of the portfolio rose from Rs 1600 at the start to Rs 2114 at the end.

Incomplete portfolio (Period 16): 2015–Present (10.6 per cent alpha relative to the Sensex; -2.7 per cent absolute returns till date)

All-cap portfolio stocks: ITC, HCL Tech, Lupin, Asian Paints, Cadila, Britannia, Marico, GSK Consumer, Colgate, Amara Raja, Page Industries, Berger Paints, eClerx Services, Astral, V-Guard, Cera Sanitaryware, HDFC Bank, Axis Bank, LIC HF, Gruh Finance.

Large-cap portfolio stocks: ITC, HCL Tech, Lupin, Asian Paints, Cadila, Britannia, Marico, GSK Consumer, Colgate, HDFC Bank, Axis Bank, LIC HF.

This iteration showcases the performance of our latest published portfolio. As can be seen, the portfolio has outperformed the Sensex by a handsome margin of 10.6 per cent over this period as well (Exhibit 188).

Exhibit 188: Sixteenth iteration summary

2015–Present*	All-cap CCP	Large-cap CCP	Sensex
CAGR returns	-2.7%	-6.6%	-13.4%
Maximum drawdown**	-5.4%	-7.5%	-10.4%
Excess returns	-1.98	-1.93	-2.05

Source: Bloomberg, Ambit Capital research.

Note: *Portfolio kicks off on 30 June 2015. Excess returns have been calculated as returns in excess of risk-free rate (assumed to be 8%) divided by absolute maximum drawdown. Maximum drawdown is defined as the maximum drop in cumulative returns from the highest peak to the lowest subsequent trough.

**Maximum drawdown took place from June 2015 to April 2016 for the all-cap CCP, large-cap CCP and for the Sensex.

The all-cap portfolio was able to outperform the Sensex and the large-cap portfolio on the back of strong performance of Berger paints and eClerx services that have generated a CAGR return of 35 per cent and 25 per cent, respectively.

Exhibit 189: Portfolio performance during the sixteenth iteration

Company	Price at Start (Rs)	Price at End (Rs)	Share price CAGR	FY14–15 PAT CAGR
Date from/to	30/6/2015	05/04/2016		
ITC	315	326	5%	9%
HCL Technologies	920	843	-11%	12%
Lupin	1,886	1464	-28%	30%
Asian Paints	755	870	20%	15%
Cadila Health	359	319	-14%	41%
Britannia Inds	2763	2641	-6%	46%
Marico	225	245	12%	18%
GlaxoSmith C H L	6272	6036	-5%	8%
Colgate-Palm	1020	831	-23%	14%
Amara Raja Batt	883	891	1%	12%
Page Industries	15,115	12,143	-25%	28%
Berger Paints	195	246	35%	5%
eClerx Services	1116	1325	25%	-10%

(*Contd*)

Astral Poly	389	416	9%	-3%
V-Guard Inds	896	893	0%	1%
Cera Sanitary.	1957	1775	-12%	32%
HDFC Bank	1067	1057	-1%	22%
Axis Bank	559	433	-28%	18%
LIC Housing Fin.	451	468	5%	6%
Gruh Finance	262	250	-6%	15%
Portfolio*	**2000**	**1957**	**-2.7%**	
Sensex	27,781	24,884	-13.4%	

Source: Bloomberg, Ambit Capital research.

Note: *Portfolio price at start of Rs 2000 denotes an equal allocation of Rs 100 in each stock at the start of the period. Portfolio price at end is the value of the portfolio at the end of the period. Thus, for this period, the value of the portfolio dropped from Rs 2000 at the start to Rs 1957 at the end.

Exhibit 190: Berger Paints and eClerx have been the best performers in the sixteenth iteration of the CCP

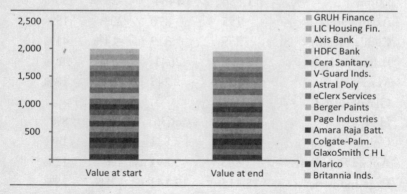

Source: Bloomberg, Ambit Capital research. Note: Value at start denotes an equal allocation of Rs 100 in each stock at the start of the period. Value at end is the value of each stock at the end of the period. Thus, for this period, the value of the portfolio dropped from Rs 2000 at the start to Rs 1957 at the end.

The Case against Churning

There is one rather obvious question that should alert the reader's mind. The Coffee Can Portfolio changes every year. This is only logical since not all companies can keep maintaining a revenue growth of more than 10 per cent every year and simultaneously deliver ROCEs of more than 15 per cent every year for ten years at a stretch. Thus, those companies that fail the twin Coffee Can filters exit the portfolio while those new companies that meet the filters enter the portfolio. This process of stocks going out and new stocks coming in is also called churn. Therefore, the question that investors will ask is: Shouldn't the Coffee Cans be churned every year as companies enter and exit? My answer is an overwhelming 'No'. I believe that rebalancing the CCP every year goes against the basic philosophy of long-term investing, which is a cornerstone of Robert Kirby's original Coffee Can construct. I offer five compelling reasons in favour of keeping the CCP intact every year for ten consecutive years:

Reason 1: Higher probability of profits over long term

As is well understood, equities as an asset class is prone to extreme movements in the short term. For example, whilst the Sensex has returned over 15 per cent CAGR returns over the last twenty-five years, there have been intermittent periods of unusually high drawdowns. In 2008, for instance, an investor entering the market near the peak in January would have lost over 60 per cent of value in less than twelve months of investing. Thus, whilst over longer time horizons, the odds of profiting from equity investments are very high, the same cannot be said of shorter time frames. In his book, *More Than You Know*, Michael Mauboussin, managing director and head of global financial strategies at Credit Suisse, illustrates this concept using simple maths in the context of US equities. I use that illustration and apply it in the context of Indian equities here.

I note that the Sensex's returns over the past thirty years have been 16 per cent on a CAGR basis, whilst the standard deviation of returns has been approximately 29 per cent. Now using these values of returns and standard deviation and assuming a normal distribution of returns (a simplifying assumption), the probability of generating positive returns over a one-day time horizon works out to be approximately 51.2 per cent.

As the time horizon increases, the probability of generating positive returns goes up. The probability of generating positive returns goes up to around 70 per cent if the time horizon increases to one year; the probability tends towards 100 per cent if the time horizon is increased to ten years (see Exhibit 191).

Exhibit 191: Probability of gains from equity investing in India increase disproportionately with increase in holding horizons

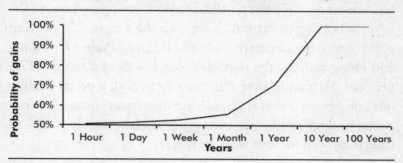

Source: Bloomberg, Ambit Capital research.

Note: This chart has been inspired by similar work done by Michael Mauboussin in the Western context.

Reason 2: Power of compounding

Holding a portfolio of stock for periods as long as ten years or more allows the power of compounding to play out its magic in a rather unusual way. Over the longer term, the portfolio comes to be dominated by the winning stocks whilst losing stocks keep declining to eventually become inconsequential. Thus, the positive contribution of the winners disproportionately outweighs the negative contribution of losers to eventually help the portfolio compound handsomely. I will illustrate the point here using simple mathematics. Let's consider a hypothetical portfolio that consists only of two stocks. One of these stocks, stock A, grows at 26 per cent per annum whilst the other, say stock B, declines at the same rate, i.e. at 26 per cent per annum. Overall, not only do I assume a fifty-fifty strike rate, I also assume symmetry around the magnitude of positive and negative returns generated by the winner and the loser respectively.

In Exhibit 192, I track the progress of this portfolio over a ten-year holding horizon. As time progresses, stock B declines to irrelevance while the portfolio value starts converging to the value of holding in stock A. Even with the assumed 50 per cent strike rate with symmetry around the magnitude of winning and losing returns, the portfolio compounds at a healthy 17.6 per cent per annum over this ten-year period, a pretty healthy rate of return. This example demonstrates how powerful compounding can be for investor portfolios if only sufficient time is allowed for it to work its magic.

Exhibit 192: A hypothetical portfolio with 50% strike rate and symmetry around positive and negative returns

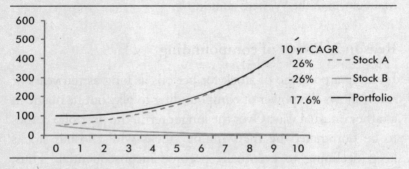

Source: Ambit Capital research.

Reason 3: Neutralizing the negatives of 'noise'

Investing and holding for the long term is the most effective way of killing the 'noise' that interferes with the investment process. In his book, *Investing—The Last Liberal Art* (2013), Robert G. Hagstrom talks about the 'chaotic environment, with so much rumour, miscalculation, and bad information swirling around'. Such an environment was labelled noise by Fischer Black, the inventor of the Black–Scholes formula.

Hagstrom goes on to ask: 'Is there a solution for noise in the market? Can we distinguish between noise prices and fundamental prices? The obvious answer is to know the economic fundamentals of your investment so you can rightly observe when prices have moved above or below your company's intrinsic value. It is the same lesson preached by Ben Graham and Warren Buffett. But all too often, deep-rooted psychological issues outweigh this commonsensical advice. It is easy to say we should ignore noise in the market but quite another thing to master the psychological effects of that noise. What investors need is a process that allows them to reduce the noise, which then makes it easier to make rational decisions.' As an example, I highlight how, over the long term, Lupin's stock price has withstood short-term disappointments to eventually compound at an impressive 33 per cent CAGR since January 2004 (see Exhibit 193).

Exhibit 193: Lupin's stock price has compounded at an impressive 33% CAGR since January 2004

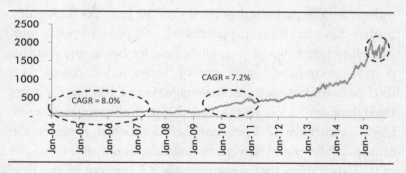

Source: Bloomberg, Ambit Capital research.

However, the chart shown above also highlights that over the past twelve years, there have been several extended time periods when Lupin's share price has not gone anywhere—such as from January 2004 to March 2008, December 2010 to March 2013 and April 2015 to October 2015. In spite of remaining flat over these periods, Lupin has performed so well in the remaining six years that the twelve-year CAGR of the share price is 33 per cent. At its simplest, this is why the concept of investing for longer time horizons works—once you have identified a great franchise and you have the ability to hold on to it for a long period of time, there is no point trying to be too precise about timing your entry or your exit. As soon as you try to time that entry/exit, you run the risk of noise rather than fundamentals driving our investment decisions.

Reason 4: No churning

By holding a portfolio of stocks for over ten years, a fund manager resists the temptation to buy/sell in the short term. With no churn, this approach reduces transaction costs, adding to the overall portfolio performance over the long term. I illustrate this with an example: Assume that you invest US$100 million in a hypothetical portfolio on 30 June 2005. Assume further that you churn this portfolio by 50 per cent per annum (implying that a typical position is held for two years) and this portfolio compounds at the rate of Sensex index. Assuming a total price impact cost plus brokerage cost of 100 bps for every trade done over a ten-year period, this portfolio would generate CAGR returns of 13.3 per cent. Left untouched, however, the same portfolio would have generated CAGR returns of 14.5 per cent. This implies that approximately 9.1 per cent of the final corpus (around US$35 million in value terms) is lost to churn over the ten-year period. Thus, a US$100 million portfolio that would have grown to US$382 million over the ten-year period (30 June 2005–30 June 2015) in effect grows to US$347 million due to high churn.

Reason 5 Back-testing results prove that rebalancing does not improve returns

I back-tested (i.e. used past stock price data) to check the effect of replacing Coffee Can stocks every year (or, annual rebalancing) instead of holding one portfolio for ten years (or, buy and hold). I tested this annual rebalancing approach as against a buy-hold approach over six ten year periods (2000–10, 2001–11, 2002–12, 2003–13, 2004–14 and 2005–15) on the listed companies universe. (There are only six ten-year periods because the CCPs from 2006 are less than ten years old, while the CCP for 2000 has already played out its holding period of ten years.) For the annual rebalancing strategy, I used the following approach: As a first step, I created the CCP for all the years starting 2000 to 2014.

For each period (say the 2000 to 2010 period for example), I start by allocating Rs 100 to each constituent stock at initiation. I then rebalance the portfolio annually by allocating the value of stocks exiting the previous year's CCP to the stocks entering the new year's CCP. For example, for the period 2000–10, the value of stocks exiting the model CCP at the end of first year (i.e. NIIT and Swaraj Engines in June 2001) was Rs 92 out of total portfolio value of Rs 297 at the end of the first year. This value was allocated equally to new entrants of model CCP for the year 2001 (i.e. Apollo Hospitals, Roofit Industries and LIC Housing Finance were allocated Rs 30.67 each). The same process was then followed for subsequent years as well.

In cases wherein there was no churn year-on-year, (i.e. all stocks from previous year's CCP made it to the subsequent year's CCP), the same portfolio was carried over without any rebalancing even if there were more stocks eligible for inclusion.

As can be seen in the results below (see Exhibit 194), the Coffee Can approach without rebalancing has outperformed the rebalancing approach on all six occasions. For example, the CCP for the year 2000, when held for ten years (from 2000 to 2010), gave a portfolio return of 19.3 per cent CAGR if the investor just bought and held the stocks, refusing to change each year as new stocks qualified to enter the CCP and old ones that missed the filters left the CCP. In comparison, an investor who kept changing his portfolio every year by replacing the disqualified stocks with the qualifying stocks would see his portfolio giving a return of 18.5 per cent CAGR—which is 0.8 per cent lower than the 19.3 per cent CAGR he would have got if he stuck to the original portfolio. Similarly, an investor who started the CCP in 2004 and held the portfolio intact till 2014 saw his portfolio return 30.8 per cent, as compared to another investor who kept buying the new qualifiers and selling the old disqualified stocks (this replacement process is also called rebalancing or churning). Taken together, the average of all six ten-year period returns without rebalancing was 24.5 per cent as against 18.7 per cent for CCP with rebalancing. These results clearly highlight the advantage of the buy-and-hold approach over an annual rebalancing approach even with the weights of repeating stocks unchanged in the portfolio.

Exhibit 194: CAGR returns over 10-year periods for CCP with and without rebalancing

	2000–2010	2001–2011	2002–2012	2003–2013	2004–2014	2005–2015	Average CAGR
CCP without rebalancing	19.3%	28.5%	22.4%	25.4%	30.8%	20.5%	24.5%
CCP with rebalancing	18.5%	22.6%	22.0%	17.0%	18.7%	13.5%	18.7%
Difference (without minus with rebalancing)	0.8%	5.9%	0.4%	8.4%	12.0%	6.9%	5.8%

Source: Bloomberg, Ambit Capital Research.

Note: All the ten-year holding periods begin on 30 June of the starting year.

I believe the findings from Exhibit 194 shown above bring out one very important aspect of the buy-and-forget investing approach, where allowing the power of compounding to work its magic is a much more important driver of long-term returns than the most ideal stock selection itself. This is similar to what I had explained under 'Reason 2: Power of Compounding' where even with a 50 per cent strike rate and perfect symmetry around the returns generated by winning and losing stocks, the portfolio when left untouched for longer periods of time compounds well. Why? Because, over time, the losing stocks become insignificant while the portfolio returns are gradually dominated by the winners. That is the central point of the Coffee Can Portfolio.

Index